Lucy

PAULINE

PAULINE

a portrait of
my younger self
1939 - 1945

Pauline Forrest

BATH UNIVERSITY PRESS

1992

20164 7 104566 120

PUBLISHED BY

Bath University Press · Claverton Down · Bath · BA2 7AY

ISBN 0 86197 115 9

Pauline Forrest's original manuscript
was edited by Michael Allen

Typeset in the Printing Unit, University of Bath

Printed by Redwood Press Ltd., Melksham

ACKNOWLEDGEMENTS

'God send you back to me'
[ADAMS / FURBER]
© Asherberg Hopwood and Crew Ltd.
Reproduced by permission of Warner Chappell Music Ltd.

'The thingummy bob'
[GORDON / THOMAS / HENEKER]
© 1941
Reproduced by permission of
Francis Day and Hunter Ltd./ EMI Music Ltd., London WC2H OEA

For my Grandchildren

PART ONE

I SHALL never know how different my life would have been if the Second World War had not broken out. But chance, or fate, plays a large part in all our lives; and, as I shall tell you, it was chance that brought me together with my husband, and chance that saved my life, more than once. For better or for worse, the war changed my life completely.

Of course, mine was but one life among millions, and millions more could tell of their experiences. But I will gladly tell you the story of my life in those important years, for going back into the past makes me feel a very happy person.

I was in fact quite young at the outbreak of war, and so very inexperienced. However, having been brought up in a home of contentment, I was quite happy with my life.

A young girl of seventeen I was, with red hair, brown eyes, and a ruddy complexion. You might say I was an average teenager, and I dearly loved my parents and my home. My youngest brother Rob also shared the delights of home, for Rob and I were the two youngest members of our family, with Rob being two and a half years junior to myself. We lived in the Georgian city of Bath, in a stone cottage on top of a hill — Primrose Hill, they called it. It was aptly named, for many primroses grew in the surrounding fields and hedgerows and it indeed was a place of beauty.

Attached to the cottage was a good acre of garden, and my Dad devoted all his spare time to keeping it so very neat and tidy. I could never forget such a garden, and whenever I think of it, it always gives me this feeling of calm and tranquillity. The fuchsia that surrounded the doorway climbed up the stone wall, settling itself around the trellis of the veranda, which opened into my parents' bedroom.

Coming out of the front door, which incidentally faced the garden, one could turn left, and there underneath the sitting-room windows lay the lily-of-the-valley beds. To me they always looked such delicate little flowers, yet their strong leaves protected them;

3

and right next door to them grew the beautiful scented lavender, from which we made tiny lavender bags which we placed amongst our clothes in wardrobes and drawers.

Then there was the enormous selection of roses. They were Dad's pride and joy, with archways of rambling roses displaying their delicate red and white petals. As one walked down the middle pathway, especially in the spring, the scented lilac trees of mauve and white captivated the eye with sheer delight. Then to the right of those beautiful trees were my favourite peony roses, and I recall thinking that their deep rich petals of red were like ruby wine; I always thought they were the strongest-looking flower in my Dad's garden. And so, what with the selection and variety of all the other different flowers, not forgetting of course Dad's favourite assortment of wallflowers, and the white scented stocks, there was an array of great beauty.

Moving on from the flowers you could come down upon the strawberry beds, raspberry bushes, American loganberries, and gooseberry and blackcurrant bushes, which stood like soldiers in a row. These lovely fruits took up almost a third of the garden, while the remaining space was for every vegetable imaginable, plus, dotted here and there, the plum and apple trees; and at the very bottom of the garden stood two large fig trees.

I can picture it now, as it was then, and I was never happier than when helping Dad, who took great pride in this wonderful garden. We had poultry too, solely under Mum's care, so we had plenty of fresh eggs and of course the occasional roast chicken. One could say we wanted for nothing, and our only visits to the city of Bath would be for meat and bacon, plus our clothes and shoes, and maybe a trip to the movies. We did in fact live a happy life, simplified perhaps, or let's say we were appreciative of the more natural things life had to offer.

It's true to say we were not wealthy by any means, for Dad's occupation was that of a motorman. He drove the local buses, for an average wage of £3 a week. However, an exception would be made if Dad drove a charabanc, this being after he had completed his fifty-two hours weekly; then there would be extra money in his pay-packet.

Mum also contributed, by doing a part-time job at our nearest general hospital, the Royal United, which was a distance of two miles away. The position she held was that of Matron's personal maid, caring for all Matron's needs and making sure that everything was spotless in her office. I thought this was an honour for my Mum, and reckoned her to be good at her job.

My brother Rob had not long been left school, and was now training to be a footman with the Pitman family. They incidentally were the great founders of the Pitman Press, and Sir Isaac Pitman was the inventor of the system of shorthand which bears his name.

As for myself, I worked in a small tailoring factory, three miles from home. It was named Todd's, The West of England Tailors, and was a subsidiary of a larger factory in Bristol, a distance of twelve miles away. It was the function of our factory to make gentlemen's trousers, from the best white cricket flannels to the finest worsted and serges. I depended on my bicycle for transport to and from work, and my weekly wage for a forty-eight hour week was twelve shillings and sixpence. It wasn't a lot, but I was happy just to be able to earn that much money.

It was always my secret wish to become a nurse one day, but at that time it was impossible, for to have me trained in the nursing profession would have cost my parents a considerable fee. As I knew only too well, they couldn't afford it, so I was careful not even to talk about becoming a nurse at that particular time. I contented myself at the tailoring factory, and Dad said I should do well at it, for my grandparents had been high-class tailors; they had specialised in making the red velvet waistcoats which were very popular in the upper classes during the latter part of the nineteenth century.

In the meantime, my life was completely routine. From Monday until Friday I worked from 8 a.m. until 6 p.m., and on Saturdays until midday. Through the week we had an hour for lunch, from 1 p.m. to 2 p.m., this giving me ample time to go home. It indeed was a wonderful break for me, for by the time I had cycled in the fresh air I was always ready for something to eat. I used to love it if both my parents were home together; then the three of us would tuck into whatever there was to eat, Rob of course having his lunch with the domestic staff at the Pitmans.

I had no interest in boy-friends, and therefore I would not go out socially on my own. I think I barely knew about the facts of life, for often I would hear conversations from the girls in the factory which to me made no sense whatsoever. They would talk of their boy-friends, and of dancing, and almost bragged about the night life. It's strange, but I had no desire to venture out and see the world for myself. Maybe I was an old stick-in-the-mud, I really don't know; perhaps I was just content and happy with my own life and was not desirous of a change.

Even a year before the Second World War broke out, we were all aware of the unrest in Europe. In March 1939 the Germans invaded Czechoslovakia, completely violating the Munich agreement, so it was no surprise when on the 26th of April 1939 there was conscription of men between the ages of twenty and twenty-one. But for all that, it was remarkable that life appeared normal: everyone still went about their every-day duties, plus the fact that we were still enjoying the peaceful times, like for instance the last weekend in August in 1939.

It was a regular practice of my Mum to meet Dad from work. She would walk across the high common to meet him, regardless of hail, snow, wind or rain, and always beside her was Joey, our black and tan mongrel dog. As it happened, the evening of the last Saturday in August 1939 was warm and still sunny. Dad was due back in the bus depot at 8.30 p.m., so Mum was ready to set off at a quarter to nine, making sure that our evening meal was all intact in the oven. When Mum slipped on her cardigan, Joey was up and raring to go, with his tail wagging nineteen to the dozen. For a mongrel dog, I thought him most intelligent, for he knew, I'm certain, that he would soon be racing through the long grass across the common. Mum then glanced at me and said, 'Fancy coming with me, Paul?' Pauline was my name, but very often I was called 'Paul'.

I jumped at Mum's suggestion. 'Be right with you, Mum. Just change my shoes.' And so in a few minutes we were strolling across the common, enjoying the light breeze that was now blowing.

On the opposite side of the common lay the golf-course, and this being a Saturday evening there were still plenty of golfers around, so we paused awhile and watched them.

By this time, Joey was really enjoying himself in the grass, jumping up and down in the long blades in a thoroughly playful mood. Occasionally he would snap off the grass and eat it; Mum always reckoned it was good for him, and believed it was a dog's best medicine.

As Mum and I continued to walk we started talking. 'Mum,' I said, 'it's rumoured there may be a war.'

'I dunno, duck,' was her reply.

I must mention this use of the word 'duck': it originates from the dialect of Berkshire, my Mum's birthplace.

'Mum,' I said, 'I can't help thinking about Hitler invading Czechoslovakia, last spring.'

Mum was looking at me with curiosity. 'I remember,' she said.

'Well, what's to stop him from invading other countries?'

'Don't worry, my darling,' was Mum's cheerful reply. 'Nothing may come of it.'

I sure hoped Mum was right.

'Ah,' exclaimed Mum, 'there's your Dad.'

Joey must have seen him too, for he was as quick as lightning, racing towards him. Then the same old ritual would start, with

Joey in so much excitement at seeing Dad that he would jump up and down at his coat, with his tail wagging furiously, while Dad was making the effort to pat his head and say, 'Good boy, good dog.' After all that performance, Joey would make for the long grass again.

Dad, pleased to see us, exclaimed, 'Hello, you two!'

I considered that Dad always looked smart, especially in his uniform, with his white shirt set off by his black tie; his shoes always had a shine on them, even after a day's work, but I do declare that at times Dad's handkerchiefs got awfully dirty, and I'm sure it was not from blowing his nose.

'Hello, Pat,' said Mum. 'Had a good day?'

'Not bad,' replied Dad. 'Had three trips to Wells, I did. And on my second journey, ran into a thunder-storm. Still, it cooled the air a bit.'

Then Dad, looking at me, said, 'How's our Polyanthus?' a nickname by which he often called me. I considered myself honoured by it, for it meant I was named after a flower, the cultivated primrose.

'I'm OK, Dad.'

'Good,' replied Dad. 'And what have you been doing with yourself this afternoon?' Knowing of course, that it was my half-day off.

'I've helped Mum a bit. Haven't I Mum?' Now looking for support.

'Indeed you have,' said Mum.

'Oh — and my bike,' I said. 'I've given it a good clean.'

'Hope you've given it a good oiling. Machines need plenty of lubrication,' said Dad.

'Gave her plenty of oil, Dad. It dripped on the ground.'

'Good old Paul.' This was another frequent saying of Dad's.

So the three of us just strolled along the red rough brick path that led home. It was quite a time before any of us spoke, and then Dad broke the silence.

'Don't like the look of things, Nell. We could be dragged into a world war at any time.'

'Oh no!' came Mum's answer, and although I knew Mum was being optimistic about the situation, she was showing signs of apprehension, for she was now squeezing Joey's leash. I could almost read Mum's thoughts; she did not want to believe that there was a possibility of a war erupting. But then Dad, convinced that there was trouble brewing, continued talking in a somewhat melancholy frame of mind.

'Mistake,' he muttered. "We should have been building up our armaments before now. We'll be left high and dry, mark my words.'

7

All Mum and I could do was just listen.

Then Dad spoke again in a brighter tone of voice. 'Enough of depressing thoughts, eh? It's Sunday tomorrow. And with us all being off work, how about a day trip to Weymouth?'

I saw Mum's face: it suddenly took on that surprised look. 'Can we afford it, Pat?' she said.

'Of course we can,' answered Dad. 'And I dare say Mrs Pitman will let Rob off for the day.'

How excited I suddenly felt, for if we went to Weymouth I would have a wonderful opportunity to wear my new bathing-suit: black it was, and trimmed with green binding.

So the quick decision was made: we would all be off to the seaside the following day. Such an outing would be commonplace for young people nowadays, but before the war it was something special.

Rob was home prompt at ten o'clock, calling out, 'Hi, everybody!' as he came through the door, so eagerly I told him the news.

'You mean, our Paul, we're off to Weymouth tomorrow?' A sudden shriek of excitement came from him, and he yelled, 'Whoopee! See, I've got the day off too!'

So there it was; we were all full of joy.

A tall fair lad, was Rob, with blue eyes. He resembled Dad very much, and he was well fitted to his job as an apprentice footman.

That very same evening, preparations had to be made for the following day. Our clothes had to be put out in readiness, and I noticed Mum had put out her new dress; it was one I had bought for her out of my pocket money, two shillings and elevenpence three-farthings, to be precise. Pretty it was, made up of blue and white cotton material, with a matching belt.

Provisions, too, had to be made up and put in the picnic basket, and it was always Dad that did the sandwiches, most of which consisted of egg and tomato; each little pile was neatly wrapped up in a clean white serviette. 'Keep 'em fresh, and keep the sand out,' Dad would say.

Weymouth, then, was one of our nearest seaside resorts, a distance of some sixty miles, and it was my Dad's decision that we go to Weymouth by train, as it was much quicker than the bus. And besides, we would be going on a cheap day excursion.

Sunday morning came around, and Dad was up first, as was always his practice, making us all early morning tea. Usually we had biscuits with our tea on Sundays, this being a special treat we had accustomed ourselves to. But this Sunday there were no biscuits, as we all would be having an early breakfast. This particular morning we were all full of joviality, so in no time at all we had our bags packed and were ready for the off, with Dad making a last-minute check on everything.

Looking across at Joey, I felt so sorry for the poor little dog. He looked so forlorn. But it was no use; this time he must stay behind. Mind you, it just needed one word of command from Dad and he'd be up off his chair, but all poor Joey got was a pat on the head, and words to this effect: 'Be a good boy, Joey.'

Having no transport, we had to walk the three miles to the GWR railway station, which was situated in the centre of Bath. Nevertheless, we all enjoyed the walk down, for it was a beautiful morning, with the early sun bright and clear, its strong beams penetrating the branches of the trees.

Dad got our tickets at the booking office, and then we all climbed the wooden stairs which led up to the platform. On the platform we waited with what seemed like hundreds of other people, all taking advantage of the cheap day excursion.

Rob and I were past the stage of bucket and spade, for now I was a young Miss, and was delighted to be carrying a square box Brownie camera, which had been given to me by my parents on my sixteenth birthday. With my very long cotton dress, I wore a large-brimmed white straw hat, and my white sandals were not only attractive but comfortable too. The only cosmetic I was allowed to use was the powder on my nose. Mum would say that lipstick and rouge were out of the question; she considered them unladylike, and was positive that they did harm to the skin.

I stood alongside Rob, who was much taller than I, and secretly I felt very proud to be beside him.

Dad pulled out his pocket-watch, glanced at it, and said, 'Train shouldn't be long now.'

Then that old big steam engine came puffing in, belching the smoke well into the station, and she moved slowly along the platform, pulling the carriages behind her. In those days the carriages were marked as to their destination, so in large letters on wooden boards that were fixed to the side it was clearly stated that this train was going to Weymouth.

Everybody scrambled on to the train, struggling to pick the best seats, with small children crying, some of them dropping their buckets and spades, while frustrated mothers and fathers were doing their best to control them. Still, for all that, we were indeed a happy crowd.

We were lucky: Dad had selected a nice clean carriage, with a mirror in it too, so carefully I placed my straw hat on the rack above. You know really I didn't need a hat, for my red strong hair protected my head from any hot sun-rays. Still, I suppose it was the fashion to wear a straw hat; it was all part and parcel of becoming a lady.

Dad had bought himself a Sunday newspaper for twopence, and sitting opposite him I couldn't help but glance at the headlines:

GERMAN TROOPS ABOUT TO ENTER POLAND

I thought the news grim. Then I thought of this so-called League of Nations, an association of countries that had pledged to help each other in times of crisis. It was all too obvious that the Germans were doing just the very opposite, wanting to enter another country, with hostile intentions. But I was determined to dismiss these thoughts from my mind; after all we couldn't let the shadow of a war spoil our day's outing.

We were all seated in the compartment when a young couple joined us with their little boy, who, when I smiled at him, deliberately put his tongue out at me. Naughty little brat, I thought.

Then, suddenly, the train gave two big jerks, and children shouted 'Hooray!' with excitement. We started moving, slowly at first, but then the train gathered momentum, and so now our journey had really begun.

Dad immediately got up to close the window, for the smoke from the engine was coming in. 'That's better,' remarked Dad, while everyone looked on with approval, for that engine smoke certainly did not smell of sweet violets.

We were going faster now, and we were being rocked to and fro. I could see that Mum and Dad were deep in conversation, and as I was sitting quietly beside Rob, I couldn't help but overhear. The expressions on their faces clearly revealed their anxiety.

'Look at this, Nell. Reservists to be called up immediately. That'll involve our Pat and Tim, you know.'

Pat, incidentally, was my eldest brother, with twenty-one years' service in the Royal Navy, whilst Tim, the second eldest, had served eighteen years with the Somerset Light Infantry.

I couldn't help but notice the worry on Mum's face. She looked sad, and her concern for her two eldest sons was evident. 'It looks bad then, Pat.'

'Afraid so, Nell.'

Quickly I intervened; I thought it a good time to do so. 'Dad, we'll soon be seeing the Westbury white horse,' I told him. I must explain about the Westbury white horse; it is in fact the outline of a horse carved into the side of a hill, the hill being made entirely of white chalk.

'Ah, there it is,' exclaimed Mum, who was sitting beside the window.

Now we were all peering out of the window, as if we were seeing one of the seven wonders of the world for the very first time. We had all seen it many times before, but it always gave us pleasure and a sense of wonder.

Our old steam train rattled on. Then Dad, glancing at his pocket-watch, remarked, 'All being well, we should arrive at Weymouth soon after eleven o'clock.' And so it was: the old train pulled into Weymouth station at exactly ten minutes past eleven.

The weather was exceedingly hot, up in the 80s I shouldn't wonder, but nevertheless it was simply glorious, and we all knew we were in for a good day. We were all off the train now, everybody making their way out of the station and getting their tickets punched by an old ticket-collector.

Coming out on to the roadway it appeared even hotter, and it was Mum's suggestion that we have some refreshment before making our way down to the beach. So, into a small café we wandered, ordering four cups of coffee with four cream slices, the total coming to one shilling.

Coming out of the café, we started to make our way down to the sea, with everyone else going in the same direction. Our favourite place was the smooth pebble beach, and it was always fun to me to run across those smooth pebbles in my bare feet. This day was no exception: off came my shoes and stockings, what a lovely feeling, and I almost danced across those warm smooth pebbles. Having my feet free was sheer delight.

Crowds were occupying all the beaches, and the popularity of this holiday weekend was certainly showing. For many this would be the last chance of a summer break.

We selected three deck-chairs — three because Rob and I were to share one between us. The charge for hire was one penny per chair per day. But before we had time to sit down, Rob said to me, 'How about it, Quinner?' He nicknamed me Quinner for the simple reason that our surname was Quintin. 'Shall we go halves for the hire of a lido-bed?'

'How much is it?'

'Two bob and sixpence, for the whole day,' replied Rob.

'Why, that's a lot of money, our Rob.'

Then, to my surprise, Rob was grinning at me like a Cheshire cat. 'Come on, our Paul,' he said. 'You'll have one shilling and threepence to spare.' He knew I had a budget of half a crown.

'OK,' I said, but it was with reluctance that I handed over my precious money. Meanwhile we had settled down in a nice spot; not much privacy of course, but then it really made no difference, for were we not all out to enjoy ourselves?

The first thing to do was to get into our bathing costumes, so while Mum placed a bath towel around me, I slipped into my new bathing-suit.

I stood up, almost admiring myself, and Rob, with his eyes upon me, said, 'I say, look at madam there.' Too true. He was justified in saying this, for I was showing off a bit. I guess it was only natural; after all it was so nice to be wearing something new.

Then Dad asked me if I'd got a bathing-hat, to which I replied, 'I was going to buy one here, Dad,' knowing that it was now entirely out of the question, for the lido-bed had taken up most of my money.

Rob, now in his trunks, shouted, 'Hey Quinner, I'll race you down to the sea.'

'What about the lido-bed?' I called out.

'We'll get that later. Come *on!*'

At the edge of the water crowds of children were happily playing, splashing and laughing at the same time. Then someone shouted, 'Here's a boat!' The children stood waiting to scream, and jump the waves as the wash from the passing boat came rolling in. I myself was fully aware of Rob's intentions: they were, of course, to give me a good splashing, but I had beaten him to it by quickly swimming out into the waves. I loved the water, and I was considered a fairly good swimmer, while Rob was in the throes of learning.

A bigger boat passed, so bigger was the wash, and louder were the screams from the children.

After a little swim I was out of the water, and with Rob I raced back over the pebbles to where Mum and Dad were sitting.

My long red hair was flattened and was still dripping when I flopped into the deck-chair, with the hot sun making me steam up a little. Mum was quick to notice, for she immediately placed a towel around my shoulders. With the heat from the sun, it was more than likely we'd all be sun-tanned before the day was out.

Now Rob smiled at me and said, 'Don't forget, our Paul. It's my turn next for the deck-chair.'

'OK,' I answered.

'You kids hungry?' said Dad. Too true! We were nothing else but always hungry, for Rob and I both had good appetites, and I'm sure the sea air always added to our pangs. Before long, out came those delicious sandwiches of egg and tomato, for Dad could accurately gauge the right amount of salt that made them so tasty.

After we had finished eating Mum decided she would come back to the sea with us, so down to the water's edge we went, with Rob this time trailing the lido-bed behind him. The fun began when we reached the sea, for Rob pushed the pretty coloured bed out into the white waves, and then he and I jumped on the thing together. Naturally we tipped the bed over, and how Mum laughed at us. But we didn't care; like Rob I was feeling so free and happy that day.

Dad came down to take our photographs, including one of me actually lying on the lido-bed. It was then that I noticed Dad was in his bare feet, letting the water ripple over them; most probably he wanted to cool them down a bit, for it was such a hot day. I felt my face and arms beginning to burn, and hoped Mum had remembered to bring the olive oil with her.

We must have been in the sea for at least a couple of hours when Dad whistled us to come out. To our surprise he had purchased a large pot of tea, so out came more of those lovely sandwiches; nothing has ever tasted better.

Then Dad decided to take us out in a rowing boat. 'We'll leave the chairs and our clothes in that hut, yonder,' said Dad, so this we did. Then, dabbing ourselves with olive oil, we all clambered into a small rowing boat; that, of course, was after Dad had paid his half-crown to the man in charge, who to me was a typical seafaring man, his skin coated bronze from the sun.

'Be only a couple of hours now,' the man shouted, as Dad started to row out.

'OK,' answered Dad.

We all had great confidence in Dad, for he could row a boat well, so it was nothing for him to take us far out to where a Naval boat lay anchored. As a matter of fact, Dad rowed right around her, and with the slight breeze blowing it was a good way of cooling down.

'Don't go any further out, Pal,' said Mum.

'I'm turning back now, Nell,' replied Dad.

I don't think any of us wanted the day to end, for we were enjoying every minute of it. But, like all good things, that lovely day had to end sometime.

Reluctant as we all felt, the time came to leave the beach and make our way back to the railway station. Oh yes, we were the same old crowd, children with sand still in their buckets and sucking sticks of Weymouth rock, and it looked as though no one had missed the hot sun, for everybody had the appearance of Red Indians. However, I was sure of one thing, we had all had a marvellous day, for everybody appeared so happy and jolly.

The old steam train came in, dead on time too, and the fireman saluted us with the wave of an oily rag. The engine driver's smudgy face grinned at us through a cloud of steam.

Once again we all scrambled on to the train, and again we were lucky, in that Dad found us a nice clean compartment; all of us were so very tired that we just flopped into the seats.

13

There was laughter and singing all around us; ordinary people like ourselves were still enjoying their day's outing.

Soon the porters were banging the carriage doors shut and shouting, 'All aboard for Bath,' followed by the guard blowing his whistle. Then we started to move, and at last we were homeward bound.

The journey back was enjoyable, and we continued to forget the troubled times and the uncertainty of everything. Already I could feel a touch of sunburn on my face and arms, but it was all worthwhile, I told myself; it had been a day out never to be forgotten.

PART TWO

MONDAY MORNING soon came around, and off I went to work on my bicycle, as usual. As you can imagine. I looked like a beetroot, but I knew I would be the envy of all the girls, especially when they heard I had been down to Weymouth.

I arrived at the factory in good time, well before the whisle blew for the commencement of work. At that particular time we had a large contract for white worsted flannel, and my job was to press the seams on a specially heated machine. I had to be very careful that the machine didn't get overheated, for white flannel soon scorched.

I was piled high with trouser seams to press, but I worked away quite happily. Naturally my thoughts wandered a bit, but they were happy thoughts of the previous day.

Another whistle blew at 10 a.m., when it was our morning ten-minute break, so we all raced along to the small canteen, or large room really, containing long tables and forms. We all sat down ready for our cocoa etc. Our conversations were all on the same topic, 'the world crisis', and every tongue spoke of war being inevitable.

I sat and just listened; after all, my own father had explained the serious situation our country was in, and the calling-up of the reservists was a true indication of trouble. Usually the girls were full of fun and laughter, but that particular morning I could sense a different atmosphere.

When our working day was over, we all waited to clock out at 6 o'clock, and soon I was cycling home. How I loved the fresh air that blew in my face. I arrived home just in time for tea, and directly after tea I was out in the garden helping Dad. He had been on an early turn so the both of us got down to weeding the strawberry beds. As we worked, I talked to Dad about the conversations I had overhead at work.

'There is no doubt about it, Paul. We could be involved in a war any time now.'

All I could say was, 'Oh dear.' Never mind; we completed our task and Dad said we still had a good crop of strawberries.

We were about to walk up the garden path when we heard a whistle. This old familiar whistle came from my brother Pat. He was married, with one little daughter, Patricia, and lived with his wife Violet in the city of Bath. Our Pat was thirty-three, and of my complexion with reddish, auburn hair and brown eyes. Well built he was, and in my opinion a fine specimen of a man. He came down the garden to meet us, his tanned face smiling.

'Hello Dad. Hi, our Paul.' Now he was grinning, which told me he was up to something, for he loved to tease me. Often he would grab a hold of me and squeeze me, and so many times Mum checked him. 'You'll hurt her,' she would say. But for all that, he was a wonderful brother in every way. Meanwhile, from the inner pocket of his sports jacket he produced a buff envelope, with an official stamp on it, and all in one sentence, he said, 'Its arrived, and I'll be off tomorrow.'

'So soon?' was Dad's reply.

'Afraid so,' said Pat. 'I've to be in Devonport before midnight tomorrow.'

Dad and I must have looked solemn, for Pat then said, 'Never mind. How about a nice pint, Dad, and a game of crib in The Retreat?'

I then noticed that Dad brightened up immediately. 'I'll go up and change,' he remarked and so he went, leaving Pat and me standing.

This was a grand opportunity for our Pat, for suddenly he made a grab at my wrist, yelling, 'I've got you now!' I could not free myself, and I could not help laughing with him, but I'm sure that at times he didn't realise his own strength, for my wrist did hurt. But that was our Pat, so full of fun and vitality.

Then, out of the blue, Pat said, 'Any apples, our Paul?' Well, a sudden impulse to get my own back came over me, and I was dying to laugh, but I knew that would spoil things. However, I was determined to have my revenge, so from a basket nearby I selected a large sour cooking apple.

'Here you are, Pat,' I said handing him the apple, and at the same time trying hard to keep a straight face. Well, he took one big bite, and immediately knew he'd been had.

'Gawd! What's this I'm eating?'

Well, I just rocked with laughter, and spluttered out, 'Those are the best apples for Mum's apple pies,' and he had to laugh with me.

So, with our joking over, we continued to walk up the garden path. Then Pat suddenly appeared very quiet; he even went as far as to place his arm gently around my shoulder, and in all sincerity said, 'Paul, look after Mum and Dad while I'm away.'

I did not speak, but merely patted his hand to give him reassurance.

The Retreat, then, was our little local as you might say, very friendly, with a most delightful garden, along with a huge veranda, on which there were tables and seats, ideally for children to sit there with their soft drinks. Attached to the little pub was a skittle alley, in which, incidentally, many good teams were beaten by our locals. Old Sam and his wife Nora were the proprietors, and no matter what time of the day you happened to be in, you would see Old Sam polishing away at the drinking glasses. 'A clean glass be the making of a good pint,' he would remark.

So Dad and Pat vanished into The Retreat while I helped Mum to prepare the supper. It was to be shepherd's pie, and when Dad and Pat did return, they both looked pleased with themselves. I didn't have to ask, for I surely guessed that they had both done well at cribbage, and winning would reap the reward of an extra few shillings, plus I dare say a little winnings on the shove-halfpenny board.

Then Mum spoke. 'How about a little supper before you go, Pat?'

To which Pat replied, 'Thanks all the same, Mum, but I'd better hurry home to Vi.'

It was time for him to go, so kissing us all he said , 'I'm not saying goodbye — just so long,' and after hugging Mum he gave her one last kiss. Then off he went, trotting down the lane, with myself calling after him, 'Don't forget to write soon!'

The outline of him was now a mere shadow. He waved, turned the corner, and was gone. I think our thoughts were fully occupied with Pat going away, for we all remained silent over our supper.

That night, as I lay in bed, I couldn't help but think of my second eldest brother, Tim. He would be the next to go to war. He was also married, with two children, a boy and a girl. Rene, his wife, was a little younger than him, and they lived on the other side of Bath.

I felt my arms: they were still sore from the sunburn. Anyway, I lay on my back, and must have gone off to sleep, only to be aroused by a knocking on the front door. I hurried downstairs, then peered through the letter-box and quickly recognised it was our Tim. I let him in, and I could see he was carrying a large suitcase. I guessed the rest. I knew he had come to say goodbye.

'Hello, Paul,' he said, 'I'm catching the one a.m. train to Aldershot.'

'You go on up and see Mum and Dad, while I'll put the kettle on.'

Having made the tea, I took it up to everyone. Tim was now sitting on the edge of the bed, talking to my parents, and I heard him mention the Suffolk Regiment. Our voices must have disturbed Rob, for now he had joined us.

'You going too, our Tim?'

'Ah,' sighed Tim.

'Well,' said Rob, 'the best of British.' In other words, he was wishing him the best of luck. 'And if you don't mind, I'll be off back to bed.' He then departed, yawning as he went.

Then Tim made his farewells, hugging Mum for a second or two. He left the bedroom and I followed him downstairs and stood with him on the front doorstep.

'Well, cheerio, Paul,' he said, 'and be good.'

I couldn't understand why he should say that. Wasn't I always good? Or tried to be. The next thing I heard was his boots clanging over the cobbled stones, as he walked briskly down the lane. It was dark, and I knew we couldn't see each other, but I called out just the same, 'Good luck, Tim!'

There was a pause, and then Tim's voice yelled back, 'Cheerio, kid!' He must have shouted as he turned the corner of the lane.

All was quiet, so locking the front door, I returned to my parents' bedroom; I wanted to collect the dirty cups. I glanced at Mum, who was still sitting up in bed, and I saw that her eyes were moist: she had been having a little cry to herself. It was understandable, with her two eldest sons going away within hours of each other. Anyway, I kissed Mum, whispered goodnight, and jumped into my little bed. But sleep was not to come, for my mind was so alert that I was restless. I tossed and turned. This thing called war was definitely on my mind, and I realised the complex state our old country was in; and as Dad had said, we were so undefended.

In the days that followed, the country and everyone in it seemed to be in turmoil. What it all amounted to was simply that we were actually preparing for war. People would say, 'We're preparing, in case there is a war.' So much was to become involved, such as the rationing of food and clothes; that meant ration books would have to be issued to every person. There was also the possibility of gas being used, and hence gas masks were issued in cardboard boxes, with a special apparatus for the babies.

Volunteers were helping in all kinds of ways, distributing and allocating all sorts of government equipment. The response was enormous, and all credit must go to the ordinary men and women of that time, who made the change-over possible.

Myself, I was already a member of the Red Cross Society, attached to the Somerset 120 division. I attended lectures twice weekly, but at that particular time I considered I wasn't much of a help to the community, for I had a long way to go before I obtained my certificate in first aid, home nursing and anti-gas.

It was on the 1st of September 1939, amongst all the confusion and bustle, that street lighting was extinguished, and drivers were forbidden to use their headlights; consequently the headlights of vehicles were temporarily masked with black paper in case of accidental switching-on. There was also a mad rush to buy torches. Again, it was not unusual to see men digging trenches everywhere, and sealing them off with sandbags for protection, and I'm afraid all this got such a hold on us that we were digging up country gardens as well as city streets. One day I actually saw a man painting the top of a pillar-box bright yellow; this was gas-detector paint.

Sunday the 3rd of September was the day war was declared. That morning I awoke just as the big clock in a mansion nearby chimed out the seven bells for 7 a.m. Actually I had never seen the big clock, yet I knew its chimes well, and the time-keeping was always accurate, which to me made it all the more mysterious. All I knew then was that this chiming clock played a part in life in the big mansion belonging to the Cook family, who incidentally were founders of the famous Cook's tours. A wall separated our cottage from the estate, with a lane in between, but I had a good view from my bedroom window of the delightful gardens around the big house. Often I would see Mr Cook himself strolling in the grounds, and always at his heels would be his two white Scottie dogs. To me he appeared a somewhat solemn kind of a gentleman, who wore only old tweeds and plus-fours or baggy pants. He was never without his walking-stick, and for all his wealth he did not look a happy man; yet I suppose he was typical of a man who was master of all he surveyed.

It was Sunday, so there was no real hurry to jump out of bed, and I lay until the big clock chimed the quarter past the hour. Then I decided to get up and make the early-morning tea, so, dressing quickly, I slipped downstairs and put the kettle on. It was always special on Sundays, and a real treat to have biscuits with our tea, so in no time at all I was knocking on my parents' bedroom door.

'Come in, duck,' called out Mum, and as I entered I could see that Dad was awake too.

'You've beaten me to it this morning,' said Dad. 'I intended to get up first.'

'Dad,' I said, 'enjoy a nice cup of tea while you've got the chance,' for most mornings he was indeed the first up.

Quite content, I sat on the side of the bed, dipping the hard ginger-nut biscuits into my tea. Mum and Dad were doing likewise. 'Open the veranda door,' said Mum, and so this I did, revealing a beautiful morning. Looking up across the fields, I could see Mr Chubb's cows grazing in contentment; contemplating such a peaceful scene one could hardly believe the upheaval that surrounded us. Then, suddenly, the bells of All Saints church echoed across the countryside. Sweet music came from these bells, which I know will forever ring in my ears, for they had something special to offer, and we were very proud of our little parish church that stood in the small village of Weston, a distance of one and half miles away.

Now I was right out on the veranda, in fact I was leaning over the railings taking in a full view of the garden, for there had been a slight dew that morning, and the appearance of the early morning sun made the flowers almost twinkle as if in fairyland, with everything appearing so fresh. The scent from the flowers was almost overpowering. How well I remember just gazing down and thinking how blessed we were with all that surrounding beauty, not forgetting of course the lovely fresh air, which Dad always said put the roses into our cheeks.

Well, with breakfast over that morning, I helped Mum with the odd jobs that had to be done on a Sunday. My first job was to collect in the fresh eggs, and fresh they were, for they were still warm. Having placed them all in glass dishes, I then proceeded into the chicken-runs to clean the huts out; a smelly job perhaps, but rewarding when they were replenished with clean straw. After washing my hands in the outhouse, I started preparing the hens' feeds of bran mash. I also scattered maize in the run; Mum bought it at 5 lb. for one shilling, at the nearby market.

Just finished I had when Mum called me in for a cup of cocoa, so taking off my wellington boots in the outhouse, I joined Mum and Dad in the kitchen. I did not speak because both Mum and Dad were listening to the wireless, and attentively too. I myself heard the announcer say that there would be a special bulletin at 11 o'clock by the Right Honourable Neville Chamberlain, our Prime Minister.

When I had finished my cocoa, I left Mum and Dad in the kitchen, for next I was about to wash out my works overall. I only possessed the one, so it could only be washed out on a Sunday, to have ready nice and clean for Monday morning. Putting the soft brown soap, with a little lump of soda, into a bowl of warm water, I carefully washed through my overall. Then came the rinse; it didn't need the blue bag which we used to make white clothes look brighter. Then, during the process of wringing out, I heard Dad shout from the kitchen. It was Mum's name he called out, for Mum would be upstairs now, probably making the beds. They took some making, those heavy feather beds, for they had to be shook from one side to the other, and when properly made up, one could sink right in the middle. Well, Mum and I reached the kitchen door together, for I had raced in from the outhouse, thinking something was wrong by the note of distress in Dad's voice. When face to face with Mum he said, 'It's here, Nell.' Mum by now had flopped herself into a chair beside him. Again Dad spoke: 'Chamberlain has just announced that we are now at war with Germany, and that further announcements can be expected.'

I think at that moment we all experienced an initial shock, for suddenly we all fell silent. I was still standing, bewildered at the outcome, when Mum's voice gave me a sudden jog. 'Look, duck, hadn't you better hang out your overall?'

I still had it clutched in my hands, with the drips splashing the floor. 'Oh golly,' I murmured, and then hurried out into the garden to peg it on the line.

As I hung up the black and sleeveless overall, I couldn't help admiring the white swan that was embroidered on the breast pocket. But suddenly my mind was full of the realisation that we now had been plunged into a war. True, we had talked many times of the possibility of war, we had even prepared for it, and the way things had been going it seemed obvious that we could not escape becoming involved in a world war. But now it was actually here — surely that was quite another kettle of fish.

Despite myself, I felt a certain wild excitement. After all, a war could be something new and adventurous. But then I felt guilty, for surely it was wrong of me to think that any war could possibly bring fun and excitement.

I was still in the garden when a voice called over the hedge. It was Bill Harding, our neighbour in the adjoining cottage. 'Heard the news, Paul?' he said.

'Yes,' I replied. 'It be bad.'

'Be Pop there?' Bill always called Dad 'Pop'.

'I'll tell him, Bill,' I answered, and off I went indoors.

The next thing was that the two men were chatting over the hedge, and if I guessed rightly, it would have something to do with the events of the day and its sudden happenings.

It is perhaps an indication of how young and inexperienced I was that the declaration of war did not spoil my appetite. The leg of mutton that was now cooking in the oven was giving off a lovely aroma, and I just fancied a dip of bread in the meat tin. 'It'll spoil your dinner,' said Mum. 'But go on, help yourself if you want to.' The temptation was too much, so I dipped the slice of bread into the lovely gravy. Rob and I always did this, from being very young; the delicious substance from the meat, mingled with fat, made a slice of bread very tasty indeed. Yet really I should not have indulged, my weight being more than it should have been.

During our dinner we all listened in to the 1 o'clock news; it was the repeated speech of Neville Chamberlain:

'I am speaking to you from the Cabinet Room at 10, Downing Street. This morning the British Ambassador in Berlin handed the German Government a final Note stating that unless we heard from them by 11 o'clock that they were prepared at once to withdraw their troops from Poland a state of war would exist between us. I have to tell you now that no such undertaking has been received, and that consequently this country is at war with Germany.'

I couldn't help but notice Mum: she remained extremely quiet, eating her dinner very slowly. It's true she had had previous experience of war, for in the 1914-1918 Great War my Dad had been away for four years on active service with a cavalry regiment, the 5th Dragoon Guards. I thought of the struggle she must have endured then, with my three brothers and sister, all small children. And here she was, having to go through it all over again. One consolation was that Dad would be at home with her this time.

Anyway, in spite of everything we managed to enjoy an excellent dinner, what with the tender mutton along with the fresh mint sauce and fresh vegetables, not forgetting of course Mum's delicious apple pie, topped with fresh cream that had come up from the farm.

Sunday afternoons were usually spent leisurely. If the weather was fine, we were outside on the lawn, maybe with a couple of magazines, and that very afternoon that was precisely what I was doing. Actually I was lying on my back, looking up into the blue sky and thinking how peaceful it all was. It was really difficult to believe we were at war.

On days such as these, especially on Sundays, we always had tea on the veranda; it made a nice change. And it was over tea that day, during a relaxed conversation, that Dad spoke of preparing something for the windows and doors for black-out purposes. 'Just wondering what we've got in the shed,' said Dad. 'I've a fancy, you know, there's some old blinds in there. Anyway I'll have a look.'

I volunteered to help Dad to look for the blinds. 'You'll get yourself all mucked up in that old shed,' said Mum, 'for there's all sorts in there.' And so it was that in no time at all Dad and I were busy turning over everything in the shed, which stood in a corner of the garden beside the chicken-run.

There was quite a collection; it must have accumulated over the years. Before long I came across this black tin box which was locked.

'Dad,' I said, 'what's in here?' I picked it up and blew the dust off it.

'Ah,' exclaimed Dad. 'Wondered where it had got to.'

Now I was really curious, and remarked, 'What's inside, Dad?'

In the dim light inside the shed, I observed Dad was smiling. 'It's your Mum's love letters. Mine too.'

I held the box closer to me now, for this indeed was something precious. I thought then of the photograph that stood on the piano, in the sitting-room. It was of Dad in uniform, displaying the regimental colours of the Dragoon Guards; standing up tall he was, holding his plumage in his left arm, while Mum was seated beside him, holding a bouquet of flowers, for they were meant for each other.

I placed the tin box reverently down, thinking to myself that an inestimable find such as this must always be treasured.

Like Dad, I looked and searched around, until I got my eye on what looked like a blind. I was tugging hard on it, to free it from other obstacles, when suddenly it gave way, and so did I, pulling on top of me a dusty roll of canvas. Now I was spluttering with the dust.

'You all right?' shouted Dad.

I got up laughing. Meanwhile Dad had salvaged three navy-blue blinds that had been lying on top of me, and they were absolutely covered in dirt and dust. Anyway, Dad was soon giving them a good wash in the big sink in the outhouse, and when he had thrown them over the line they looked almost brand-new, without a bit of fade in them.

'They've come up well,' I said, as I looked at them dripping on the line.

'Um,' said Dad. 'It puzzles me where they came from in the first place.'

'Out of the big house maybe,' I answered, for they could only fit very large windows. Well, we got them dried off quickly, and in no time at all I was helping Dad to cut them and fix them up on the front window. I'm afraid they looked far from elegant. Perhaps it was because we had never been used to them; for after all it wasn't necessary before, as we had complete privacy.

One whole week passed, and everyone remarked how quiet things were, apart from the trying-out of the air-raid sirens. Practice warnings were announced in the local paper to give the public a chance to distinguish which siren was which, for when the wobble-siren went it was a warning of approaching enemy aircraft, and the 'all clear' was the long uninterrupted siren. I always thought Stothert and Pitt's engineering works' siren was louder than the Gas Works'.

Another week perhaps went by and then we received a letter from Pat, saying he was on the aircraft-carrier *Courageous*. And so I answered his letter quickly, as I liked writing, giving him all the news; I even sent him a photograph of myself taken on the lido-bed at Weymouth, and for a lark I wrote on the bottom of the photograph, 'I'm still on my battle-ship. Are you?' I never thought, of course, of what could happen during the days that followed; at the time it was a joke on my part, and I did not realise it was some kind of premonition.

Immediate changes were taking place at the factory. We were finishing all civilian clothing, and a rumour got around that we would soon be on khaki and air-force trousers.

Our manager, a Mr Joe Gould, sent for me to see him in his office. I wondered why. Had I done anything wrong perhaps? Anyway I tapped on his office door, and then I heard Mr Gould's powerful voice call out, 'Enter.' When he saw me, he smiled, yet I felt a little nervous as I stepped into his office, perhaps in suspense as to what this meeting was all about. A robust man he was, with a pleasant disposition. He was also a man who appreciated good workers, leaving them entirely on their own, with those deserving merit always being rewarded by increases in their weekly pay-packet. So on the whole we all thought of him as a fair and just manager.

'Ah, lass,' he said. 'Sit ye down.' A Yorkshireman to the full.

I sat perfectly still on a stool, ready to listen to what he had to say.

'I've been thinking of putting you in the press room, young lady. As a matter of fact on a Hoffman press, for you being a strong lass, and capable of doing a good job, you would be well fitted as a presser. There'll be an increase in your wages, of course.'

I must have looked a bit taken aback, but nevertheless I was prepared to listen further to what Mr Gould had to say.

'It's like this, lass,' he said. 'Shortly we'll be going on to government work, and we'll need to get the orders out fast. That's why I could do with you on the leg-press.' Now he was smiling. 'You'll soon learn, love.'

Mr Gould surely had confidence in me, so what could I do but smile back at him?

'Quite happy about it, Miss Quintin?'

So the one and only word I spoke was, 'Yes.' The next thing I

26

knew I was being introduced to the girls in the press room. On the other leg-press was Edna, while Nancy was on tops, and the trouser-bottoms were done by Betty; they all appeared pleasant girls.

The big day arrived when I was to go on the huge Hoffman press. But how to operate it? Well, this Nancy had to show me, and she was so patient that I picked it up quite quickly. One had to pull the top of the press down by means of a handle, and a small lever on the handle operated the steam which could be adjusted for the amount required. There were also two foot pedals, one for the vacuum which sucked up the steam, whilst the other was for the release of the top of the press, which used to spring up.

I must admit that I was very clumsy at first. However, I soon got into the way of it, and I was very proud of the first pair of trousers I pressed. I had to get used to the atmosphere too, for ventilation was very poor: just one small window, which was always open, summer or winter. It was almost a confined space that we worked in, the temperature was always up, and I would perspire heavily; in fact we all did, for every time you put the pressure of steam on, it somehow came up into your face, just like a Turkish bath. I'm sure that was why we were so susceptible to a lot of head colds.

The first consignment of khaki arrived. It came in huge bundles, tied with string, and already cut out by our factory in Bristol. Very busy, that's what we were, for every sewing-machine was put to use to get the trousers stitched up as quick as possible. Then the completed trousers came into the press room for pressing. Nancy would do the tops first, then throw them on to a rail behind her, whereupon Edna and I would press the legs. Then, when we had finished with them, they went in to the examination room to be passed by a Mr Smith, better known as 'Nobby', he being the one and only final passer. So the rail behind us was always piled high, and we were kept going the whole of the time, and if any of us wanted to go to the toilet it would have to be a case of the utmost urgency.

I quote an old saying, we worked like Trojans, but in spite of the hard work we had time to laugh and sing. It was funny, but it seemed to me that the harder we worked, the more trousers we were given to press, and when the machinists went on piece-work our little press room was jam-packed with pile upon pile of trousers. The only solution was to work overtime, so instead of finishing at the usual time we often worked on until 7 or 8 o'clock.

There were times when I felt too tired even to ride my bicycle home, and when riding in the black-out it was easy to get my wheels caught up in the tram-lines; consequently I often enough fell off my bike.

I remember very clearly the 17th of September 1939. At work I had been kept busy as usual, so by 1 o'clock I was ready to go home for a meal. As I cycled along I was taking in deep breaths of lovely fresh air, which was most appreciated I must say after a stuffy press room with all the khaki flying around. However, when I did arrive home I found Mum a little agitated.

'Anything wrong, Mum?'

'I dunno, duck,' she answered. 'Only...'

'Only what, Mum?'

'Well, it was on the one o'clock news,' said Mum. 'One of our aircraft-carriers has been sunk.' There was no mistaking it, Mum looked worried. 'What was the name of our Pat's boat?' she said. 'I've been trying to find his letter.'

I knew the name of Pat's boat. It was HMS *Courageous*, one of the biggest aircraft-carriers in the British Navy. I wanted to blurt out what I knew, but I hesitated. Some sudden impulse made me refrain from telling Mum. I only wanted to save her from worrying, and I secretly hoped that this aircraft-carrier which had been reported sunk was not Pat's boat, not forgetting in God's mercy all those that had perished.

'Mum,' I said, 'I don't remember the name of our Pat's boat.' How I hated myself for telling this little white lie, but I just had to spare her from being concerned. 'Did they mention the name of the boat that had sunk?'

'That they didn't,' replied Mum. 'Anyway, I'll put the one-thirty news on. We may get more information.'

I think it was Richard Dimbleby who announced the 1.30 news on the wireless. 'It is regretted,' he said, 'that our largest aircraft-carrier, HMS *Courageous*, has been sunk with the loss of many lives.'

I suddenly felt sick, and there was no mistake about it, Mum had noticed my reaction.

'It *is* Pat's boat isn't it?'

Words failed me. I just couldn't answer Mum, I could only fling my arms around her and hold her tight. 'Mum,' I said, 'I'm sure our Pat's all right. And you know, Mum, you always said he would never drown because he was born with a caul over his face.' I let go of her gently, then looked at her. Her eyes were misty, yet did I not detect some highlight in them, as if I had said the right thing at the right time? Perhaps my reminding her of the caul Pat was born with could be considered an old wives' tale. I don't know. Nevertheless, it was always said that a baby born with a caul over its face would never drown, and any captain of a ship with such a man in his crew considered himself lucky, for it gave him hope that he himself would never perish at sea.

Dear Mum, she was trying hard to smile through her grief, and what a blessing it was that Dad would be finishing soon that day. It was time to go back to work, but I felt reluctant to leave her.

'Mum,' I said, 'shall I stop home with you this afternoon?'

'Oh no, duck. You must get back to work. I'll be all right. Besides, your Dad will be home in a couple of hours' time. Meanwhile, duck, we'll just have to put our trust in the Good Lord.'

So Mum came to see me off at the front door, as she always did, and all I could say was, 'Don't worry, Mum. I'm sure our Pat's OK.'

I jumped on my bike, and soon reached the bottom of the lane, whereupon I braked and stopped and then waved to Mum. Turning the corner I was speeding down the hill towards the Pitmans' house when an idea struck me: perhaps I could see our Rob.

I parked my bike beside a hedge and then went up to the back door that led to the servants' quarters. There I gave a pull on the big iron bell, which echoed so loud I felt I'd pulled it too hard. However, a pantry maid answered the door.

I spoke first. 'I'm Pauline, Rob's sister. Can I see him a minute?'

'Half a tick,' she answered. 'I'll fetch him.' She then disappeared.

The next thing, Rob appeared, looking very surprised at seeing me. Anyway, quickly I told him the disturbing news, whereupon the poor kid turned white.

'Hey,' I said. 'You all right, our Rob?'

He smiled and said, 'Don't worry, our Paul. I'll go up and see Mum right away, for the Pitman family are all out, so they'll not need me.'

Anyway, I said cheerio to Rob, and went off again, cycling down the hill as fast as I could. I only just made it before the whistle blew to commence work.

Within minutes I was on my Hoffman press, and feeling terrible too. I guess it was the shock of Pat's boat going down. Anyway, I worked away, secretly praying for Pat's safety.

Then Nancy spoke. 'Heard the news? We've lost a big aircraft-carrier.'

'I know,' I answered. 'It's my brother Pat's boat.'

It appeared that everyone suddenly stopped working, while Nancy gasped, 'Oh no!' All were sympathetic and ready to share my grief.

The afternoon seemed to drag. I tried to kill time by working as hard as I could, but it was of no use, for Pat was on my mind the whole of the time. Then I thought about Violet, his wife: I was sure Dad would see her as soon as possible. And then Mum, dear Mum, waiting in uncertainty. They say no news is good news, but I knew that waiting for news of this kind would be an absolute torment.

I must say all the girls in the press room showed much understanding. They even wanted to see Mr Gould to allow me to go home, but when I explained I could do nothing, even if I went home, they agreed I was right. One thing was in my favour: there was no overtime that day, and we would be finishing at 6 p.m. When that time arrived, I was on my bicycle like a shot and heading for home.

Before reaching home, however, I had to push my bike up the twenty-five yard slope which we called the slipway. I wanted to hurry, yet as I got closer to our cottage, I began to feel afraid.

What would be the outcome? Could it be tragedy for us? Could our Pat have gone down with the ship? All these thoughts flashed through my mind. Oh dear God, I thought. Please be kind to us. It was the first month of the war, and already this had happened to us. Was it only a few weeks ago that our Pat was skylarking with me in the garden, and had grabbed my wrist? Oh, I thought, if only he were here with me now, I wouldn't have cared, he could have broken my wrist. Dear brother Pat, may God have kept you safe.

I opened the front door, and called out, 'Cooee,' but there was no answer. Then I distinctly heard voices coming up from the garden, and for a minute I felt my heart pounding with fear that had suddenly come over me. It was no good, I just flew down the garden, only to find it was just Mum and Dad talking to Bill over the hedge. I must have interrupted their conversation when I gasped out, 'Any news?'

'No news, Paul,' answered Dad.

I looked at Mum, and thought how pale she looked, and I knew she had been crying for her eyes were still red.

'Oh, Mum,' I said, giving her a big hug, and while I was embracing her, Joey started yelping, jumping up and down for my attention, whereupon I gave him a couple of pats on his head. That was all he needed to reassure him, and that was the advantage of being a dog, I thought.

Mum had now braved a smile. 'Let's go up for some tea now.'

I think we were all ready for something, and it surprised me to see that Mum had been baking, making a large fruit cake and some scones. Bless her, she had kept herself occupied that afternoon, and if I knew Mum she would have been silently praying the whole time she was cooking.

Through tea there was little conversation; in fact we hadn't the usual appetities to eat. What had happened to us? Our happy home which was always filled with laughter had suddenly vanished, and now we were experiencing a change. Sad to say there was an atmosphere of gloom and uncertainty.

That evening we were anxious to hear all the news on the wireless, so we kept it on all the time, and I was pleased to see that Mum and Dad managed to smile at some parts of the programmes. When the time reached 8 o'clock I knew that Dad would not be going into The Retreat for his usual game of cribbage.

I think we were all pleased to see Rob come in at 9 o'clock. His very presence uplifted us all, and much to our surprise he spoke of joining the Territorial Army.

'You are too young, my boy,' said Dad, for Rob was only fifteen.

But I could sense the keenness that was within Rob, and he remarked, 'I could always advance my age.' Meanwhile Mum made no comment; she just continued darning socks.

It was after the 10 o'clock news that we all made up our minds to retire, so kissing Mum and Dad goodnight, I was the first upstairs. I seemed to be lying awake for such a long time. However, I must have fallen into a sound sleep, for suddenly I was startled out of my sleep by someone banging on the front door. I think I almost fell out of bed, and just flew downstairs only in my nightie.

'Who's there?' I called out.

'It's me, Vi.' I couldn't get the door unlocked quick enough. Violet now had suddenly grasped hold of me, and exclaimed with excitement, 'Pat! He's all right!'

Without any hesitation, I raced back upstairs and burst into my parents' bedroom, almost yelling out, 'Our Pat's OK!'

It was then I heard my Mum's quiet voice say, 'Thank God.'

By this time Vi had followed me up, and she explained how she had received a telegram at 11.30 p.m.

'And you've walked all the way up here on your own?' said Dad.

Then Mum spoke. 'Little Patricia, is she all right?'

'She's all right, Mum,' said Vi. 'A kindly neighbour came in to stay with us, just for the night of course. But I did so want to let you know about Pat.'

'How about a nice cup of tea for us all?' said Dad.

'Righto, Dad,' I replied. 'I'll go down and put the kettle on.' I was about to mash the tea, when I was overcome with emotion, for tears were now just streaming down my face. They must surely only have been tears of joy for my brother Pat, for he had survived. Before going upstairs, I dried my eyes, and the tea, it was so refreshing. I even took Rob in a cup, only too glad to tell him the good news.

'Just had that feeling our Pat was OK,' said Rob.

31

Now that our anxiety was over, we all felt at ease, and it was time for Vi to return home. 'If you like, Vi,' I said, 'Joey and I will see you best part of the way home.' I immediately went into my bedroom and dressed. Dad suggested coming with us, but I persuaded him not to, knowing he had to be up early for the workmen's bus, which took the men to the big underground arsenal at Corsham, a distance of some eight miles away from Bath.

So Vi and I, not forgetting Joey of course, made our way down the lane, myself carrying a walking-stick. Making a detour of the common, we walked down Sion Hill.

Joey must have thought it great having such a run in the middle of the night, for he raced backwards and forwards as we walked along. It indeed was a beautiful night, with a full moon shining, lighting up everywhere, but for all the extra natural light, we still missed the old street-lamps. Vi and I did not stop chattering, so it was no surprise at all that we soon arrived at the top of the street where she lived.

'You'd better go back now,' said Vi. We then exchanged kisses and farewells, and I started my return journey. I had Joey, and of course Dad's walking-stick, ample protection, so I felt no fear. Going back up Sion Hill, I was aware of the beauty in the sky, which was patterned with rows of white cloud, like waves upon a high sea. The stars too were shining brightly, and I was looking for the constellation Pat had told me about, the one shaped like a letter V. He used to tell me it was a sailor's guide. And so there it was. I had located it, but only just, along with the Waggon and Horses, or Plough, stars that resembled such and which everybody knew of. And then there was no mistake in observing Venus, the big and beautiful bright star. In fact the whole heavens looked so peaceful and tranquil, and how well I remember wishing that the whole world could be the same.

But, unfortunately, the night and my peaceful thoughts were suddenly disturbed by the wobble-siren, giving warning of an air raid. 'Come on, Joey,' I shouted. 'We'd better run for it!'

I ran as I had never run before, with Joey at my heels, and running uphill too. It was no wonder I was panting by the time I reached home. However, Mum and Dad were up and I reckon they were pleased to see me back.

'See if Rob's getting up,' said Mum. I went upstairs into Rob's bedroom, and in the dim light I could see he had his head covered with a sheet, so I had to give him a couple of shakes to rouse him.

'Come on, Rob,' I said. 'Dress quickly, Jerry's around.'

Rob muttered something, and if my guess was right it could only have been, 'Oh damn.'

Then Dad called out, 'Don't put any lights on,' and soon we were all in the sitting-room. We huddled together, talking but listening and waiting just the same.

Then we heard it; a single plane going over. It somehow had a different drone to ours. 'A reconnaissance, or a straggler,' said Dad.

'It's probably lost, or even dropping spies,' replied Rob.

We waited what seemed ages, and then the 'all clear' blew. By that time we were all ready to go back to our beds.

During the weeks that followed many other things happened. My brother Tom, the third eldest of the family, had been called up for service, and was attached as a driver with the 5th Field Ambulance Corps, which at the moment was still stationed in England. Brother Tom was also married, with a lovely wife, Dorothy, and their small son Jimmy; they lived in the Bath suburb of Twerton.

Meanwhile Pat came home on a month's furlough, and imagine how pleased we all were to see him. It was rather strange, but he spoke very little of his experiences; it was my guess that he was still suffering from the loss of his pals, especially one in particular, his bosom friend, Percy Minns. He did speak of him. Found him on the top deck he did, with both legs trapped. The pathetic thing was, Pat was unable to release him; and the most hurtful thing was that Percy was conscious, and asked Pat that if he should make it, would he go and see his wife and kids. Here indeed was a heroic man, about to die for his country. It must have been a terrible ordeal that Pat experienced, leaving his best pal on board ship, able to do nothing in so short a time and helpless in such a situation. It is without doubt that it must have preyed on Pat's mind, and as he talked of the sinking of the *Courageous*, his face showed signs of sadness and remorse.

We all knew it must have been disastrous, with the loss of over 500 men, clinging on to the sides as she went into submersion so very quickly. Pat's own story of the sinking was brief. Apparently a German submarine had followed them for days. Pat had just come off watch, and was lying in his bunk reading a book, when he heard and felt this terrific thud. Bells were heard for immediate action stations, and so with others Pat raced to the top deck.

Then Pat heard someone shout, 'We've a bloody torpedo through the magazine! We're bleeding sinking fast!'

From then on it was every man for himself, for she was going further under every minute. There was no fight in her, this fine aircraft-carrier the Navy was so proud of, and gracefully she had to submit to the depths. Imagine men grabbing what they could to keep afloat, clinging on to pieces of wood, anything, and the sea, Pat said, was icy cold.

'I was one of the last to leave,' he said. 'I dived into the water and started swimming away from the boat, and when I had swum a good distance, I turned around and saw the last of the *Courageous* as she finally disappeared, taking with her all those who were frantically holding on to the sides. I went on swimming, having no idea where. I then got the cramp in one of my legs. Almost gave up, almost gave up I did. It was then I started struggling. Then I couldn't remember any more, until I felt myself lying on some deck, and I heard a voice say, "The poor bugger." Still lying there I must have been absolutely exhausted, yet aware of thankfulness at being still alive.'

That's what he told us, so that's how we remember it.

It was while Pat was home that I asked him if he had ever received my photo, the one taken at Weymouth on the lido-bed.

'Yes, Paul. I got it the very morning the *Courageous* was sunk. A coincidence wasn't it, asking me if I was afloat. What was it again? "I'm still on my battleship, are you?" It's funny, our Paul, it's as if you knew the old girl would get it.'

'Uncanny, wasn't it, Pat?' I answered. And then I thought of the old saying, that there's many a true word spoken in jest.

After Pat's recuperation, he rejoined the Navy in a corvette, and for the remainder of the war was placed on convoy escort duties.

The loss of the *Courageous* was a big enough blow to the Royal Navy, but almost a month afterwards, on the 14th of October 1939, the *Royal Oak* was sunk at Scapa Flow.

My only sister, Nell, lived in Sheffield, and her husband, being a miner, was exempt from active service. They lived in a small house, with their small daughter of eight years. We didn't see much of them, but we exchanged plenty of letters, and it was in one of her letters that she proudly stated she was doing crane-driving in a big steel works. In detail she explained how she was manipulating an overhead crane, and it was Dad who remarked after he had read the letter, 'Whatever next? Young women doing jobs like that!'

Secretly, I was very proud indeed. Anyway it was proving something — weren't we as good as the men?

It was getting near Christmas and I knew this festive season was going to be different, for the simple reason that we would not be together as a family. At previous Christmases, when the whole family was reunited at home, it was always a wonderful time. Just to be together was just something great, but this year, as we expected, Christmas Day passed over very quietly. One thing I must mention. On this special Christmas Day, and on all Christmas Days to follow during the war, when Big Ben chimed out the time of 9 p.m., we would raise our glasses while Mum would sing a song to the family. So Pat, Tim, Tom and Nell, no matter where they were, or what they were doing, would hear Mum's song in their thoughts, at precisely 9 p.m. each Christmas night. A sentimental song it was, and it spoke for itself, and went like this:

'Love, you have left me
Weary and lonely,
Sailing so far away.
Ah how I miss you,
Daily I'm praying
Safely you'll come home some day.
God send you back to me,
Over the mighty sea.
Dearest I want you near.
God dwells above you,
Knows how I love you,
He will bring you back to me!'

When Mum sang this song for the first time, I was very moved, for I realised that Mum's heart was within us all, and although we were separated, in our thoughts we were closely linked.

So the new year came in, 1940, bringing with it a blanket of snow. By now Rob had somehow managed to join the Territorial Army, and one day, to our amazement, he brought a very large drum home to practise on. How we all laughed at Rob trying to get the right beats in. Joey would join in, giving us the occasional waul, to accompany the bangs on the drum.

About this time Dad too had now joined the LDV (i.e. the Local Defence Volunteers, later called the Home Guard). My old headmaster, Mr Pike, also joined; for years he and Dad had been the best of friends. Talks were, of course, of the possibility of an invasion, so we just had to be prepared, and these gallant bands of men were formed. They consisted mostly of retired gentlemen, who in fact were still very active, and although they engaged in apparently schoolboy exercises, they did relieve the Army of some of its routine patrols, such as being pickets on buildings; they also did a certain amount of ARP work (Air Raid Precautions). Many was the time I would see Dad return from the manoeuvres that they used to go on, often enough covered in mud. I had a sneaking fancy that Dad and his pals would cross over the Weston fields and make their way up to the Blathwayt Arms, the little pub that stood next to the racecourse; and I dare say that a pint of beer would be most welcome after the walk they'd had. Looking back, Dad had quite an Army record. His career started when he was a young scout in the South African War, or the Boer War as it is so often called. Then he did fifteen years with the 5th Dragoon Guards, often enough escorting HRH Queen Victoria. He also rejoined for active service during the 1914-1918 Great War, still doing his bit for his country. Mum too was working longer hours at the hospital, so in some way or other all our family were engaged in contributing to the war effort.

At my own job I still worked hard on the Hoffman press, and one incident I shall always remember. We had just completed an order for some 5,000 pairs of khaki trousers when they were returned faulty, the fault being that the trouser legs all measured short. This indeed was a problem, especially for our manager, and how well I remember him coming into the press room mopping his forehead; his perspiration was caused by anxiety, I felt sure. On his arm he carried a pair of khaki trousers. Then, glancing at me, he spoke: 'Hey, lass, we're in dead trouble. But I've got an idea. We'll try and stretch 'em.'

I was ready and only too pleased to make the experiment. I placed the trouser leg on the press, measuring the inside leg at thirty inches. Then I pulled the top of the press down, giving a full pressure of steam, and without using the vacuum to disperse the steam, I lifted up the top arm of the press, and pulled the trouser leg down as hard as I possibly could. Without any hesitation Mr Gould then pulled his tape measure out and measured. He found that the leg measured thirty-one and a half inches.

'Bravo!' yelled Mr Gould with delight. 'We can do it!' And so for the days to follow, Edna and I concentrated on steaming and stretching 5,000 pairs of khaki trousers, working some nights up until 9 p.m., by which time the palms of our hands were hot and sore. Every night Mum would soak a bandage in glycerine and wrap it around my right hand. She insisted I keep the bandage on all night, and it certainly prevented blisters occurring. Never mind; in spite of everything we still got our laughs. One morning at the factory things started happening and I found myself giggling so much I couldn't stop. Well, actually the alert was on, and it was mid-morning.

'Everybody take cover under the tables!' shouts Mr Gould.

Immediately all the machinery was switched off, and now all we could hear was the hissing of the steam in the press room. All us young girls were in a scrimmage to take up our positions, and the majority of us were in fits of laughter, squeezing ourselves under the little wooden tables for shelter. As you can imagine we joked about it. We thought it crazy of Mr Gould to tell us to do this, but he had his reasons, I suppose. He emphasised his concern by once again shouting, 'It's the flying glass! Ye'll be all well protected under them tables.'

Talk about sardines in a tin, I certainly felt like one, with two heavy girls almost lying on top of me. We all remained quiet, apart from the chatter and laughter from the girls, and try as I may I was still giggling, for to me it was all so amusing.

Then there was silence. A single plane was circling overhead. No mistake, it was Jerry all right. Then we heard more planes approaching, and we guessed they were ours in pursuit of the enemy, for we distinctly heard machine-gun fire.

What were my thoughts? Same as the others', I expect, for Jerry could easily drop right down on top of us, blow the tables and us to kingdom come. All was silent. Then someone spoke: 'Our lads will soon chase Jerry out to sea.'

Soon afterwards the 'all clear' sounded, so immediately we emerged from underneath the tables, and in minutes we were all back on our jobs. As one could imagine, Mr Gould was cursing the interruption.

While I worked away at pressing the legs of the trousers, my thoughts drifted to the German pilot up there in his plane, alone perhaps. I wondered how he could have felt, flying over enemy territory and outnumbered by enemy planes. Should I feel sorry for him, this unknown German pilot? After all, he did belong to someone, and someone would be praying for his safety, just like we were for our own boys. Deeper my thoughts became. If then we wanted the enemy destroyed, were we not destroying someone's hopes, someone who prayed for the safety of that German pilot, whoever he may have been? And remembering that we all prayed to the same God, and pray we would for the same thing, it seemed that to wish ill to anyone, even to our enemy in war, must surely be doing an injustice to ourselves. We then were no better than the enemy. I thought of the precept 'Do unto others as you would have them do unto you.' The meaning was right enough, but we were apt to forget it in times of war.

I realised that my mind was in a state of confusion and I thought it best now to concentrate on my work. I was aware that my right hand was extremely sore that morning, so, dipping my handkerchief in cold water, I tied it around my hand, where the pressure was greatest.

Nancy spoke: 'As bad as that Pauline?' I nodded, but smiled. An understanding girl was Nancy. Then she said: 'I'll take over for a little while. Then you can carry on doing tops.' The change was much appreciated. I liked doing tops anyway, and manipulating the little press was easy; it would give my hand a chance to rest.

Another Friday arrived, and Friday was always our pay day. We received our pay in small buff packets, and here was Mr Gould coming around with them. When he came into the press room he was all smiles and said, 'I kind of appreciate you lasses, for the amount of work you've got through has been outstanding, so you'll all find extra in your packets.'

I opened my packet slowly, scarcely knowing what to expect, and then I pulled out two pound notes. Glory be, I thought, I'm rich.

As I gazed upon the notes, a sudden impulse of generosity swept over me. Definitely I would give Mum extra, and buy a treat for her too. I knew exactly what I was going to do — I would stop on the way home and buy her a box of Black Magic chocolates. She'll love them, I thought, and as yet sweets and chocolates were still not rationed.

The 1 o'clock whistle blew for lunch, and I must have been first out of the factory, for soon I was on my bicycle and heading for home. But first I must stop at the little confectioner's opposite the Gas Works, where I purchased the box of chocolates for one shilling and threepence. Happy with my buy, I placed the chocolates in the saddle-bag behind my seat, jumped on my bike, and started pedalling fast. When I reached home I was pleased to see that Dad was there too. Well, the three of us sat down for lunch, exchanging conversation as we ate. And it was after we had finished a cup of tea that I slipped out to my bicycle to fetch the chocolates, and now in the kitchen I hid them behind my back.

Then I said to Mum, 'Close your eyes now,' and lift up your pinny. I've a little surprise for you.'

Mum then opened her eyes, exclaiming, 'What's all this? It's not my birthday.'

'Surprise, surprise!' I answered.

'But —'

'It's all right, Mum, I got extra wages this week.' I could not hold back the excitement as I told my parents what I had received in my wage-packet. Both looked surprised.

'Two whole pounds!' gasped Mum.

'Yep,' I answered. 'And all for Mum.'

'Hold on young lady,' said Dad. 'You can't go giving all your money away. The time has come when you must start to save. I'll go back a little sooner. Call at St Andrew's Post Office I will, and get you a post-office savings book.'

It was now time to go back to work, so kissing Mum and Dad I was soon on my bicycle and away.

Always Dad kept to his word, and that same night when he returned home he gave me my very own savings book. I held it in my hand, and as I looked upon it, it somehow gave me a feeling of security. On its cover it read, 'St Andrew's, Bath, No. 2078.' On the first page, clearly written, was my name, and down the first column was the first deposit of ten shillings.

I looked up at Dad, who was now smiling at me. Then he spoke: 'Make it grow, Paul. It's your best friend. Come in handy one day.'

'Oh Dad!' I said, throwing my arms around his neck, and at the same time giving him a big kiss.

'One thing more, young lady. Let your eyes be your guide, and your money the last thing you part with.' Dear Dad, his words were always affable and understanding.

Spring of 1940 came around, bringing with it new life to the countryside, and the 'Dig for victory' campaign started, with the flower-beds being turned into vegetable plots. This was so very necessary for survival.

Some important events were happening within those weeks. The Bank of England transferred itself to a Hampshire village, and large numbers of people were still being evacuated from the big cities which were likely to be bombed. It was reported that, in all, some three million children, mothers, hospital patients, and blind people were transferred to safety zones throughout Britain. Many of the evacuee children came from slum conditions which were quite unknown to country folk.

The newspapers were full of Hitler's victories, for on April the 9th he invaded Norway and Denmark. Meanwhile British involvement in the war seemed remote, for activity on land, sea, and air, was on a small scale. Very often things appeared quite normal. Many was the time I would sit in the garden, enjoying the spring sunshine, and maybe I would be writing letters; anyway, I was aware of this wonderful peace and serenity that surrounded me, and so it was impossible to believe that we were at war, fighting each other. And for what? I suppose it was the lust for power, this being the dominating factor, as in all wars. I knew that the ordinary man desires no war, yet was obliged to serve the cause; it was as if we were all slaves in a community that was ordered to obey, and if necessary to die for our King and country.

One evening I was sweeping the paths in the garden when I heard a voice call over the hedge, 'Hello, Paul.' I looked up and it was Bill Harding from next door. 'They must be expecting trouble over Bristol,' he said, and now Bill was pointing to the skyline, facing west. My eyes followed his direction, and lo and behold, there on the skyline was what looked like a series of black dots.

'Never seen the likes before,' I exclaimed. 'What are those, Bill?'

'They be balloon-barrage, me dear. Supposed to hinder enemy aircraft.'

'Goodness,' I answered. I was now peering hard at the black objects that almost disfigured the beautiful setting of the sun. They were not a pleasant sight to see, yet as time passed they proved a boon, for Bristol alone experienced quite a number of air raids, some nights more serious than others. From home, when Bristol was getting it bad, the skyline would almost glitter with a pale red glow. I know us Bathonians considered ourselves lucky, and it was a saying amongst us, 'Poor devils. Getting it again.' The Bath Fire Brigade and Ambulance Service were constant visitors to Bristol, giving aid where necessary, and this is where I came to play a part.

The Red Cross division of which I was a member was in urgent need of ambulance drivers, and so desperate were they that they offered to teach driving to anyone interested in learning. An invitation such as this was too good to miss, so I volunteered; after all, I was now eighteen. Before my first lesson I was given a uniform; it was of black serge, consisting of a jacket, trousers, and a peaked cap, along with a white blouse and black tie. And how well I remember Dad saying, when first I put it on, 'A pretty uniform isn't everything. To drive, and to drive well is the most important thing.'

It was one Sunday afternoon when I had my first introduction to an ambulance. I must say I was very keen to drive, and so eager was I that I arrived at the ambulance depot in James Street a half-hour before I should have, and so there I sat and waited in what appeared to be a small office. Was I nervous! I was conscious of twiddling my handkerchief around my fingers, yet I knew I was full of enthusiasm.

I glanced around me. There was a switchboard, and above it was a large wooden notice-board; on it was the check-list of ambulances, both in and out, along with details of the personnel, drivers and their attendants. I counted: there were twenty-five vehicles in all, which I thought was especially good for Bath, for we were not a big city.

People started coming in and out, to check the notice-board I suppose, and some even gave me a glance. Then a man's voice spoke: 'Hello there. It's Miss Quintin, I presume.' He was smiling, putting me at ease straightaway, and I observed that he was a man well into his fifties. 'I'm Mr Penny,' he said, holding his hand out for me to shake.

Timidly I shook his hand, saying, 'Pleased to meet you.'

Still smiling he said, 'I'm your instructor, so come along then, I'll introduce you to Old Jane.'

I followed Mr Penny outside, scarcely knowing what to expect next. Then I realised that Old Jane could only be the old Austin ambulance standing in the corner.

'Afraid the old girl has to be started on the handle,' said Mr Penny, whereupon he went across, caught hold of the handle, and gave a quick turn. Jane spluttered, then shook as the engine finally started up, and I noticed that the old ambulance was making some peculiar vibrations. There was no doubt about it, she had seen better days, so I guess allowances had to be made.

Before long I was sitting alongside Mr Penny. 'I'll drive her out of town,' he said. 'Then I'll let you have a go.' So along the Bristol road we went, and soon we were on a quiet stretch of road. Mr Penny then pulled into the side and stopped, and still sitting in the driver's seat he carefully explained the technique of driving. He described the different gears, what to do and not what to do, emphasising that an ambulance was different from any other vehicle. 'For the simple reason,' he said, 'that you'll be carrying sick people, maybe injured. So the driving of an ambulance must be done with the utmost care and proficiency.'

We changed seats, and I was now in the driving-seat, feeling perhaps a little apprehensive.

'Now,' said Mr Penny, 'just relax, and do exactly as I say.'

There was no doubt about it, I had a good instructor, so I was determined to be a good pupil. Pressing down the clutch pedal, I engaged first gear. I then touched the throttle with my right foot, releasing the clutch pedal at the same time, and giving my hand signal. I was about to move out, and at that moment I blundered, for I realised I had let the clutch in a little too quickly; consequently I gave Old Jane quite a few nasty jerks. Mr Penny was not perturbed by all this; perhaps he expected me to do it on my first attempt. Anyway he merely said, 'Don't worry, Miss. You'll soon get used to it.' He was right. With Mr Penny's careful instructions, I did indeed get the hang of it.

I have a vivid memory of my first lesson. I was doing nicely, and almost feeling proud of my achievement at being able to master Old Jane, when we came across workmen digging in the middle of the road. On approaching them I slowed down considerably, but my judgement of distance was incorrect, and to my dismay I only just managed to squeeze past them. I glanced at the mirror, only to see one of the men shaking his fist at me. I blushed with guilt, and hoped Mr Penny hadn't noticed me. However, once again I relaxed, and felt much better when Mr Penny told me, 'You are going to be all right, Miss.'

By this time I was so enthusiastic that I hadn't noticed we were now near Bristol. As a matter of fact, we were on the outskirts of the town, when suddenly the alert siren started blowing.

'Well I'll be damned,' said Mr Penny. 'Looks like trouble. Pull into the side, Miss, and I'll take over. Since we're this far, we might as well make our way to the Bristol depot. I can phone in to Bath, and give our location. Then if we are required here, they'll know exactly where we are.'

I now sat back and admired the way Mr Penny drove Old Jane. It was as if he was driving a Rolls-Royce, so it was no wonder he was eligible for his position as an instructor, having qualities of both patience and tolerance.

We had only just arrived at the Bristol ambulance depot when we distinctly heard aircraft overhead, followed immediately by 'thud, thud.' It was obvious that Bristol was in for it again.

Mr Penny spoke to several men and women. Evidently he had been there previously, for the co-operation between Bath and Bristol was obvious. Then, within seconds, 'action stations' came into operation, and information received indicated that the docks were the target. An announcement was made that all personnel on call would proceed to the Avonmouth docks.

Mr Penny arranged for a message to be sent to Bath, and then he looked at me and said, 'I think I'd best go down to the docks too. They may need a bit of extra help.'

And it was in a feeble voice that I exclaimed: 'Is it all right, Mr Penny, if I come with you?'

His face was now showing concern. 'Do you really want to?'

'I would rather,' I replied.

I sat quietly beside Mr Penny as we made our way down to the docks, and as we got nearer we were aware of lots of different noises around us. It's true I felt afraid; however, I did my best to hide my fear. The loudest noise was our own big guns blasting off, followed by machine-gun fire from aircraft. By now it was dusk, and strong beams from searchlights were trying to focus on enemy aircraft. I was amazed at Mr Penny's calmness amidst all this upheaval.

'How's your first aid, Miss?'

'I'm qualified,' I replied.

'Good,' said Mr Penny. 'Looks as if we are going to need you.'

Somehow I gained extreme confidence from what Mr Penny had just said. Somewhere, I thought, someone will be needing my help.

Arriving on the spot, I was confronted with horror, never having seen the likes of it before. The docks had got direct hits all right, and all the warehouses seemed to be on fire, with firemen desperately fighting the flames. It appeared to be an impossible situation, with everything in a turmoil, dust rising from the rubble, and the broken glass was everywhere.

We stopped, Mr Penny and I all ready to jump out of the cab, when a stranger shouted to Mr Penny, 'Those houses on the right there! A direct hit! See what you can do.'

Back now in Old Jane, Mr Penny drove up as near as he could to the bombed houses. We then jumped out of Old Jane, grabbing our first-aid kits as we did so. Then both of us hurried over the rubble to the site of the onslaught. Special constables and ARP wardens were working desperately to free the people that were trapped, and so it was alongside Mr Penny that I found myself administering first aid. My first casualty was a man who appeared to have a broken leg. Quickly I looked around for some kind of support, but Mr Penny looked over my shoulder and said, 'Use his other leg for support, Miss.' So, strapping the man's two legs together, I went on to the next victim. Some of them no longer required any help, so all we could do was to cover them with newspapers. I had never encountered death before, not with people. With animals it was different, and just seeing dead people like that made me kind of shudder. This then was my first experience of hostility with the enemy, and I was stunned and horrified at it all.

I remember so well bandaging up a little boy's head that had been cut by flying glass, and thinking to myself, 'This is not war'; for here were innocent civilians being absolutely slaughtered. Was I not right in thinking that, in the past, men had fought men, and *that* was war. This then was surely not war. Could it be the origin of something more terrifying? Was this not past all human endurance?

Mr Penny and I carried the injured to Old Jane. Poor Old Jane — she wasn't even equipped for service; it had been intended that she should end her life gracefully, with learner-drivers. With no stretchers for the injured it was awkward, but we were fortunate enough to have a good supply of blankets; placed on the floor, these acted as beds for the stretcher cases.

We made several trips, transporting the injured to the casualty section of the Bristol General Hospital. On our journeys to hospital, I sat amongst these poor people, all of them being in a state of shock, and all I could do was try to comfort them.

After the activity had subsided, we returned to the Bristol ambulance depot, whereupon a Superintendent thanked Mr Penny and me for services rendered.

It must have been well into the evening when we made our return journey to Bath, a distance of twelve miles, and I imagined Mum would be wondering where on earth I had got to. We must have been about three miles from Bristol when Mr Penny pulled into the side of the road and stopped.

'Would you like to take the old girl back home?' he said, meaning of course to drive Jane back to the depot. When we exchanged seats I glanced at Mr Penny and I thought the poor man looked so tired. It was strange; I knew very little of this man, yet I couldn't help but admire him for his way of coping with everything. To me his courage and personality were absolutely outstanding.

After we got back to the depot, I happened to glance at myself in a long mirror that hung up on the wall. My lovely new uniform was now covered in dust and lime, and even my face was black and scratched. I looked a mess, but before leaving I thanked Mr Penny kindly for his tuition.

'I'm only sorry, Miss,' he said, 'that it turned out the way it did. But rest assured, I know you are going to be all right. Sure enough, you'll make the grade, as we all have done. And if it's any satisfaction to you, Miss, your first aid was tops.'

'Thank you again for everything, Mr Penny,' I said. I then left the depot.

Once in the road outside, I couldn't make up my mind whether to walk home, or to catch the bus up as far as Sion Road. However, I did decide to walk home, a distance of some two and a quarter miles. I felt as if I wanted to be alone with my thoughts, and walking home was a good chance as any, so up the Lansdown Road I walked, and so deep in thought was I that I scarcely was aware of traffic passing me. It was those poor people that had been injured that day. I couldn't get them out of my mind; it was as if I had been through a fantasy, for so much had happened in so short a time. It was just hard to believe. I had merely been going for a driving lesson, when it developed into a chain of circumstances in which both Mr Penny and myself were involved in unexpected action.

I carried on walking, still thinking of the previous happenings. My heart was almost aching. Many, I knew, had lost relatives besides their homes. Much damage had been done to the warehouses, but fortunately, it being a Sunday, there were fewer people around the docks at that particular time, or the casualty toll would have been exceedingly high.

I was almost home, and glad to be there, so when I turned into the lane, I ran. I shouted 'Cooee!' as I entered the front door, and as always Mum and Dad were pleased to see me, but they were surprised to see me in such a state. It was good to be home, but I'm afraid my feelings got the better of me for without hesitation I blurted out what happened, and tears I couldn't stop simply flowed down my cheeks. 'Oh, Mum,' I sobbed, 'it was awful!'

The next thing I knew, Mum had her arms around me trying her best to comfort me. 'It's all right, darling. Come, dry your eyes, while I make some tea.'

I looked at Dad. 'Sorry I cried, Dad. I'm not as tough as I thought.'

And it was in a sympathetic voice that Dad answered, 'Paul, I've seen grown men cry when they've been in action. Best you did cry. Does no good bottling things up.' My Dad was right, for already I was beginning to feel better. 'Anyway,' said Dad, 'you haven't told me yet how your driving came on.'

'Reckon I'll be all right, Dad,' I said, and then eagerly I told him all about Mr Penny. 'He's so efficient,' I said, 'and my next lesson will be next Sunday.'

'Good for you,' replied Dad. Meanwhile Mum had made me a nice cup of tea, and between sips I laughed and chatted with my parents, and so very soon I had recovered from the events of the day.

Sunday evenings were mostly spent listening to the radio, and a favourite programme of ours was the evening service, which often enough came from St. Martin-in-the-Fields, a church in London. One night, after the service had finished, Mum said she was going to visit a certain lady, a Mrs White, who lived in Lansdown Place West — No. 7 to be precise. Mrs White was elderly, the widow of the Reverend William White who recently had passed away. Mum would describe her as a dear old soul and she was living alone apart from the domestic help she had in daily. Often enough the old lady would have her problems, in that the staff wouldn't turn up, and so she used to send for Mum to help her out. And so, as Mum said, 'Cheerio, won't be long,' I could almost guess the reason why she went to see Mrs White.

Dad was now in his armchair, occupied with his newspapers, while I sat at the table writing letters. Anyway, it wasn't long before Mum returned and began to tell us of Mrs White's predicament.

'It's her two daily maids, they are both going to leave her. One's joining the Women's Land Army, whilst the other is taking a job in a munitions factory, somewhere in the Midlands.' So it had left the dear old lady absolutely stranded, for already good domestic staff were hard to come by.

Mum, I was sure, could come to her rescue, but like Mum said, her job at the hospital took a lot of time up, without doing any extras; yet knowing Mum, I was sure she would find a way of helping the old lady.

'Can't help but feel sorry for her, being alone in that big house on her own.' Then Mum looked at me and said, 'Just suppose, duck, you could keep her company at night time. It would make the dear old soul so happy.'

'You mean for me to sleep there?'

'Yes. You could manage it, Paul.'

Myself, I wasn't struck on the idea of having to sleep away from home. On the other hand, I wanted to please Mum, knowing her judgement to be sound in all matters. And again, perhaps I felt obliged. After all, an elderly lady needing my company would give me the opportunity of doing some good, for that's what we were brought up to do; yet at the back of my mind I felt somehow unsure. I had my job at Todd's plus my involvement with the Red Cross and Civil Defence.

'Oh, Mum,' I said. 'Will I be able to manage any more?'

'It's up to you, duck. I dare say you could always give it a try.'

So, at this point, how could I refuse? Well, the very next evening, Mum took me along to No. 7 Lansdown Place West. It was dusk when we walked down Sion Hill and up the small hill that led to the house.

I was still dubious. 'Are you sure Mrs White would like me along?' I asked.

'Positive. She'll be glad of you.'

Anyway, my bag was all prepared. I was taking with me my night-dress, toothbrush, and a small alarm clock.

Mum had a key to No. 7, so we were able to let ourselves in. I followed Mum along the thickly padded carpet, my feet almost sinking in, and up the broad stairs we went. Mum then stopped outside a door; she tapped on it gently, whereupon a sweet voice answered, 'Come in.'

Mum entered first, with myself close behind. Immediately I realised that the room was a study, but before I had time to look around Mum said, 'Madam, this is my daughter, Pauline.'

Mrs White took my hand as I held it out, and her hand felt as soft as silk. She then beckoned Mum and me to be seated. I couldn't help but glance around, for this was indeed a fantastic study. It was as if I had suddenly come face to face with the Reverend William White himself, for the room had an intellectual atmosphere. I was sure it had all belonged to him, the solid oak desk and the table-lamp. And the books — what a lot of them, all neatly arranged on book shelves protected by sliding doors.

I was now looking at the lady herself, sitting in an armchair worthy of its surroundings, for it was upholstered in red velvet, trimmed with gold braiding. I couldn't guess her height, but she was a little overweight maybe, with a most charming smile which gave her face an expression of a definite character and refined goodness. Her hair, it was in abundance, lily white in colour, and so without doubt she was a lady of distinctive attractiveness.

Madam spoke. 'How would Pauline feel about coming to stay with me?'

Mum gave me a reassuring glance, as if hoping that what she had to say was the right thing. 'I must tell you, Madam, Pauline has never been away from home, except of course when she stays with her grandmother at Maidenhead.'

'I see,' said Mrs White, who was still smiling. 'Maybe if Pauline could come a few nights a week, I would be most grateful. To be alone, especially through the night, is not very pleasant.'

I now felt the dear lady's eyes upon me. Oh dear, I thought, how could I refuse to come to the aid of a lonely old lady?

'I'm willing to pay, of course,' said Mrs White. 'Just ask what you wish.'

So all was settled. I would come to Mrs White for five shillings a week.

Mrs White then spoke to Mum. 'If you like, Mrs Quintin, you may show Pauline her room. The front bedroom on the third floor.'

Mum and I then excused ourselves and off we went in pursuit of my bedroom. I had never seen the likes of it before; Lansdown Place West, leading on to Lansdown Crescent, is, after all, one of the most famous streets in Bath. How exquisite, I told myself. Fit for a queen. 'Oh, Mum. Isn't it just beautiful?'

I placed my night-dress on the top of the bed, noticing the bedside table, with the prettiest lampshade. Then, hanging up my coat in an empty wardrobe, I went across to the large windows, which were arrayed with the most delicate lace curtains. I peered through the glass, and with a moon shining I could see a little. There was no mistaking the clean-cut grass across the road to the left, and scattered everywhere were many very old trees, which were now in bud. I reckoned it would look more beautiful in the morning.

Mum then kissed me goodnight, saying, 'Don't forget, duck — breakfast at six-thirty sharp, because I'll be on my way to work at seven.'

'OK, Mum, I won't be late in the morning.'

When Mum had gone, I rejoined Mrs White in her study, where we chatted awhile. Then, seeing the dear lady to her bedroom door, I went further up the stairs to my bedroom. I closed the door quietly behind me. Going over to the windows, I closed the green velvet curtains together. Now it was really pitch dark; however, my fumbling hands touched the pretty lampshade and I switched it on, revealing the prettiest of colours and making the room almost glow with warmth and comfort.

It's strange, but I was kind of lost in such a large room. However, I was soon into bed. It was very comfortable, yet I missed my own little bed at home. I was ready for sleep, for I felt tired, but it was difficult just to drop off, and I tossed and turned restlessly.

Sooner or later, I must have fallen off to sleep, for I didn't hear any more until I was awakened by the ringing of the alarm clock. I immediately stopped it, for fear of disturbing Mrs White. I dressed, made my bed, and was along to the bathroom in minutes. A bathroom was a luxury indeed. I reckon it was the first proper bathroom I had ever been into, for we had to make do with a tin bath at No. 7 Primrose Hill, and looking at the white enamel bath and wash-basin made me realise that these things only belonged to the rich. Yet I was not envious of another's better fortune, and I forgot about it as I hurried down the stairs towards Mrs White's bedroom. I tapped gently on the door, and then Madam's voice called out, 'Come in.'

I entered her room. She too had a pretty lampshade, reflecting pink light, which made it all so cosy. The dear old lady herself was propped up in bed with book and glasses lying beside her. She gave me a smile and said, 'I hope, Pauline, you've had a good night?'

To which I replied, 'Yes, thank you, Madam.' Then, very boldly, I spoke out. 'Would Madam like a cup of tea before I go?'

'That would be very nice.' I was just about to excuse myself to go down to the kitchen in the basement, when Mrs White pointed to a cabinet on the far side of the room, saying, 'Press the button on the side. It will open up, and you will find everything you require.' So this I did, and I was amazed at my findings: an electric socket for boiling the kettle, teapot, cups and saucers, along with a barrel of biscuits. I thought of my Dad — wouldn't he just love this in his bedroom to make the early morning tea?

I made tea in minutes, giving Madam a cup, and her appreciation was now showing in her smile. 'Do have a cup with me,' she said. It was nice, sipping the tea out of a real china cup.

We finished our tea together, and then I carefully rinsed out the cups and saucers in the hand-basin and put everything back as I had found it. I was now ready to make my way home. 'It's time for me to go now, Madam.'

'Yes, my dear, you mustn't be late in getting home. And I'll be looking forward to seeing you tonight.'

I made my departure and I was now walking briskly down the road. The morning air felt good, and in my hand I grasped the key that Mrs White had given me to let myself in. I remembered her last words: 'I'll be looking forward to seeing you tonight.' As I turned into the lane, the Cooks' clock chimed the half-hour, and when I opened our front door I was met by the delicious aroma of English bacon.

'Hello, duck,' said Mum. 'Everything all right? Tell me all about it while I pop the eggs into the pan.'

'Well, Mum, I think I kind of like the old lady. But I was a long time going off to sleep.'

'Only natural,' answered Mum.

'Oh, and I made her a cup of tea before coming away.'

'I am pleased,' said Mum, who was now dishing out the eggs with the bacon, and on top went the slices of fried bread. Still Mum talked on. 'She's a dear old soul really. And to be left on her own, too. Mind you, Paul, the Rev. himself was a real gentleman. Devoted they were.'

In the following minutes we were enjoying breakfast, and when we had finished I told Mum I would wash up as I had plenty of time before going off to work. And so Mum gave me a kiss before she went off herself.

Dad was already out on the early turn, driving the 4 a.m. workman's bus that left Bath for Corsham. So there was only Rob I could make a cup of tea for, and when I went up into his bedroom he was still snuggled up in bed.

I reached over, gave him a shake, and said, 'Come on, lazy bones — time you were up.'

'Any tea, Quinner?'

'Yes, your lordship, with two lumps.' I chuckled, while Rob grinned, and then he sipped his tea.

Weeks seem to fly by, and so many changes occurred. On May the 10th Neville Chamberlain resigned, making room for another Prime Minister, Winston Churchill, who also took on the title of Minister of Defence. As time passed he turned out to be a good leader, for he encouraged hope rather than despair, and I must say how marvellously the community responded to his appeal for steadfastness in the dark days, when we all knew we were struggling. Really, right from the beginning, Winston Churchill faced a desperate situation, for the very day he took office, Hitler had invaded Holland, Luxemburg, and Belgium. Nevertheless, he inspired us all, and quite clearly I recall a speech he made to Parliament: 'I have nothing to offer, but blood, toil, tears, and sweat. . . . You ask, What is our aim? I can answer in one word: Victory.'

Amongst the members of Churchill's Government was Ernest Bevin, Minister of Labour, with Kingsley Wood, as Chancellor, presenting his first budget. It was a tough one, for he introduced purchase tax for the first time. It was described at the time as the 'pain in the neck' budget: income tax and surtax were raised, and the prices of beer and cigarettes also went up.

People worked long hours in the factories, making guns and ammunition etc., and women were replacing men in all walks of life. Even the children played their part in collecting salvage.

In June we acquired another enemy, the Italians. Their statesman, Mussolini, pledged to help Hitler. Together, he said, they would rule the world.

Many regiments had been sent to France, and my brothers Tim and Tom were both there. Building up resistance against the enemy, that was the reason why so many of our troops were there.

What was happening on the Home Front? We still had intermittent air raids. Refugees were still coming into Britain, and already we had 60,000 Germans and Austrians, and 8,000 Czechs, soon to be joined by Belgian and Dutch refugees, including Queen Wilhelmina. Aliens, however, were suspected as potential collaborators in the event of an invasion, and many were interned.

For myself, life was purely routine. I was always trying to beat the clock, as so many of us were. I would go along each evening to Mrs White, usually around about 9 p.m., and by this time I realised that I had got very attached to the dear old lady. Many nights in the study we would have long conversations, and she indeed was very wise. I never knew her age, but she must have been well into her eighties, and what a remarkable brain she had: I was most impressed with her knowledge in general. Her elegance too, was most outstanding, and this had an influence on me; in fact, it made a quick and remarkable change in my outlook on life. I knew I was changing, and I felt myself getting more and more confident. My standard of dress certainly improved, and Dad insisted that I should have the use of the five shillings a week which I received from Mrs White. 'A young lady should always be dressed well.' That was his opinion, and in fact if I ran short of clothing coupons I could always depend on Dad.

Of course, rationing was necessary. Everybody had a ration book: it was 4 inches by 6 inches, printed on cheap paper, and contained a dozen or more leaves. After a page or two of instructions, it consisted of solid pages of small coupons, the coupons on each page successively labelled Sugar, Butter, Cooking Fat, Bacon, and Meat. The instructions told you to pick out tradesmen with whom you wanted to do business, to register with them, and to inscribe their names in the blank places. Then, each day when shopping, these tradesmen were to tear out the coupons necessary to cover the purchases. A week's allocation went something like this:

Meat — two shillings and twopence

Cheese — 1 oz

Tea — 2 oz

Bacon or Ham — 4 oz

Sugar — 8 oz

Fat — 8 oz

The actual allowances varied during the war. Shell eggs were also controlled, and one packet of dried eggs was allowed each month, while jam and tinned food were rationed on a points system. A similar system was adopted for clothes, and each item cost so many of the 66 coupons allocated to everyone each month.

I might add something which I considered good about rationing: it ensured that the majority of people did not suffer from obesity, and in consequence we were far healthier people. On the other hand, one had to beware of certain people who tried to get rich quickly, like the many shopkeepers who hung on to the goods, keeping them 'under the counter' for their best customers. There were too the racketeers who managed to secure rationed or unrationed food which was in short supply, and resold it on the black market for exorbitant sums. I remember once hearing about some oranges being sold at the enormous price of sixpence each.

I still worked hard on my Hoffman press, like we all did, yet we had time to laugh and joke.

'For a bit of fun,' said Edna, 'we'll write our names and addresses on pieces of paper and put them into some air-force trouser pockets.' And it was Nancy who made us all laugh, when she said, 'Put the slips of paper in the tall 'uns, mind, the ones with the slim waists, not the short fat blokes!' Eventually, some replies to these letters were received, but they never led to anything.

At this point I was doing well with my ambulance driving. Under Mr Penny's guidance, and with more practice runs, I was beginning to feel as good as anyone else. But one Saturday afternoon I blotted my copy-book. Mr Penny was with me, and I had been promoted to drive a more modern ambulance. I felt kind of honoured at being allowed to do this, and I was driving along the London Road. Full of confidence I was, and I guess my foot was further down on the accelerator than I anticipated, the result being that I was travelling at quite a speed, and I recall passing a green single-decker bus. What I did not know at the time was that Dad was behind the wheel of that green bus.

51

Meanwhile, when we got back to the depot, Mr Penny stated that I was almost ready for an ambulance driving test, a special test that I would have to undertake before becoming competent. Naturally this immediately boosted my ego, so when I did arrive home I was in high spirits. Perhaps I was disappointed when no one was in, but there was a little note from Mum, saying that she was across the common meeting Dad, and wouldn't be long.

I could smell some delicious cooking, and peeping in the oven I saw that Mum had baked an oven pie (meat with pastry on the top). The table was set, and everywhere neat and tidy, so there was nothing I could do but wait for Mum and Dad coming home. I then decided I would have a stroll down the garden: almost all the vegetables were now planted and all the trees were in full bud. I looked up at the lilac trees: soon they would be showing their array of beauty in the variation of colour, white and mauve.

Then I heard Joey bark. Mum and Dad were home; and after our delicious meal, we all sat back and relaxed.

Then Dad spoke. 'How did the driving go today, Paul?'

'Very well,' I answered. 'Mr Penny thinks I'm ready for my test.'

'I'm pleased to hear that,' said Dad. 'But take my advice, young lady. You mustn't become over-confident.' The tone of Dad's voice made it sound like a reprimand. 'You passed me on the road today, you know. Your ability, I feel sure, is good, but in my opinion, my gal, you were travelling far too fast in a built-up area. No need for it, Paul, and speeding is dangerous.'

I blushed to think I had given Dad anxiety, and what could I say? Only, 'Sorry Dad, I'll try and remember in the future.' After all, I knew Dad to be right in what he said, he himself being an excellent driver — none better in fact. However, our little misunderstanding was soon dissolved, for I had to admit to myself that I was at fault.

On my way to Mrs White's one night, a policeman appeared from nowhere. 'Good evening, Miss,' he says. 'I must ask you to accompany me to the station.'

'Whatever for?' I gasped.

'I don't rightly know, Miss. The only thing I can tell 'ee, you be a suspected suspicious person.'

'Why that's ridiculous!' I replied.

'Well of course,' said the policeman. 'It is ridiculous, I've to acknowledge the fact. But anyway, Miss, it's best you come with me to the police station.'

I thought it ludicrous, but knew it best to do what I was told, especially when it concerned the law. I was accompanied then by the policeman to the local police station, where I came face to face with the Sergeant at the desk, who looked at me in such a peculiar way that I began to think I was about to be interrogated as the No. 1 suspect and spy. Still eyeing me up and down, he twirled at his moustache, and in a deep voice said, 'Now young lady, I must ask you for some identification.'

'But why?' I asked. 'I'm sure I've nothing to identify myself with, for it isn't necessary for me to carry anything. I live on Primrose Hill, and each night I walk along to Lansdown Place West, to stay with a Mrs White. I'm her nightly companion, you see.'

It was no good, I could see the Sergeant was not convinced.

I plucked up my courage. 'Please tell me who has been kind enough to lodge this complaint about me.'

Now the Sergeant was fully occupied with scratching the back of his head. 'Well now,' he says. 'I suppose there is no harm in telling you, girl. It's the old Major, that lives in the big house on Sion Hill.'

I suddenly felt my cheeks go hot; evidently the old Major had been watching me for some considerable time.

'I'll have to take some particulars,' said the Sergeant.

Then a thought suddenly flashed through my mind. 'Sergeant,' I said, 'would you be good enough to ring the Civil Defence ambulance depot. They will verify that I am Miss Pauline Quintin, attached to the Somerset division of the Red Cross Society.'

I'm sure I now had the Sergeant baffled. However, he picked up the receiver and dialled a number. He spoke. 'Enquiring, please. Do you have a Miss Pauline Quintin on your staff?' Pause. 'Oh yes. Thank you.' So at last I had finally convinced the Sergeant, for immediately he said, 'OK, Miss, you may go. And if I get the chance, I'll have a word with the old Major myself. And I'm sorry, Miss, for any inconvenience this may have caused you.'

The next thing was, I was hurrying up Sion Hill, for it was past 10 p.m., and I imagined Mrs White would think I was never coming. However, when I did reach her I soon poured out my story to her.

'How ridiculous,' exclaimed Mrs White.

The next morning I arrived home prompt at 6.30 a.m., and I was full of excitement as I told Mum all that had happened the night before. When I told Dad he just laughed and said, 'What a silly old fool the Major must be. Imagining a slip of girl to be a spy!'

Well, by now I was beginning to see the funny side of it, and I giggled to think that the incident had caused so much embarrassment.

The middle of May 1940 brought Tom home on leave from France, and when we did see him he had the fattest of faces; he had in fact got an abscess in his gum, due to a decayed tooth. I felt so sorry for him, for he was in much pain with it, yet it didn't stop him from going into The Retreat with Dad for a game of cribbage. Well, I just knew I must help him to alleviate the pain somehow, so filling a small canvas bag with salt, I heated it up over the electric hotplate, and dashed into The Retreat with it.

'Hold this to your face, Tom,' I gasped.

But Tom looked surprised at my command. 'Hey, what's this?' he exclaimed.

'Just something to ease the pain.' And it was the third hot bag I took in that yielded results, for it gave Tom such relief.

'Well I'm blowed,' he said. 'Florence Nightingale to the rescue.'

Anyway, the next morning, Tom attended the Royal United Hospital, where they extracted the troublesome tooth and gave him a permit for an extension of leave. Despite the discomfort, this was a lucky break for Tom, for it meant that he missed the ordeal of Dunkirk. The German armies were now making a breakthrough into France, bringing the war nearer home. Consequently, an invasion was now a real threat, and the French were unable to hold back the advance. And so it was that on May the 20th 1940 the Germans reached the Channel coast, and the British Expeditionary Force was cut off in the country behind Dunkirk. Evacuation was the only solution; about 340,000 men had to be taken off the beaches and shipped home. So Dunkirk was tragic; it was a major blow, yet all credit must go to the bravery of the men who came to the rescue, in whatever boats they could handle, some of which were unseaworthy.

Something like 860 ships took part in Operation Dynamo. Fishing-boats, steamers, yes, even the Brighton Belles and Brighton Queens played their part. One can imagine these boats leaving their innocent foolish world to sail into the inferno, only to defy bombs, shells, magnetic mines, torpedoes, and machine-gun fire, for the sake of rescuing men.

Amongst the thousands saved was my brother Tim, and how well I remember him coming home, for the very first words he uttered were, 'Our Tom — our Tom, is he all right?'

'He's all right now he's got rid of his bad tooth,' I said.

Tim looked at me, puzzled. 'His tooth?' I guess he wondered what the devil I was talking about, and it was only when I explained briefly about Tom's leave being extended that the frown disappeared from his forehead. 'Good God, our Tom's been lucky.'

Soon afterwards, I overheard Tim's conversation with Dad. 'We were in a hell of a mess, Dad, had to leave all our equipment behind.' Pathetically he told Dad how he came across Tom's mob (the 5th Field Ambulance Corps), and how, surrounded by Germans, he ran from one ambulance to another only to find dead men slumped over the steering-wheels.

'You know, Dad,' said Tim, 'our Tom would have copped it, if he had been there. For they just machine-gunned us as we waited on the beaches. Dive-bombing they were, with their guns blazing. Oh Dad, it was just one hell of a carnage. We were mowed down like rabbits.'

I looked at Dad and saw that he understood it all. Perhaps it had been different for him, as an old soldier in a different kind of war, yet he knew the meaning of hostilities.

When Tim and Tom finally met up with each other, they had much to talk over, Tom being in a state of melancholy, knowing he had lost many of his pals.

A few nights passed, and then one night at about 7 p.m., our air-raid warning siren went, so once again we were sheltering in the sitting-room. By now we had a Morrison shelter, a square box of steel, designed to protect us if the house collapsed; Mum had put a mattress on the bottom of it to make it more comfortable.

Almost immediately we heard enemy aircraft going over, followed by heavy thuds; it was obvious that Bristol was getting it again. I suddenly thought of my encounter at Avonmouth Docks. That had been bad enough, and I shuddered to think how much worse it would be at night.

After an hour or so, the 'all clear' blew, so out we crawled, and on Dad's suggestion I was to go into The Retreat and fetch Mum in a little drink. So, taking a little white jug, and sixpence, I went into the pub to get it filled with best port wine. Now, Mum was not a habitual drinker by any means, but occasionally she would enjoy this special treat.

I went down the stone steps to The Retreat, crossed over the crazy paving, and then opened the front door. I thought it strange, Old Sam having his door closed, for usually it was always wide open at this time of a night to welcome customers. All was quiet. I then tapped my shoe on one of the flagstones in the passage. 'Hello?' I shouted. 'Anybody at home?'

I then heard footsteps. It was Old Sam himself, and the poor man looked startled. 'The "all clear" bain't gone yet, has it?'

'Oh yes, Sam,' I replied, 'about twenty minutes past.'

'Well I be damned. Never heard it.'

We were joined by Nora, his wife, who was also surprised at not hearing the 'all clear'. Anyway, I purchased Mum's refreshment and the port wine was just brimming to the top of the little white jug; I was almost tempted to take a sip out rather than spill it. However, I walked slowly with it, keeping my hand as steady as possible, and up the steps I went into the lane. There I was suddenly confronted by two young men. The light was dim, yet I noticed they were both smiling at me, maybe because of the awkward way in which I was standing from the effort of trying to steady the little white jug.

Then one of the young men spoke. 'Excuse me, Miss. Do the Quintins live somewhere around here?'

It was silly, but suddenly I felt myself blush, and when I spoke I hoped they did not observe the nervousness that was within me. 'Um, I'm Pauline Quintin.'

'Well I never,' remarked the other young man. 'Don't you know me? I'm your cousin Cecil.'

'Why of course,' I replied timidly. 'You're Uncle Edwin's son. I'm sorry I didn't recognise you.'

'Must be years since I last saw you,' said Cecil. 'By the way, this is Timmy, a mate of mine.'

I could not shake his hand, my own hands being occupied. However, I did say, 'I'm pleased to meet you.'

My cousin and Timmy then followed me up the back lane, Cecil opening the door for me. Down the steps, one behind the other we went, into the kitchen, where Dad was busy banking up the fire, and was he surprised when he turned around and saw the three of us standing there.

Dad recognised Cecil immediately. 'Why hello, Cecil, nice to see you. And this young man?' said Dad.

'It's Timmy, Uncle Pat, a pal of mine. We're on the same boat. Merchant Navy.' That explained why they were not in uniform.

Then Dad called out to Mum, and when she did appear, Dad said, 'Do you know who this is, Nell?'

Well, Mum looked a little vague at first.

'It's Cecil, Edwin's boy.'

'Why of course,' said Mum. 'The trouble is, you've all grown up too fast!' Mum then looked at the other young man.

'Oh, Aunt Nell, let me introduce you to Timmy.' Mum then shook hands with the boy. 'I came up especially, Uncle Pat, to see if your lads were all right. For Dad was saying that Thomas and Timothy were at Dunkirk.'

'Tim was,' replied Dad. 'But thank God he got home. Tom was in England and missed it.'

'So glad,' said Cecil.

By this time I was sitting on a stool beside the fire. There was not a lot of heat coming from it really, yet my cheeks felt hot: it was myself blushing again, affected by the presence of Cecil and Timmy, who were both fine young men. I was just happy in listening in to their conversations.

'Good of you to come up,' said Dad.

Then I was aware that Cecil now had his eyes fixed on me, for he remarked, 'You know, Pauline, I can remember the last time I saw you. You were still at school. And I see you still have your freckles.'

Well, I went crimson didn't I, for now I sensed Timmy's eyes upon me. Oh dear, I thought, what will they think of me? The truth was, I was suffering from bashfulness.

Then Dad spoke. 'How would you lads like a pint? We can have a nice chat over a glass of mild and bitter.'

'Splendid, Uncle Pat,' replied Cecil. Both lads looked pleased, and they both jumped up off their chairs. 'Well, goodbye, Aunt Nell,' said Cecil, giving Mum a kiss. And then he said, 'Cheerio, Pauline,' and without any hesitation he gave me a kiss on my cheek. And before I knew where I was, Timmy did likewise.

'Best of luck to you, boys,' said Mum.

I think I almost stood rigid at the thought of being kissed by two young men. Such a thing had never happened to me before.

'I do declare,' said Mum, after they had gone. 'You are still blushing.' I smiled at Mum, who gently placed her arm around my shoulder. 'Funny,' she said 'I was just like you at your age — extremely shy.'

Well, it was time I was getting along to Mrs White's, so after kissing Mum goodnight I was on my way, and walking along underneath the trees my thoughts drifted to Cecil and Timmy. They were both very nice. Pity I blushed though. I guess I had very little control over my feelings, yet secretly I was pleased I had made their acquaintance.

It was on the 17th of June 1940 that France fell; an armistice between France and Germany was signed on the 22nd. Britain now stood alone, facing a German-occupied Europe, and the Channel no longer gave us the same defence as in the days before bomber aircraft.

The Government and everyone else feared a general panic if ever German forces should actually land. It was understood that the British people could expect anything now, so it was no surprise when German air attacks on British convoys through the Straits of Dover began in earnest.

The battle of the Atlantic brought with it a drastic reduction of five million tons in imports, so the meat allocation alone was reduced from two shillings and twopence a week to one shilling and twopence. The Government also feared inflation. Too much money would be chasing too few goods, this being the classic condition for inflation, so the Government took the advice of John Maynard Keynes. This meant, of course, increased taxation of the working classes, but at least some of the money collected in taxes would be repaid after the war, in post-war credits.

Summertime came, and I think everyone took advantage of the sun — that's if they had time, of course. Holidays, even day trips, were out of the question; nevertheless, the warm sunny days were a tonic to us all, in spite of the uncertainty we had to face, for enemy action, both in the air and on the seas, was coming closer to our shores.

The reality of war was soon brought home to our family. It all happened when we had an unexpected visit from Uncle Edwin. I think we were all surprised to see him, and when I first saw his face I knew something was very wrong. He almost spoke in a whisper when he said, 'Hello, everybody.' Then his next sentence came as a shattering blow to us all. 'We've lost Cecil.'

Immediately Dad steadied him down on to a chair. Dad started to speak but did not finish his words.

'Yes, Pat,' replied Uncle. 'Cecil was killed on active service.'

'Oh God,' said Mum.

'And Timmy?' said Dad.

'He got it too. As you know, they were on the same boat, and both gunners.'

We were stunned. No one could speak, and a state of silence came into being. Then Mum disappeared and came back holding a small glass in her hand. 'Edwin,' she said, 'drink this, it will help.'

What Mum gave him appeared to steady him for next he spoke with more strength. 'All I know is, they came into some kind of skirmish. I don't rightly know where.' Uncle was now bending over, holding his head in his hands.

'I'm sorry, Edwin,' said Dad. Mum did not speak, and only the paleness of her face revealed her thoughts.

For myself, I was shocked. I just couldn't believe that Cecil and Timmy had been killed, for only a few weeks previous had I not blushed at their very presence? I remembered how they had both kissed me. I thought then of dear Auntie Min. Cecil was her youngest son.

The next thing I remember, Uncle Edwin was telling Dad that Cecil could have had a sea burial, but Min preferred his body to be brought home and buried at Haycombe cemetery.

Quietly, unnoticed, I slipped into the scullery and put the kettle on; what we all needed was a good cup of tea. After settling everyone, I wandered out into the garden, and being alone I suppose I started crying. I then strolled over to the chicken-run, and watched the hens scratching up the dirt. Finally, drying my eyes with the bottom of my dress, I went inside, making myself busy with the washing-up, lest anyone should see my red eyes.

Then Uncle Edwin said he must go. 'I'll walk a little way back with you,' said Dad. 'Our Joey there, he'll enjoy a run.'

I would have loved to have gone with them, but did not want to intervene where two brothers were concerned.

When they had gone, I sat down beside Mum, who was by now almost staring into space.

'Nice boys,' she said. 'And oh so very young.'

PART THREE

IN AUGUST 1939 William Joyce, an American-born Mosleyite, decided to leave London for Berlin, where he took a job in broadcasting. So a propagandist he became, and by joining the fifth column he became without doubt a traitor. On a certain wavelength on the wireless, one could pick up the propaganda station, and our Mr Joyce was thus re-christened 'Lord Haw Haw'. He would start his announcements with this introduction: 'This is Germany calling, Germany calling.' He was in fact trying very hard to intimidate us. The aim of his propaganda broadcasts was to break down British morale; and in all sincerity, and with a perfect English vocabulary, he endeavoured to convince the British people that they were going to lose the war. He boasted about our defeats, and was full of hilarity when he spoke of German gains.

Hitler by now had found a new weapon — and a very peculiar one it was too, as I found out at first hand. One dark night, I set off from home to meet Mum coming from the Royal United Hospital. It was a strange night: the atmosphere was humid, bringing with it a fine drizzle. I was pleased Joey was with me, and strangely enough he kept to my heels. I came down the slope and passed the farm; then, on my way down the long Weston hill (now called Weston Park East), the Pitman estate lay on my left, fine old trees casting shadows in a somewhat weird way.

Somehow I wished I could have whistled, for at least it might have broken the uncanny atmosphere which now surrounded me, and I was aware of the unusual stillness of the night air. On my right I passed some meadows. One field in particular was used solely for archery, and often we would enjoy watching the archers from the roadway. In this sport, the women were as keen as the men, but unfortunately it was a game for the upper classes only. It always fascinated me just to watch the arrows leave the bow and speed towards the target which stood on an easel, with painted rings of all colours. Secretly I felt as excited as the archer when an arrow would hit a bull's-eye.

I walked on. Perhaps it would have been better if I had started running, for at least I would have heard my own heels clicking.

However, eventually I did hear something, and I realised it was a drone from a single plane. It was getting closer, and now it appeared to be right above me. It was so low, too. Must be one of ours, I thought, so I stood in my tracks and listened.

I sensed that something was wrong, and on impulse I grabbed at Joey's collar, pulling him close beside me, for at that moment I felt I needed some kind of reassurance, if only from a dog. I waited in anticipation, for it felt as if the plane was right on top of me. I was frightened, but I knew that whatever I did I must not panic or show any light from my torch. To some extent I felt safe and protected in the dark, but the situation I now found myself in appeared somewhat disturbing. There was only Joey and I on this lonely road, with a mystery plane just circling above me. Could it be something unnatural from outer space? It could be coming right for me, maybe to make a grab for me, like some terrible phantom.

Now I was thinking stupid. Such thoughts I knew were ridiculous. Best disperse them from my mind, I thought. But suddenly, almost without thinking, I made a jump into the hedge, pulling Joey on the top of me. All I could do then was peer out into the darkness.

At first I could see nothing, yet I was still aware that the plane was above me, and if I had let my imagination run away with me I could have sworn the aircraft was stationary in mid-air. I continued to gaze into the uncanny blackness that surrounded me. Then suddenly I saw it: an object was falling out of the sky. I felt my heart beat faster. I couldn't make out what the object was, yet I did observe that it was light in colour. Could it be a parachute? Then I saw the outline of it fall right in the middle of the archery field.

Beads of perspiration were now on my forehead. What was I to do now? I listened for the plane, and was I relieved when the noise from its engines subsided; at long last, it was going away.

On the road now, I peered at the object. It did not move. I knew I must not be alone in this, and that I must get help quickly. Further down the road was Ben's cottage — Ben was Mr Pitman's chauffeur — so immediately I started running as fast as I could with Joey at my heels.

I reached the cottage, and panting I was. However, I gave three taps on the door, and when Ben answered he was more than surprised to see me.

'Hello, young lady. Why, it be Pauline,' he said. 'What can I do for you, me dear?'

'Need your help Ben,' I blurted out. 'They've dropped a parachute or something in the archery field.'

'Coo. Be 'ee sure?' replied Ben.

'I saw it,' I answered. 'Came from a plane it did.'

'Ye best come on in a minute, have a chat with our Peggy.'

Peggy, incidentally, was Ben's wife, and she too was surprised to see me. 'Why, it be Polly Quintin,' she said, and oh dear, how I hated being called Polly.

Then Ben said, 'This calls for action,' whereupon he picked up the phone and dialled a number. I overhead him say, 'Sorry to bother you, Sir, but I've just received information of something falling, out in the archery field.' Pause. 'Yes. Yes, Sir. Very good, Sir.' With which Ben replaced the receiver. He then looked at me and said, 'Were thee going to meet thee Mam then?'

'Yes,' I answered.

'Well, don't thee be worrying then. Mr Pitman is taking the situation in hand. Reckon he'll notify the Army first. Anyway, he's coming down to investigate himself. Can depend on the Master, he knows what to do for the best.'

I waited with Ben and Peggy, curious to see what was going to happen. Besides, I knew Mum wouldn't have left the hospital yet, and with a bit of luck my delay would just mean that I would meet her half-way. Sometimes that used to happen, so I wasn't concerned.

Well, Mr Pitman arrived, carrying his shotgun too, and accompanying him were two of his gardeners, each armed with a garden tool.

Mr Pitman spoke: 'Who saw the object fall?'

'I did, Sir. It came from a plane hovering over me.'

'Damn funny thing,' remarked Mr Pitman. 'We've had no warning siren. I must make enquiries about this. Unless, of course, it was one of our planes. And what precisely was it that dropped? Rather a puzzling affair. Still, we must investigate the matter.'

By now I couldn't help studying Mr Pitman. I hadn't been this close to him before. He was a typical gentleman, with fine-cut features and a moustache that gave him much distinction. A man who I would say was in his forties.

The next thing, Mr Pitman was giving orders to his men to move with all caution up the road. By this time Ben had joined them, carrying a heavy spanner. 'We'll cross into the archery field,' said Mr Pitman. 'But on no account must anybody go near the fallen object. It'll be up to the Army to tackle it.'

I myself said a quick cheerio to Peggy and proceeded on my way to meet Mum, with Joey anxious to be on the move. My steps quickened, and then I spotted Mum on the bend of the road. I could hardly see her through the mist and drizzle, but there she was, and really pleased I was to see her. So was Joey; he was jumping up and down so much he nearly knocked her basket out of her hand.

I couldn't wait to tell Mum about the mystery plane and its fallen object. 'Strange,' says Mum. 'There's been no warning.' Anyway, we now made our way back up the Weston hill, and when we reached the archery field we came across a couple of Army jeeps parked on the side of the road. Then, looking across the field, we saw torches flashing, and heard the sound of men's laughter.

'Wonder what they've found?' I said.

'Your guess is as good as mine, duck!' Mum paused. 'Paul — did you really see something fall? It wasn't just imagination, was it? The darkness can be so deceptive, you know.'

'Oh Mum! Really I did see something fall.'

'I believe you,' came a voice from behind us. It was Mr Pitman.

'Good evening, Sir,' said Mum.

'Your young daughter, I must say, is very observant. And as it happens we did have an enemy straggler over. Can't imagine how the devil he got through, though. But he did, and dropped two very large canvas bags which were tied together, each containing thousands of propaganda leaflets. I can only think it was a very weary pilot, wanting to get rid of his load quickly.' Then Mr Pitman gave a chuckle. 'Tomorrow, in daylight, we'll make one huge bonfire of them. Well, goodnight ladies.'

'Goodnight, Sir,' Mum answered. I bade the gentleman goodnight too, but in a mere whisper. And so Mum and I continued our way home. We had almost reached home when Mum said: 'Fancy. A German plane getting through like that. Wouldn't credit it. Could easily have dropped bombs instead.'

Mum was right, of course. Radar was only in its infancy, and it was quite understandable that an enemy plane should get through unspotted. However, I got the idea that nothing would escape Mr Pitman's enquiry into the matter.

Dad was in when we finally reached home, the table was set, and Mum's Irish stew was slowly being re-heated on the stove. Through supper I talked of my encounter with the enemy.

'I just had that feeling, Dad, that the plane above me was not ours.'

'Bet it put the wind up you, Paul!'

'It did,' I replied. 'I was frightened.'

'It was a blessing,' said Dad, 'that it was only leaflets.'

That evening I had plenty to tell Mrs White. 'You poor child,' she remarked. 'You must have been frightened nearly out of your wits.'

'I was, Madam,' I answered.

That night in bed, after I had said my prayers, I thought what on earth I would have done if what had dropped into the archery field had turned out to be paratroops or spies. Remembering the plane, and just how close it had been to me, I shuddered to think any more.

The next morning, at work, I told the girls in the press room all about my ordeal the previous night.

'Goodness gracious,' said Edna. 'You should get a medal for your observation.'

I wanted no medal, I was just pleased to be alive.

From the 11th to the 18th of August 1940, the Battle of Britain was at its height. German attacks on British convoys were also becoming more persistent. Hitler now had one aim, to conquer us. He made plans for Operation Sea Lion, which was the invasion of England.

We stood alone on an island. Before aircraft were invented, we had the protection of the sea, but now it was all so different. Together with increased activity on the seas there came the bombing of our airfields. Hermann Goering ordered the Luftwaffe to destroy the Royal Air Force by bombing the Kent fighter bases. One night, 600 German planes were used in three raids on south-east England.

Reports from London stated that the first flights of German bombers were now coming up the Thames. Hitler launched an almost continuous succession of mass raids on London, leaving the city ringed with fire. But the courage of our fighter pilots saved us. In one day, the Germans lost 180 planes, and the British 60. The Luftwaffe's effort to knock out the R.A.F. and secure a safe sea-passage for the invaders failed, and Hitler had no alternative but to call off Operation Sea Lion.

Churchill spoke for the whole nation when he gave thanks for our fighter pilots. His famous words were as follows: 'Never in the field of human conflict, was so much owed by so many to so few.'

Despite our victory in the Battle of Britain, the blitz continued. Every night, the searchlights sent up straight, hard fountains of light that seemed to dissolve into infinity. But eight of Christopher Wren's churches, the Guildhall, and the Houses of Parliament, all suffered direct hits. Destruction spread beyond the City into the West End of London. Actually I was not a witness to the happenings in London, but they say it was eerie to walk along streets and see houses lying flat in their own gardens. And in the East End, it was estimated that there was a square half-mile of devastation: all life, all semblance of human habitation had disappeared from the crushed and flattened acres.

The roof-top spotting system came into being. It helped to localise the air-raid warnings and prevent disruption of a whole city at once.

There was very little absenteeism caused by the raids, but one would see men staggering at their work from lack of sleep. It must have been the high courage and resolution that spurred us all on. Praise is due not only to wives and mothers, but also to the crowds of nurses, secretaries, clerks, telephone girls, shop assistants, and waitresses, who morning after morning turned up for duty, looking as neat as ever. After the war, even the Windmill Theatre could boast that it had never closed!

The Women's Voluntary Services were doing a great job. They were responsible for setting up emergency canteens, aided by the Government, which took responsibility for the welfare of the blitzed. The Ministry of Food also set up emergency services for those, rich and poor alike, who needed sanctuary and food.

It was during Hitler's invasion attacks that Southampton, Bristol, and Birmingham were badly hit, and Plymouth suffered five terrible nights of raids. I think incendiary bombs and fires were the worst hazard. The public were told to leave a bucket of sand outside their front door, sand being the best thing to use to put out incendiary bombs.

The firemen became the heroes of the day, but I'm afraid the service was badly strained, because 800 firemen lost their lives, and 7,000 were badly injured. With such a sacrifice, it was necessary to ask for help from the public, so compulsory fire-watching was introduced. Every man between 16 and 60 took a turn for 48 hours each month.

The newspapers of the time were full of photographs of people taking shelter in the underground stations. Men, women, and children were just lying down on blankets on the platforms, feeling more secure and safe down there perhaps. It was also known that Epping Forest, in Essex, became a nightly camping ground for many hundreds fleeing the blitz.

It was Saturday night, and I was just about ready to go along to Mrs White. I was alone, Dad was on a late turn, and on that particular night Mum was working extra time at the hospital. I was about to switch all the lights off when I got a surprise visit from my eldest brother, Pat. I thought he looked extremely well, and I dare say time itself had helped him to recover from his ordeal on the *Courageous.* He appeared disappointed when he heard that Mum and Dad were not at home, but anyway he said he was on a week's furlough and would be up again the following day.

'Aren't you going into The Retreat?' I asked.

'Bit late now, Paul,' he replied. 'Anyway, you'll be going along to the old lady's — I'll walk along with you.'

This to me was indeed a pleasure, to be escorted along the road by my big brother. I always felt proud of him, especially when he wore his sailor's uniform. We laughed and chatted as we walked along, and as a matter of fact Pat was curious to know if I had any boy-friends. That was our Pat, kidding me as usual, so I thought I would do likewise.

'Oh yes,' I said. 'Got myself a marine.'

My last remark made him suddenly stop in his tracks. 'You haven't, our Paul.'

I couldn't help it, I burst out laughing, and of course this gave the game away, didn't it? Then brother Pat said, 'You wait, young lady, one of these days you'll meet Mr Right, and then you'll be swept off your feet.'

I stopped at the top of the road leading to the common, thinking that Pat would be going that way home, as he usually did. 'Well, cheerio, our Pat,' I said.

'Hold on,' said Pat. 'I'm not leaving you yet. Tonight I shall escort you right to the door, Madam.'

Now I put my arm in his as we walked down Sion Hill. Suddenly the warning siren went, and my reaction, as usual, was to start running. But Pat reached out and held me back.

'Don't be in such a hurry,' he said. 'We could just run into trouble.' And funnily enough I had never thought of it like that before.

The next thing we heard was the sound of aircraft overhead. 'Aye aye,' said Pat, looking up worriedly. Then we heard the whistle from a bomb falling, and without any hesitation Pat pushed me into the gutter. Taken unawares I went down on my knees with such a thud, and then Pat was almost lying on top of me, protecting me with his own body. In seconds we felt this terrible vibration underneath us.

'God,' said Pat. 'That's been a close 'un. . . . You all right, our Paul?' Now he was helping me on to my feet.

'I'm OK,' I answered. 'How about you?'

He chuckled and said, 'I'm still in one piece, Paul.' But faintly I could see that the side of his face was bleeding, for something had hit him. Myself, I felt my knees were full of gravel; they were sore, due to the impact I got when falling to the ground.

Pat then pulled his handkerchief out of his pocket; he dampened it with his own saliva, and wiped the side of his face. Meanwhile, a number of alarmed voices were heard as people came out to see what had happened, and just a matter of thirty yards away we observed a big crater. The bomb had landed on the junction between the roadway and common, making the heavy iron railings that separated the two disappear completely. It was a blessing it fell where it did, for there were no casualties, but I imagine that the little animals which roamed the common at night would have been terrified.

We then heard a voice shout at us. 'You two all right there?'

Good heavens, I thought, it's the old Major himself. It was the very same old boy who had thought I was some kind of spy, and had had me held for questioning at the police station. He must certainly have recognised me again, but this time he showed some kindness by saying, 'Please come into the house. Wash and tidy up.'

I could not bring myself to express any ill will towards the man, and was glad to accept his hospitality. So, obeying the old Major's wishes, we entered the big house that stood on the corner of Sion Hill, whereupon a maid ushered us into a large kitchen. There, at the sink, we bathed our wounds. We then thanked the Major, came out, and made our way down to investigate the crater.

'Coo!' I gasped. 'Quite easily get a double-decker bus in that hole.'

'Yep,' answered Pat. 'It's a whopper. Well, better see you up to the old lady's now.'

It was on Mrs White's doorstep that I kissed our Pat goodnight. 'See you tomorrow then,' said Pat, with which he disappeared into the darkness.

I let myself in, putting the big bolt on the door, and then walked up the stairs to Mrs White's study. I gave a gentle tap on the door before entering and I immediately noticed that the dear old soul looked very pale; the bomb had evidently given her a fright.

'Are you all right, Madam?' I asked.

'I'm all right now,' was her reply.

Sitting beside her, I told her all that had happened.

'Yes,' she said, 'it gave me an awful fright. You see, I was having this little nap in the chair when the explosion startled me. Many blessings to the Almighty that no one was hurt.'

Mrs White then gave a glance at my knees, for I had a big hole in each stocking.

'Goodness me, look at your poor knees,' she said. 'Go straight away to the bathroom, Pauline. There you'll find all you need in the first-aid box.'

I hastened to the bathroom, and soon made dressings of zinc and castor oil ointment for my knees; and how soothing it was. I then returned to the study, where a cup of tea was awaiting me. And so we chatted, much longer than usual, I'm afraid.

'I wonder,' said Mrs White, 'if the blast from the bomb has damaged any of my windows.'

'I'll check for you, Madam,' I said. The front windows were OK, because they all had strong shutters which not only blotted out the light but protected the frames as well, but during my investigations I found that two back windows were badly cracked. That was all, so when I told Mrs White of my findings she was much relieved.

'Could have been worse,' she said. And how true, I thought.

Arriving home next morning, I had plenty to tell Mum, and at the same time showed her my knees.

'Goodness me!' gasped Mum in consternation. 'You've had a miraculous escape. The two of you could have been killed.' And, of course, she was absolutely right.

The following day, Sunday, I was looking forward to some driving tuition from Mr Penny. This to me was something very special to look forward to, so after helping Mum with the chores I was ready to go. My brother Rob then called out, 'Taking your bike, Paul?'

'No,' I replied. 'Taking a nice walk to town instead.'

'Can I borrow it for a couple of hours?'

'OK,' I said. 'But treat her kindly.'

It indeed was a beautiful morning, and I had plenty of time, so I just strolled across the common. I sat a while on one of the wooden seats that were placed along the pathway. How peaceful it all was; the breeze was brushing the long grass beside me, and the trees were crowned out in full leaf, giving me shelter from the hot sun. I then saw a figure approaching, and soon recognised the blue uniform of the Air Force. However, when the young man got nearer, I realised who it was: it was an old school pal of mine, Billy Biss.

When he got up to me, I started blushing, and I was glad he was the first one to speak.

'Hello, Pauline. Hope it's me you are waiting for.'

'Hello, Billy.' I couldn't think of anything else to say for a moment.

Now he sat down beside me. Nothing seemed to change about him; he was still the same good-looking lad, and being tall and slim he looked quite smart in his uniform.

'I'm just on my way to town,' I said, and explained where I was going.

'Mind if I walk down with you?'

'Would you be offended,' I said at once, 'if I asked you not to?' I just had to be outspoken; after all I did not want to become involved in any romantic affairs, not just yet, at any rate. But I could see I had disappointed him.

'I see,' he said. 'Always the very shy Pauline Quintin. Still, I must admit I like you. And always will.'

We then parted, walking in different directions, and myself feeling a bit of a heel for turning him down like that, for I dare say I would have enjoyed his company. But for me, at that particular time, having a boy-friend was out of the question.

Reaching the end of the common and walking between the two concrete posts, I happened to look up Sion Hill, and in the distance I could see men busy filling in the big crater, which incidentally reminded me that my knees were still sore. I thought it a miracle that the bomb had dropped where it did, for quite a lot of big houses stood in the vicinity.

It was about 10.15 a.m. when I reached the ambulance depot, and Mr Penny was already there and waiting.

'Hello, Miss. Nice morning.'

'Good morning, Mr Penny,' I answered.

'This morning,' he said, 'I'm going to let you take Old Jane out. I'll be beside you, of course. But I shall give you no instructions, because I want you to be entirely on your own, for tomorrow you'll be taking the special ambulance driving test.'

Suddenly a thrill of excitement swept over me. Anxiously I asked Mr Penny what time the driving test would be, because I knew it would be necessary for me to ask permission for absence from work.

'It's two-thirty p.m. from the depot, Miss.'

It then flashed through my mind that I would have to ask for the whole afternoon off. I knew Mr Gould would understand, yet I knew it might not be so easy, for absenteeism was not popular. Well, anyway, first things first. I must concentrate on getting Old Jane out of the depot. This I did with great confidence, especially with Mr Penny sitting beside me.

'Choose your own route, Miss.' This I did, and before long I was driving Old Jane up the Lansdown Road. My journey took me past the Bath racecourse, past the old Lansdown battlefields, down into Weston Village, and eventually along the Newton Road to the depot.

When I finally stopped, inside the depot, Mr Penny remarked, 'Jolly good. And if you drive the same tomorrow, I'm certain you will get through the test. So don't forget now, two-thirty tomorrow.' He then shook my hand, and wished me the best of luck. 'And I might add, young lady, you've been an excellent pupil.'

His last words were indeed complimentary, and from then on, I was determined to do my best. It was on the tip of my tongue to say something, and I did. 'Mr Penny, I wish to express my gratitude, to thank you for your splendid tuition, and all your help and kindness.'

He acknowledged me with a smile, and so I knew when I left him I just had one aim, and that was to pass.

Coming out of the depot, I was greeted with a 'Boo!'

Oh no, I thought, but yes it was, it was the young man I had met earlier, Billy Biss. As you can imagine, I was flabbergasted. Of all people, it had to be Billy.

'What on earth are you doing here?' I exclaimed.

'I came to meet you. And now I can see I've made you cross.'

Billy was wrong about me being cross. On the contrary, I was feeling somewhat happy. Surprised at seeing Billy, of course; well, I was really astonished to see him. I just couldn't help it, I burst out laughing. 'Honestly! Really! I never expected seeing you.'

'Well,' he said, 'I'm here,' and he was now laughing back at me.

I suppose in a way we had always been the best of friends, especially in our school-days, so as we walked we chatted freely. I told him about my driving, and how I worked in a factory, and then he told me all about himself, the life in the Air Force, and where he was stationed.

As we were going up the Lansdown Road, we came across a little sweet shop. 'Fancy an ice, Pauline?' And before I could make up my mind, he was in and out, with two cornets. It reminded me of when we were kids, licking the tops, and then sucking the ice-cream through the bottoms. Walking on, we talked of our school-days, how we used to run across the fields to school, passing All Saints church, zigzagging through the gravestones, then down the steps into the schoolyard, often enough only just in time for the whistle blowing for assembly. And how many times did Billy pull my hair? Still, weren't we all happy kids together? We played, laughed, and even cried in innocence.

I was surprised to find we were almost home now, and I heard a bicycle bell behind me. There was no mistake, it was my bicycle bell I heard and Rob was ringing it, and he didn't even stop, just raced past us.

'Hey,' said Billy, 'it's your Bob.'

'I know,' I answered. I was now smiling to myself, for knowing our Rob he would go straight to Mum and Dad with the news that I was actually keeping company of Billy Biss.

Anyway, when we reached our front door, Billy said, 'Cheerio, Hope to see you again sometime.'

'All the best to you, Billy,' I said. 'Oh, and thanks again for the ice-cream.'

'Well, so long,' he said, and off he went. Billy then lived further up the lane, with his mother and father, in one of a little row of cottages which had originally been owned by the Cook family, but had been sold and then rehabilitated by separate owners. Billy too had older brothers and sisters, but like our family they were all away, and now Billy was the last to leave home.

Rob must have given his information to Mum and Dad about Billy and me, for Mum was the first to speak: 'Hello, duck. Enjoy your driving then?'

'Rather,' I replied.

'Bill Biss is home on leave then?'

'Yes, Mum,' I answered. 'I walked up from town with him.'

'Well, well,' said Dad, with a twinkle in his eye. 'Our Polyanthus is blooming! Anyway, how did your driving go?'

'I drove on my own initiative, entirely alone.'

'Without any instructions?' asked Dad.

'Yep,' I replied. 'And I take my test tomorrow. Isn't it exciting?'

'Well done, Paul. Did you hear that, Nell?'

'I did,' replied Mum, and then her face beamed into a smile. 'I'm so proud of you, duck.'

I quickly laid the table, and soon we were enjoying our lunch of roast beef and Yorkshire puddings. I glanced at Rob, who perhaps looked a little guilty, and I wondered what he really had told Mum and Dad about Billy and me. Still, I soon forgot about that, and excitedly talked of my driving test the following day. 'I must see Mr Gould, first thing in the morning,' I said.

'You need to take the afternoon off,' said Dad.

'I know, but I'm afraid he'll be displeased, for we have such a lot of work on.'

'I'm sure he will understand,' said Mum.

'I hope so.'

It was after lunch that Dad said to me, 'Paul, if you pass this driving test, what will you do? Join one of the services?'

'Oh no, Dad,' I exclaimed, 'I want to stay at home.'

'But Paul, you'll be called up like the rest, when the time comes.'

I smiled and full of confidence said: 'Dad, I shall find a man's job to do, rather than leave home.'

'But Paul, what can you do regarding a man's work?'

Perhaps I had shocked Dad by thinking that I was a man's equal. But I really did believe I would find a man's job, when the time came.

'Hey Quinner,' said Rob. 'Can't imagine you doing a man's job.'

'I could always try,' I replied. 'Anyhow, what about our Nellie in Sheffield? She's doing crane-driving.'

'Ah yes,' replied Rob. 'But she's a grown woman. You're just a girl, with no experience.'

Rob's last statement made me blush, for I knew Rob to be right.

After helping Mum with the washing-up, I went into the garden, taking a book with me. My intention was to have a nice quiet read, but somehow I could not concentrate; my mind was so active, thinking of course about the following day. Then I began to wonder — was it ridiculous of me to even want a man's job? Did I want to give up my femininity? Well no, not really. It was just the idea of leaving home. I felt my parents were entitled to have me at home. After all, three of our family were on active service, and my sister was doing essential war work. Really I did not want to leave Mum and Dad.

Then, smiling to myself, I thought about Billy Biss. Nice lad, but I knew he was not for me. True, when we were children, we had been very friendly, but things were different now, Were we not now mature people living our different lives in a world of turmoil and uncertainty?

I was still in deep thought when Mum called out to tell me that tea was ready. I was surprised that the time had gone so quickly.

That particular day we were having tea in the kitchen, as it was a little breezy for having our Sunday tea on the veranda. How well I remember those Sunday teas. There was always a big glass bowl full of winkles. Owing to the restriction on fishing in the war they were sometimes a little difficult to get hold of, but there were always the trifles and home-made cakes and scones, and, in spite of rationing, freshly baked bread.

It was during tea that Dad suggested we all take a walk across the fields, up as far as Lansdown racecourse maybe, so out came the thick shoes and walking-sticks. With Joey taking the lead, the four of us just walked, chatted, and laughed. When I was a girl, I would run and jump over the hairpin stiles, but now I was too big for that sort of thing, and I gracefully walked through them as did Mum and Dad. I suppose I envied our Rob, when I saw him jumping over things, especially the five-bar gates.

We reached the Blathwayt Arms just on opening time, and we sat on forms outside the little pub, enjoying our refreshments. In those days it was always a glass of grapefruit juice for me, while Mum enjoyed her port wine and Dad had his usual pint of mild and bitter. I noticed too our Rob drinking a shandy. How peaceful was the atmosphere that surrounded us. Not far from us could be heard the skylarks; singing high in the sky they were, while behind us the sun was beginning to set. Such calmness everywhere. I suppose all of us in England experienced this peace and serenity at some time or other, for the first few months of hostilities were often called the phoney war, when nothing much happened; and throughout the war there were lulls in the action.

Walking back across the fields, we could see Primrose Hill in the distance, neatly tucked way in the hillock. 'Safe from any danger,' Dad would say, quite wrongly as it turned out. Getting closer, our own little cottage came into view, and the colours of the different flowers surrounding it made it all so picturesque. Next to us was the Hardings' cottage, and then further to the right was The Retreat, and below it were the nursery gardens, owned by a Mr and Mrs Woods. With the help of old Ned, an ex-gardener of the Cooks, they kept the nurseries up to a good standard. How often I would call at the nursery, and obtain a pound of best English tomatoes for threepence. Dad too was able to buy quite a selection of various plants for the garden, not forgetting the load of manure he got from the farm for seven shillings and sixpence. Mr Chubb was the farmer, and I recall him saying, 'Good manure that, Pat. Make thee marrows grow!' See Mr Chubb and you saw a typical farmer: a plump little man, with an oval face and a ruddy complexion that never changed from summer till winter. And you know he was one of the kindest people, always smiling too. When I was little he used to say to me, 'If thee be wanting mushrooms, Polly Quintin, take short cut cross farmyard. But don't thee be letting the cows out!' I always respected his wishes.

We reached home then, all tired and hungry. The walk and fresh air had done us all good.

After an early supper, we had a surprise visit from my brother Tim, who said he had now been posted to Essex; and, not surprising to hear, he had been promoted to Sergeant Instructor. I really think Dad had expected Tim to move up to a higher rank, for Tim had previously served for years in the regular Army.

Anyway, Tim stayed until 10.30 and then decided to make tracks home, so after he had gone we all retired to our beds.

Monday morning was here, and wasn't it just special for me? All ready to go to work, I kissed Mum, jumped on my bicycle, and was off. As I cycled I couldn't help thinking of the outcome the day would bring, but first I would have to see Mr Gould. And what a bit of luck, he came into the press room early.

'Mr Gould,' I said, 'may I have a word with you please?' I had to shout to make myself heard, for Nancy's press had a leaking valve, which was making the steam hiss out with such force.

'Can't hear you, love. Better come into my office.'

I followed Mr Gould, not quite into his office, but to where it was less noisy. 'Mr Gould,' I said, 'I've to take my driving test at two-thirty today. Would it be asking too much if I asked for the afternoon off?'

I must say he looked startled at my request, for I had never asked to be off before. Anyway, half smiling he said, 'Can't really spare you, love. But seeing it's a driving test, for a good cause, I best let you off.'

'Oh, thank you,' I said, now relieved to know I was OK for my test.

Then, smiling at me, he said, 'Best of British, love.'

Thanking Mr Gould once again, I returned to my press, where Nancy and Edna were pleased that I had been granted time off.

'Only snag is,' said Nancy, 'you'll be stacked to the high heavens with work in the morning, when you come in. Can't promise to keep your work down, but I'll do my best. So don't you be coming in tomorrow, saying you've failed.' And so it was that with everybody's good wishes I left the factory at 1 p.m.

Cycling home was great, the weather was good, and the lovely feeling that I was off for the afternoon made it all so appealing; and no mistake, I was beginning to feel excited. I didn't even feel hungry, and this was unusual for me. Nevertheless I enjoyed Mum's salad when I got home.

I quickly washed, then dashed up into my bedroom to change. And there, laid out on the bed were all my things ready: a clean white blouse, my black trousers pressed, and the buttons on my tunic were shining. Bless my Mum, she intended that I would be smartly turned out for the occasion; even my black lace-up shoes had been highly polished, giving off a brilliant shine.

Mum was washing up when I came downstairs. I placed my arms around her, and gave her a kiss. 'Thanks, Mum.'

She stood back now, eyeing me up and down, and with approval she said, 'Now you do look nice, duck.'

I smiled back at Mum, at the same time remembering Dad's words: 'A pretty uniform isn't everything.'

It was time to leave, so Mum came to the front door to see me off. 'All the best, darling,' she said. We hugged, then kissed, and I walked off briskly down the lane.

I intended to be at the depot in good time, and when I did arrive everywhere seemed quiet. However, I passed my time chatting to the telephonist. A nice girl, she was to be married shortly to a sailor. Meanwhile the door opened, and in walked Mr Penny with another gentleman. I stood up and they both approached me.

'Hello, Miss Quintin,' said Mr Penny. I smiled. 'I'd like you to meet Mr Brookes. He's the regional Government Transport Examiner.'

We shook hands. I noticed that in his left hand Mr Brookes held a folder, containing no doubt sheets of notepaper and assessment forms.

'Come along then,' said Mr Brookes. 'Might as well get started.'

I glanced at Mr Penny, who then gave me an encouraging smile. 'We're taking Old Jane,' said Mr Penny. 'There'll be room for the three of us in the front seat.' And what delighted me most was the fact that Mr Penny would be coming with us. And so it was, with the three of us now comfortably seated, that I was ready to move off.

'Miss Quintin,' said Mr Brookes. 'What should you have done first, that I notice you haven't done?'

A little hesitant perhaps, but I spoke: 'I should have checked everything. Sufficient water in the radiator, checked the oil, checked the distilled water in the battery, and tyre pressures.'

Mr Brookes smiled, as if satisfied I had answered the question right. Mr Penny too looked at me with approval. 'Right, young lady, you may proceed.'

'Which route would you like me to take, Mr Brookes?'

Then Mr Brookes glanced at Mr Penny. 'I think the Weston route will be as good as any, don't you?'

Mr Penny smiled, then nodded. So with great confidence I drove towards Weston, aware that both men were watching me.

Well, I was on home territory, wasn't I? I knew those roads like the back of my hand. One particular lane they took me on was all uphill for two miles, with more bends and twists than a cork-screw, and on each side a two-foot grass verge. At the bottom of the lane, Mr Brookes asked me to pull into the side and stop. This I did. He then spent the next ten minutes explaining why an ambulance was so different from any other vehicle, and emphasised the importance of driving with all care and consideration. 'The idea being,' said Mr Brookes, 'to ensure that both sick and injured are gently transported.'

What Mr Brookes explained was common sense, after all, but he was justified in emphasising the importance of it.

'Now, Miss, let's see you reverse up the lane. With one important point to remember. We'll assume that the grass verges are injured people lying on the ground. So on no account must your wheels come in contact with the verges. Come as close as you like, but you are not to touch them. All right, Miss, it's all yours.'

Now was the crucial moment. I glanced at Mr Penny, who said, 'Nice and easy, Miss.'

This I knew was the most important item in the test. So much depended on it. However, I put Old Jane into reverse gear, moved my whole body around, and then began to move slowly backwards. At the first bend I went into a wobble, but rectified myself by slowing down considerably, and so the other bends in the lane were made satisfactory by my steady pace. I was aware of onlookers too, who happened to be walking up the lane at that particular time, yet their presence did not disturb me. I concentrated on what I was doing, and when I was nearly at the top of the lane Mr Brookes asked me to stop.

'That's fine young, lady,' he said. 'Now drive back down the lane, and back to the depot.'

Once again I glanced at Mr Penny, who looked quite pleased. I knew he had great confidence in me, which had given me encouragement to do my best, and so I relaxed a little when driving back to the depot. On arriving, I positioned Old Jane in a herring-bone fashion, alongside other ambulances that were standing there. It was all over. Now for the verdict.

I was the first to jump out of the cab, followed by Mr Brookes and Mr Penny. Then Mr Brookes shook my hand and spoke: 'My examination of your ambulance driving test has been satisfactory.'

Oh what golden words to be spoken, especially where I was concerned.

'So, Miss Quintin, you have passed the required standards, and you are eligible to drive ambulances.'

I then shook hands with Mr Penny, who congratulated me on my success. 'Mr Penny,' I said, 'I owe everything to you, for the excellent tuition you have given me. And I appreciate all the kindness you have shown me.'

He just stood and smiled at me, saying, 'Welcome to the Ambulance Brigade.'

Inside the depot, the telephonist looked at me and smiled, then held her hand out for a handshake, saying, 'I'm pleased you've made it. Congratulations.' The next thing was, she was giving me some tea out of her flask, so between sips of tea and calls coming in we conversed sporadically.

By now I had got to know her name; it was Flo, and with much enthusiasm she talked of her wedding in three weeks' time, saying how she would have liked to have got married in white, but couldn't get sufficient clothing coupons, so she had had to settle for a navy-blue and white outfit.

When I enquired the time from Flo I realised that I had best start making my way home. So thanking her kindly or the tea I said cheerio and left.

Suddenly a flood of excitement came over me. I suppose it was the realisation of having passed my driving test. And of course it was all a reaction, for I marvelled at myself for being so placid throughout it all. No wonder I could have almost jumped for joy, for at the age of eighteen I had become a fully qualified ambulance driver. I couldn't wait to get home, where I knew I might even catch Dad, for he was on a split shift.

I saw a Lansdown bus coming, and just caught it as it was moving away. I flopped into the nearest seat, paid my fare to the conductor and got in a settled position. The bus then stopped at the next stage, and who should get on but Dad himself. His eyes lit up when he saw me, and I too was happy to see him. Full of excitement, I told him of my good news.

Dad then placed his hand on my forearm, and said, almost in a whisper that only I could hear, 'I'm proud of you, Paul. And so happy for you.'

We got off the bus at the top of Sion Road. Another five minutes' walk, and we would be home. Well, I was so full of the afternoon's happenings that I chatted incessantly and didn't give Dad a chance to get a word in edgeways. However, when we finally reached home, I had exhausted myself with talking, so it was Dad who broke the news to Mum.

'What do you think, Nell, our Polyanthus has done it!'

'You mean,' said Mum, 'she's passed her driving test? Oh, duck!' she said, flinging her arms around me. 'Well done! I somehow knew you could do it.' Then Mum said something right out of the blue. 'Is it still OK for Sunday, Pat?'

'Of course,' said Dad. 'Why not?'

This conversation between Mum and Dad had me puzzled. I just couldn't wait to hear the rest, knowing it was some secret or other. 'What's all this then, Mum?' I said.

Mum was now smiling. 'Shall I tell her, Pat?'

'Why not?'

'It was really a surprise for you, duck, that if you passed your driving test, your Dad and I decided we should hire a car out for Sunday. Seeing we'll all be off work, you'll be able to take us for a drive.'

'Me!' I gasped.

'Yep,' answered Dad. 'Now's the time you must learn to shoulder responsibilities, especially now you're able to drive ambulances on your own. You know one thing, Paul. For young shoulders you've achieved more than I. A victory, love. A deserving victory.'

When Dad called me 'love' he was always extremely pleased with me. And when Rob came in he too was thrilled. 'Good for you, Quinner!'

The very next morning, I was naturally full of high spirits, with Nancy and Edna sharing my success. Of course news always travels fast in a factory, especially where young girls are concerned, so it was not surprising that the press room had many inquisitive callers, and I overhead one girl say, 'Would you believe it? Pauline Quintin, an ambulance driver!'

My closest friends and colleagues were indeed impressed, but they were worried that I might just leave the tailoring factory. Nancy, who was always outspoken, said, 'Hope the devil you don't decide to leave us.'

What could I say? Only, 'Not just yet.'

I looked behind me and I saw I had a great pile of trouser legs to press. Edna said she would help me, so between us the heaped pile of trousers had soon shrunk.

With the morning over, the 1 o'clock whistle blew, and as usual we all started hurrying out to the cloakroom, but this particular day something happened. Catastrophe — someone had accidentally knocked a fire extinguisher off its hook on the wall. In seconds, white foam was spurting everywhere, and over everyone too.

Some of the girls became hysterical, laughing and even screaming, so naturally the disturbance brought Mr Gould almost running up the factory floor. I could see he was furious, and it was he himself who replaced the stopper on the cylinder. At once the white foam stopped spurting.

'Now you girls, you'll all walk back to your places. And in future everybody will walk to the cloakroom. Anyone found hurrying or running will be instantly dismissed.'

I heard someone snigger. It came from behind me, and I guess from one of the younger girls. It was a good job Mr Gould didn't hear her, or that definitely would have made the situation worse. It was bad enough seeing Mr Gould looking so annoyed. However, I was soon cycling home, and pedalling fast, for the little incident with the fire extinguisher had cost some precious time. I was cycling so hard I was keeping up with the tramcar, but only as far as the bridge, where we got separated.

Mum was busy hanging out some washing when I arrived home, but she stopped to put our lunch out, and through lunch I told her what had happened, and how Mr Gould was very cross with us all.

When I arrived back at work, I noticed on the middle table in the press room something covered up with a tea-towel. I had just started pressing, when there came this outburst of singing:

'For she's a jolly good fellow. . .
And so say all of us.'

I couldn't recall anyone's birthday.

Nancy then went to the table, and removed the tea-towel, exposing a bottle of something, four sherry glasses, and eight little queen cakes sitting on a plate.

Edna, now beaming, said, 'For you, Pauline.'

'For me?'

'Celebrating your triumph of yesterday.'

'Oh golly,' was all I could say at that moment, for it was a surprise, to say the least.

'We pooled together, didn't we, girls?' said Nancy.

How on earth could I express my feelings towards this genuine bunch of friendly girls?

'Come on, Pauline, open up the bottle!'

I did, reading the label at the same time: 'Fine old English sherry.'

Someone then called out, 'Speech, speech!'

'From the bottom of my heart,' I said. 'I appreciate the kindness you all have shown me.' I then poured the sherry into the tiny glasses, and as we worked we sipped the sherry, making sure the glasses were well hidden underneath the presses. And the little queen cakes, well we just nibbled at them.

After a while I felt a little light-headed, as we all must have done, for the intoxicating liquor was taking effect, and the more I sipped out of my glass, the more it was topped up by Nancy.

Then we all got the giggles, didn't we? It could have been the funny story Edna was trying to tell us. And in the midst of our laughter, to crown it all, the warning siren went.

Immediately it was action stations, with the electricity being switched off, and Mr Gould coming into the press room, telling us to take cover underneath the tables.

Well, us pressers joined the other girls, scrambling to take cover under the wooden tables. Nancy, Edna, and myself had by now had quite a good drink of sherry, and not one of us was used to drinking, so it had had quite an effect on us. In consequence, we were hysterically happy, laughing and giggling at practically nothing. Naturally the other girls noticed, and one of them remarked, 'Such hilarity.' Then someone else had to butt in. 'The press room girls have been drinking. Celebrating. One would think it was Christmas.'

Nancy must have overheard, for she said, 'Come on girls, don't be so catty.'

Then we talked about the fire extinguisher again. Well, this was making everyone laugh, and I laughed so much, tears rolled down my cheeks. Then, we were all jolted into reality, for suddenly we heard a couple of thuds, followed by a shattering of glass all around us.

Mr Gould shouted, 'Everybody stay where you are!'

The girls were murmuring amongst themselves, and it must have been a good half-hour afterwards when the 'all clear' siren blew.

Slowly everyone emerged from underneath the tables, and exclamations like, 'Blimey, what a mess!' were heard, for indeed almost everything inside the factory was covered in glass. It was on top of the work-benches, under the sewing-machines, and amongst the material that lay about. We even crunched the glass as we got on our feet. I realised now that Mr Gould had been right — had we not sheltered under the tables, many of us would have been cut by flying glass.

I noticed one girl who was standing on a stool, peering out of an empty window-frame. Then she shouted out, 'Two ambulances on their way up the road!'

I knew this could only mean tragedy — someone was hurt. Meanwhile every girl in the factory was helping to clean up the glass, using cardboard to brush it together and collect it up. The one and only window in the press room had vanished, taking its frame with it. Personally, us girls in the press room relished this fact, for the hole provided more ventilation for us. It was only later that we heard that a death and many injured had been the result of the raid.

By this time we had forgotten all about our little celebration, so once again the steam presses were banging up and down. Working hard was a sure way of killing time.

Mr Wyatt, our mechanic and handyman, was coming around with stiff cardboard to board up the windows, so you can imagine how sorry we were when our window was dealt with, for not only did we lose ventilation but we lost light as well.

I reckon we were all pleased to finish work that day. For me it was a mixture of events, and when at home I talked to Mum and Dad about our little celebration in the press room, Dad obviously considered it somewhat reprehensible.

'But Paul, wasn't it wrong of you girls to be drinking during working hours?'

Dad was right, of course, and I felt quite guilty, but it was Mum who lightened the situation when she said, 'Don't you think, Pat, our Paul was confronted with an odd situation, for surely it was the proper thing for her to be appreciative of those girls' kindness?'

I felt sure Dad was understanding, for he let out a chuckle, and said, 'Well, next time, young lady, you'll do your celebrating after working hours.'

I fully accepted the reprimand.

'Anyway,' said Dad, 'let's talk about Sunday. The thing is, where to go?'

'Let's go to Deddington, Dad, and visit Aunt Dot.'

'Oh, that would be lovely,' said Mum.

Then Dad spoke. 'May be a bit too far. See, there's a petrol allowance to be considered. However, if I can manage to get sufficient petrol we'll be off to Aunt Dot's.'

Deddington was a distance of some ninety miles, and Aunt Dot was my Mum's sister. Unfortunately she was a widow, but I did remember her husband, Uncle Jack. After Uncle Jack's death, Auntie still kept on The Volunteer Inn, a place I always loved going to, even from being very young. The old place had history; it had once been a meeting place for Cromwell and his men, who escaped from the Royalists by sliding through a secret passage into the cellar; then they would jump on their horses and disappear into the night. All so very romantic.

I first knew of the secret passage when I was very small, and I can remember my first encounter with it. The entrance was not very conspicuous: it was a small door in the oak panelling on the wall of a very large room in the upper chambers. Almost on my bare bottom I slid down the passage, amidst cobwebs and dirt, and landed with such a bump on the rough flagstones in the cellar. And that wasn't all; I was given a good scolding in the bargain, for getting myself so dirty. Nevertheless, the whole atmosphere of the Inn always fascinated me. And dear Aunt Dot, she was a lady I loved and admired. To this very day I can picture her as she always was, tall and elegant, with jet-black hair, tied with a neat bun at the back of her head, wearing always a white starched apron. So, if Dad could obtain sufficient petrol, it would be a sure thing that we would be off to Deddington first thing on Sunday morning.

Well, Dad was lucky: he was given more petrol coupons than he anticipated, and was delighted to tell us of the good news, so it made us all happy with the thought that we were going to have a good run in a motor car on Sunday.

Soon Saturday morning was here. At work I spent a busy four hours pressing, and the last half-hour was devoted entirely to cleaning and oiling the presses and machines. We used to have to crawl on our hands and knees to clean out the fluff that used to settle between the presses; and when the cleaning and oiling was over, we placed clean covers on each press, so that they were all ready for a Monday-morning start.

So, when the whistle blew we were all ready for home. My bike was on top of the pile, and I was almost the first out of the door. Usually on Saturdays I would cycle into town, but this Saturday was an exception and I was cycling straight home.

When I arrived only Rob was there to greet me. 'Hi, Quinner.'

'Hello, Rob,' I said. 'Where's Mum?'

'Gone to town with Dad,' he replied. 'I think they had some shopping to do. Hey, looking forward to tomorrow. Don't forget you'll be driving, you lucky thing.'

'Never mind, Rob,' I said, 'your turn will come one day.'

Suddenly, an unpleasant smell entered my nostrils. I noticed Rob too was making a sniff. 'What on earth is that?' I said.

'It's Joey,' replied Rob. 'Just look at him.'

I looked down, and there was Joey crouched under the kitchen table, all covered in cow's muck. I scolded him, and would have smacked him but for getting my hands covered. 'Hot water, Rob, quickly. We'll have to give him a bath, before Mum and Dad get home.'

While Rob was preparing the water in the old tub, I made preparations for myself, tying an old sack around me. And so started the procedure of giving Joey a bath. I had to drag him out by the collar, then make him jump into the water, and there he stood, motionless, while I washed him down with an old rag.

'What a naughty boy you are! Just a smelly old dog, aren't you?' But all I got in return was the pathetic look from his brown bloodshot eyes. I shouted to Rob for the flea-powder, but first I had to get Joey out of the tub and dry him. I rubbed his black coat, which was now shining, and it was a shame I had to use the flea-powder at all, but I sprinkled it gently all over him; this was a regular thing, of course. Well, after I had finished, Joey was free, whereupon he gave a couple of shakes and then flew off down the garden.

Now to clean up the mess, for whenever I bathed Joey I always seemed to get myself soaking. This time was no different from another, and it was in the midst of cleaning up that Mum and Dad arrived home, laden with parcels.

'I say, you kids,' said Dad, 'we'll have to make preparations for tomorrow.' It was remarkable that, for all that Rob and I had grown up, Dad still referred to us as kids. 'I suggest we go up to the Bear Flat Garage, after tea of course, and pick the car up. Then in the morning we can be off early.'

Dad and Rob left directly after tea, for the garage was situated on the other side of Bath, a distance of some four miles.

After Mum and I had washed up, I was curious as to what Mum had bought during her shopping spree. I knew only too well that it was seldom Mum bought anything for herself, so imagine the surprise when she said, 'Come upstairs. I'll show you my new dress.' Maybe this little flutter was necessary; after all she would be visiting her own sister tomorrow. So out of the box it came, and it was the loveliest of dresses. It was made of navy-blue velvet, the neckline and sleeve edging trimmed with swansdown.

'Oh Mum,' I said. 'Do try it on.'

She did and how beautiful she looked in it, revealing a still smart figure.

Then Mum opened up the end of another parcel. 'Take a peep, duck. It's a new sports jacket for your Dad. Oh, and I've something for you as well,' she said, handing me a small parcel.

This indeed surprised me, especially when I unwrapped it and finally revealed its contents. It was a jar of Pond's best powder-cream, plus a Pond's pale lipstick. It really astonished me.

'Mum!' I exclaimed. 'Is this really for me?'

'Yes, duck.'

'You mean, I may use cosmetics?'

Mum smiled, 'You can use it now, but only in moderation. Anyway, most young ladies are wearing it these days. But don't forget to apply it lightly.'

When Mum had gone downstairs, I went into my bedroom. I stood before my dressing-table mirror, and applied my exciting powder-cream and lipstick.

Looking at myself in the mirror then, I definitely knew I had grown up, and considered myself well and truly an adult. And when I went downstairs, Mum noticed my cosmetic, and smiled.

Dad and Rob had returned, and I could see Rob was full of excitement, for they had brought the hired car home, and it was parked on the top road.

'We'll go along and see it,' said Mum, so this we did. An old Morris car she was; nevertheless, she was clean and tidy. She also displayed a canvas hood, which could be pulled back, weather permitting of course. Looking at her, I knew I could handle her all right.

On Sunday Dad was up very early, making the tea, biscuits being excluded, for we would be having an early breakfast.

Wasting no time, I dressed quickly, wearing a white wool polo-neck jumper that Pat had given me. I must say it was far from feminine and far too big for me for really, yet it was nice and warm, and contrasted well with my black trousers.

The time came when we were all ready to go. A last-minute decision was that we would take Joey. After all, he did have a bath the day before, out of sheer necessity, of course.

Dad decided that he would drive the old Morris through Bath, and so out to Bathford he drove, saying I could take over from there. Dad, of course, was an excellent driver. He could change a gear with such perfection, and it was impossible to detect exactly what gear he was actually in; it was always an absolute pleasure to be driven by Dad.

On reaching Bathford, we changed places. The early morning was nice and sunny; there were a few scattered clouds maybe, but the roads were ideal for motoring.

All was silent as I drove off, but the silence was soon broken by laughter from Rob. 'Hey Quinner,' he said. 'Watch your driving.'

'Just leave her alone,' said Dad. 'She's doing all right.'

The journey then to Deddington was quite pleasant, stopping only twice; the last stop was to give Joey a run across some fields. I was now driving up through the High Street in Deddington, continuing on until I came to the crossroads, where I turned sharp right down the country lane which I knew so well. And there it stood — The Volunteer Inn. It was situated back off the lane, so driving up to the entrance, I finally stopped the car.

The outside had the appearance of a big house, rather than that of an inn, for beside it stood a tall stone arch, which opened into a large courtyard. Its origin surely must have been mediaeval, yet to this very day it all looked so picturesque, with its surrounding stables, and the small oblong dark-grey cobbles which gave the ground that very old look. And right in the centre of the courtyard stood the remains of a fountain, which long past had seen its days of service. One could imagine the clatter of horses' hoofs upon these cobbles in days gone by, when Cromwell and his men were desperate to make a quick getaway from the Royalists.

The very same old cobbles? Could be.

I parked the old Morris at the side, and we all got out, with Joey shaking himself. Walking to the back entrance, I was surprised to see so many sandbags stacked up on each side of the doorway. However, Mum did open the door, and called out, 'Anybody at home?' There was no reply, so Mum made her entrance, and we all followed. Again Mum called out, 'Anyone at home?'

Then a voice answered. It wasn't Aunt Dot's, but Grandmother's. 'Is that you Nell?' Immediately Mum and Gran embraced. It was indeed a lovely surprise to see Gran. Now it was my turn to hug Gran and give her a big kiss. 'Lovely to see you, Gran,' I said.

Gran, to me, always remained the same. In her early eighties she was quite independent and able to look after herself, living in her own little cottage down Cherry-Tree Garden Lane at White Whaltham, near Maidenhead. She was really remarkable; she did all her own gardening, kept poultry, and everything in her cottage was shining, with a perfume of moth-balls everywhere. And all on her pension of ten shillings a week; how she managed financially, no one knew, yet she did, and would not accept any financial help from her daughters. Might I add that my Gran was an extra lovable person, who was always ready to help, giving of her love and understanding.

Auntie Dot always called my Mum 'Blyber', obviously a nickname of a sort, so the first words Aunt Dot spoke were, 'Hello, Blyber! Nice to see you all.' She kissed Mum, then Dad, and looked at me and said, 'Why, it's Pauline! Quite a young lady now. And just look at Robby. All so grown up now.'

Over coffee everybody was busy chattering, and then, to my delight, Aunt Dot gave me permission to help out in the bar. This I enjoyed, pulling down the big handles on the pumps to release the draught beer. I was surprised to see that almost half the customers were servicemen; I suppose it was understandable, with a big Army base nearby.

Many of the young soldiers I served tried in vain to chat me up, and no mistake, I was embarrassed and constantly blushed. However, I continued to fill up the pints of mild and bitter. My intention was merely to help Aunt Dot, who I knew would be busy preparing a big lunch. The aroma of beer was pleasant, but when it mixed with the aroma of roasting beef, coming from the oven, it had the most appetising effect on one's salivary glands.

I was thrilled at ringing the bell for last drinks, so after washing up all the dirty glasses, and emptying the ashtrays, I bolted the big door.

It was exactly 2.30 p.m., and by this time I was feeling very hungry, and so when I went into the kitchen I offered my help, but I could see that Mum and Aunt Dot were coping admirably. In spite of rationing, Aunt had prepared and cooked a most delicious lunch, the proof of which showed up in all our empty plates. Content now, we relaxed over a cup of tea. This indeed was a lovely reunion, and where we were concerned I dare say the war was at its remotest ebb.

So, after helping Aunt with the washing-up, I then wandered around the old Inn, aware of the nostalgia. I suppose nothing had really changed, only perhaps the absence of Uncle Jack, who was always so kind when we were children.

I just had to go up into the old council room, now occupied by crates of bottles from the brewery. I looked for the secret panel. It was still there, and relieved I was that I could still open it, and observe the same secret passage. It was no different; there could be more cobwebs though. I imagined that with infrequent use, the spiders were free from disturbance.

Arrangements had been made for Gran to stop a few days with Aunt Dot. This I knew had pleased Mum, so I watched Gran with her two daughters, the three of them in deep conversation. I did not want to interrupt, as I imagined they had much to talk over, and I knew time was running short. And Mum, she was absolutely radiant in her new dress.

After tea, it was time for our departure. We had in fact spent a very pleasant day with Gran and Aunt Dot, who both came out into the courtyard to see us off. So, exchanging farewells and kisses, I started up the old Morris, and then moved slowly out of the courtyard, back under the arch, and out into the lane. So we had started out on our journey home.

Quite a cool breeze was blowing now, so before long I pulled in while Dad and Rob pulled the canvas top over. It had celluloid flaps attached to the sides, to imitate windows; they still let the light in, and, of course, gave us some protection from the breeze.

Dad gave me much encouragement. He told me that my driving was all right, and to keep to the speed limit of 30 m.p.h. 'At this speed,' said Dad, 'we'll reach home before dusk.'

Meanwhile, about twenty miles from home, strong winds started blowing, making the hood flap continually. Before long I was driving through heavy rain, and then — disaster. The hood blew back.

I immediately pulled into the side, and we all jumped out to retrieve the canvas hood, trying hard to pull it back into position. Finally we did, but in those few minutes we got soaked, and were glad to get back into the car again. Luckily Mum had a couple of hand-towels, which we used to mop our faces and rub our hair.

When we arrived home, Dad mentioned that he would have to return the old Morris that night. 'I'll come with you, Dad,' I said, knowing we would have to walk back, and thinking that I would be company for him. So, after a snack, Dad and I made the return journey to the Bear Flat Garage.

As we expected, the garage was closed when we got there. However, Dad parked the old Morris against the wall, making sure it was locked, and put the car keys through the letter-box.

While walking home, we talked of many things, so time passed over quickly, and we were back home before we knew where we were. After a cup of cocoa, we all retired to our beds, tired perhaps but having the satisfaction of knowing that we had all enjoyed the day.

I must confess I felt quite pleased with myself. It had made me feel proud and privileged to know that my parents and my brother Rob had depended on my driving ability. I had ensured both their safety and their pleasure, a gift which was mine to give.

*　　　　　*　　　　　*

Christmas of 1940 was well behind us, and the early months of 1941 brought about many changes and happenings.

In January 1941, the *Daily Worker* newspaper was closed down by the Government. In March, the Essential Work Orders were introduced; these made it possible for industry to retain key employees. Also in March, the Lend-lease Act was passed by the United States; from then on the US could supply defence equipment to any country whose survival was considered essential. In this very same month too, Plymouth was blitzed, time and time again, like so many other towns.

At this particular time there was a slight change in my routine. It all happened one morning. After making Mrs White her usual cup of tea, I thought that she did not look so well, and before I left she said, 'I wonder, dear, when you go home, would you kindly ask your mother if she would give Miss Hewitt a ring, and ask her to call and see me?'

So when I reached home, I gave Mum the message. 'Mum,' I said, 'who's Miss Hewitt?'

To which Mum replied, 'She's the secretary of Mrs White's solicitor. Unmarried lady, I would say in her forties. I'll ring Miss Hewitt from the hospital.' She then kissed me, and went on her way, while I washed up before going off to work myself.

During the next week, Miss Hewitt was a constant visitor to Lansdown Place West, caring for Mrs White's needs daily, and often enough I would go along in the evening and find her still there. I began to wonder if Miss Hewitt wanted to stay with Miss White permanently, and after talking to Mum and then Mum talking to Mrs White, it was arranged and agreed upon that Miss Hewitt would take my place. In one sense I suppose it was better for me, for now I could volunteer to do nights at the ambulance depot. The only thing was, I would miss the dear old lady. She had taught me so much, and really I felt beholden to her, for she had taught me elegance and elocution. I also recall something she had said to me that has stuck with me to this very day. Her very words were, 'My child, you'll never want for anything in this life.'

And so it was that I was to spend my last night with Mrs White, and it was in her study that we chatted longer than usual.

'You will come along and see me sometime?' This I promised. And after wishing Mrs White goodnight, I went into my luxurious room for the very last time.

The following morning we had our usual cup of tea together, and then, from her bedside table, she produced a little box. Holding it out to me, she said, 'This is for you, dear. I want you to remember me by it. It's a little gift of appreciation really, for the happy times we have had together.'

Carefully I took the little box in my hand, scarcely knowing whether I should open it or not. Then Mrs White said, 'Please open it.' I did, and to my surprise, I lifted out of the box the prettiest pendant.

'Madam,' I said, 'it's beautiful! I thank you kindly.'

Whereupon she gave me my two half-crowns, then placed her hand on mine. 'God bless you, child.'

Suddenly I was seized with this inner power, whereby I just couldn't help myself, for I just threw my arms around her and kissed her. Perhaps I was impetuous, disregarding formality. I had always treated her with respect, but at that moment, I did what my heart told me to do.

'You will come along and see me, won't you?'

'I will,' I replied. It was hard to keep back the tears, but I managed, forcing myself to say, 'Goodbye, Madam.'

I noticed the tear-drops in Mrs White's eyes, so the poor darling was feeling the parting also. Then, and it took all of my time to do it, I gave her my best and biggest smile. In return she smiled back, with a little wave.

I closed the door of No. 7 Lansdown Place West, and walking home I was overcome with emotion, for tears ran freely down my cheeks. It didn't matter now; it was one way of giving vent to my feelings I suppose.

Mum was up as usual when I got home. 'Hello, duck,' she said. Then Mum must have noticed my red eyes. 'You've been crying. You kind of got attached to the dear old soul. Still, don't fret. You can always go along and see her any time.' Mum's words were comforting. 'Now, bathe your eyes under the cold tap, while I put your breakfast out.'

Mum's kind words gave me consolation, so I soon rallied round and showed Mum my pendant, holding it in my hands and admiring its exquisite beauty.

In May 1941 Rudolph Hess, Hitler's deputy, landed in Scotland. This German was caught almost as soon as he landed. His reason for coming to England was a mystery, but he may have imagined that he could make peace between the two countries — who knows? In any event, he became our prisoner for the duration of the war.

Spies, or so called fifth columnists, were a constant concern of the public and the authorities. Tommy Handley, a popular comedian, introduced a comic character called 'Funf', the very image of a feared spy, in his BBC programme ITMA ('It's That Man Again'). And much credit must surely go to the entertainers in general who provided the shows for the forces, particularly through ENSA (Entertainments National Service Association). Vera Lynn was actually called the Forces' sweetheart.

It was estimated that some radio programmes had audiences of 10 to 12 million each week, and I must say the BBC gave us all a tremendous uplift, even in the darkest of days. Songs such as 'Run, rabbit, run', and 'We're going to hang out the washing on the Siegfried Line', were very popular. I also remember a frequently heard dance tune, written in appreciation of the women's effort in industry, which went like this:

> She's the girl that makes the thing
> That drills the hole that holds the spring
> That drives the rod that turns the knob
> That works the thingumebob.
> She's the girl that makes the thing
> That holds the oil that oils the ring
> That takes the shank that moves the crank
> That works the thingumebob.
> It's a ticklish sort of a job,
> Making a thingumebob,
> Especially when you don't know what it's for.
> But it's the girl that makes the thing
> That drills the hole that holds the spring
> That works the thingumebob that makes the engine roar.
> And it's the girl that makes the thing
> That holds the oil that oils the ring
> That works the thingumebob that's going to win the war.

About this time, a conversation in the press room gave me serious food for thought. It started off when Edna said, 'What do you think, there's talk of conscription of women. Seemingly they cannot get enough for the services and factories.'

'We're all right,' said Nancy. 'We're doing essential government work, so that should make us exempt.'

'No,' said Edna, 'we are not exempt.'

'What?' exclaimed Nancy, now looking surprised.

'Well now, off the cuff,' said Edna, 'but I overhead a conversation between Mr Gould and an inspector, and what I gather, they both agreed that although we were on government contract work, we were definitely not exempt. So it just means we'll all get called up when the time comes. And according to the newspapers,' went on Edna, 'women will be called up in alphabetical order, plus of course the age group.'

'It's not fair. There should be enough men to go around,' said Nancy.

I made no comment, realising that I myself could do more essential war work than pressing servicemen's trousers. Fortunately, my surname, starting with a Q, would put me on the tail end. However, thoughts about leaving home had seldom entered my head; that is, not until now. I had love and protection from my parents, so it was only natural that I was smug and complacent, and desired no change.

I felt now that I must have a serious talk with Dad. I needed his advice, knowing it was always staunch, and that very evening the opportunity came.

'Dad,' I said, 'I've been thinking. I'll maybe call at the Labour Exchange on Friday night, I think they are open until seven o'clock.'

'Whatever for?' remarked Dad.

'To see if they can offer me a man's job.'

'But Paul,' said Dad, 'they could give you anything. Maybe something you would not like doing. Remember too, you're a fully qualified driver now. And in my opinion, young lady, I would rather see you in one of the services than in a job you were not suited to.'

'But Dad,' I exclaimed, 'I just don't want to leave home.'

'I know, duck.' This time it was Mum answering. Then looking at Dad, she said, 'Let her give it a try, Pat. She'll not be obliged to take on a job she doesn't want.'

'OK,' said Dad. 'You must do as you please. But don't say I haven't warned you. Anyway, Paul, if that's what you want, behopes you get something decent.'

I was happy now. I could go ahead with approval from both my parents; it made all the difference.

Friday came around very quickly, and with the day's work over it was time to go home. But this particular evening was different: I was going into town, to the Employment Exchange.

I finally arrived at the very large old building. Lots of people were coming in and out as I entered. The time was around 6.30 p.m., and inside everywhere appeared very busy. However, I managed to find my way to the ladies section after going through some swing doors; a long counter stood before me, and lady clerks were standing behind it, looking very efficient and full of their own importance.

I myself felt shy; I'd never been in the place before. However, I walked over to one of the ladies who was unoccupied. I smiled and said, 'Excuse me please. I wish to do a man's job. Have you any vacancies?'

Well, I did come straight to the point. Perhaps I surprised the woman, I don't know, but she didn't speak at first. Instead she looked at me in a most peculiar manner. I felt a little perturbed, for now she was eyeing me up and down. Then, finally, she did speak.

'I'll have to take you through to the male section. They will deal with you there.'

It was obvious that, for some reason or other, she objected to my request. She came round, and I followed her into the male section, which was similar to the ladies, and there I stood in front of another long counter.

This time I was being stared at by a male clerk. Meanwhile the lady clerk had whispered something in his ear; then, ignoring me, she brushed past me, leaving me standing facing the gentleman.

Conscious of the atmosphere around me, I felt myself blushing. I felt that I had suddenly been plunged into an odd situation. Nevertheless, I remained quite calm, reminding myself that there was still a war on, and all I wanted to do was to volunteer for a man's job.

I felt the male clerk's eyes upon me. Now he was looking at me over the top of his glasses, and in a sarcastic tone of voice he said, 'And what have we here, a conscientious objector? Afraid of being called up, are you?'

I thought the man downright impudent, and the very thought of him thinking I was a coward made me feel embarrassed. Being brought up with good manners, it was difficult for me to return any sarcasm, though I knew he jolly well deserved it. But I did speak up for myself .

'I think, Sir, you have misunderstood me. Already I do voluntary duties with the Civil Defence. And as a matter of interest I am a qualified ambulance driver.'

I knew immediately that I had put the male clerk to shame, for he did not speak; instead he turned around and began to sort out some slips of paper lying in a tray. Then, with correspondence held in his hand he came back to the counter. Knowing that this man could not withdraw what he had said, I could not help but feel sorry for him, so that when he looked at me and I almost detected a grin on his face I could do no other but smile at him.

'Now, Miss,' he said, 'I have something here that may be of interest to you, seeing you have the qualifications for driving. It's the Pierrepont Garage. Do you know where it is?'

I must have looked vague; well really I was trying to think where the garage was situated. Then the clerk spoke again.

'It's opposite the GPO sorting office.'

'Oh yes,' I said. 'I know of the garage.'

'Well now,' said the clerk, 'if you go there and ask to see a Mr Griffin, he's the proprietor, he'll most probably fix you up. He's requiring a girl to replace a man, to serve petrol, and to do odd jobs in the garage, like mending punctures. Maybe you could fit into his requirements. Anyhow I'll give you a green card, so take it along with you when you go for an interview. Should he then be prepared to start you, he will fill in the necessary on the green card and then send it back to us.'

I took the green card, thanked the clerk, and then left in a dignified manner.

Out in the fresh air, I felt happy. My first step was now over, so all I wanted to do now was to go home to my parents and discuss the possibilities of working in a garage.

Conversing with Mum and Dad, they came to the conclusion that it was entirely up to me, so taking the bull by the horns I decided I would see Mr Griffin the following morning.

'Your Dad will come with you,' said Mum.

'Oh Mum, I'll be quite all right to go to the garage alone,' I said firmly. Dad was now smiling, and I could tell that he was all in favour of my independence.

The following morning was Saturday. I finished work at 12 o'clock on Saturdays, so I made up my mind that I would go straight to the garage from work.

Mum had suggested I wear my best coat and shoes, so that I looked smart when meeting Mr Griffin, so when I arrived at the factory everyone was curious as to why I was all dressed up, and one remark was made that I could be meeting a boy-friend. With Nancy and Edna I could not keep back a secret, so I eagerly told them all, and they both agreed I was doing the right thing.

The 12 o'clock whistle blew and it was time to leave the factory for the weekend, so jumping on my bicycle I headed for town — destination, the Pierrepont Garage.

I arrived at the garage much quicker than I anticipated — I expect it was because my thoughts were fully occupied — and putting my bicycle against a wall I took a quick glance at my surroundings.

On the forecourt, six petrol pumps stood alongside a small wall, which was the demarcation between the garage and the public footpath. I slowly walked into the garage, through one of the two huge sliding doors, and I was amazed at the space; it was a much larger place than I had thought, and parked cars were everywhere.

Standing momentarily, I observed a car pull in for petrol, and a fair young man came out in attendance. The display sign swinging from one of the petrol pumps clearly stated that best BP was selling at two shillings and three ha'pence per gallon; it also said that petrol was sold only with coupons.

When the young man had finished serving, I went quietly up to him and asked if I could see Mr Griffin.

'Yes, Miss. He'll be in the big house next door.'

'Thank you,' I timidly answered. 'Oh,' I said, 'will it be all right if I put my bicycle in the garage?'

'Why of course,' he replied. Then he said, 'Here, give it to me, I'll look after it,' with which he took my bicycle and wheeled it into a safe place. Again I thanked him.

I approached the big house next to the garage. I rang the old-fashioned bell, pulling it out on its wire, then letting it go back on its own, and making quite a din too. Afraid I was that I had pulled it out too far; however, I hopefully waited, but not for long, for suddenly the big oak door opened, and I now stood face to face with a tall, dark-featured young man, who I would say was in his late twenties.

'Yes, young lady?' he said.

Aware of my shyness, I started blushing; however, I answered the young man. 'Would it be convenient to see Mr Griffin, please?'

'Come in and follow me.' Which I did, up two flights of stairs. Then the young man paused outside a door and knocked twice. I heard this powerful voice shout out, 'Come in!' We both entered.

'A young lady to see you, Uncle.' I was quick to learn, then, that the young man was Mr Griffin's nephew; and here I was looking at Mr Griffin himself, who was seated at a large desk covered in correspondence.

I must say I was astonished at his appearance. He was in fact a well-developed man, with very broad shoulders; his face was oval-shaped, yet his square chin was pronounced, and his head, his whole head, was clean-shaven. His appearance was so unusual. However, I reminded myself that I had come for an interview, and not to criticise other people's looks; no doubt there would be a reason for his shaven head.

This gentleman was now looking straight at me, when he said, 'What can I do for you young lady?' His voice was pleasant, which put me at ease straightaway.

'Please, Sir,' I said, 'I've come from the Labour Exchange. They have recommended me to see you. You see,' I blurted out, 'I need a man's job.'

Did I surprise Mr Griffin by my last sentence? I don't know. Maybe too much enthusiasm, being eager to come to the point. However, he smiled and spoke.

'I could give you a man's job, but I must be honest with you. It's a dirty, greasy job, and you would have to wear a boiler suit. And what's more, young lady, if you were in my employment, you would have to be treated in the same way as a man. So therefore I could show no leniency towards your sex. You do understand, Miss?'

'Yes,' I replied. So here was a challenge all right. Anyway, I thought, why not, a woman could do equally as well as a man.

'Well, Miss, should you decide to come and work for me, it would have to be on a trial basis, of course. Maybe for a month — give us both time to adjust. Are you working at the moment, Miss, er . . .?'

'Miss Quintin,' I answered. 'And, Sir, I work in a clothing factory, as a presser.' I then expected Mr Griffin to ask me why I wanted to leave, but he didn't, and I was glad.

'So, young lady, if you would like to work in the garage, I suggest you give a week's notice to your present employer. Then you could start for me, a week come Monday. About wage — will you be happy with four pounds per week? There will be an increase, of course, depending on your ability for this kind of work. You see, I've never taken on a girl before. But losing so many of my lads for the service, I've been obliged to take on any kind of labour. With no disparity to you, Miss, or your sex. So how do you feel about starting?'

Knowing now I had to make a quick decision, I said, 'I'll be happy to accept the position you have offered me.'

'Right then,' said Mr Griffin. 'I'll put you on the six a.m. to two p.m. shift. So be here sharp then.'

'Oh,' I said. 'The green card.'

'Righto, I'll attend to that. And I suggest, Miss, you get yourself a boiler suit, and a turban for your hair.'

'Thank you, Sir,' I said. I then excused myself and left the room. I hurried back down the stairs, thinking to myself that £4 a week meant a financial gain, compared to what I got in the factory.

I felt excited as I walked into the garage, whereupon the young man brought my bicycle over to me. 'There you are, Miss.'

Timidly, I said, 'Thank you.'

'I say, Miss,' then said the young man. 'You wouldn't by any chance be coming to work here?'

I felt myself blushing again. 'Oh yes. I'm starting here a week come Monday.'

'Why, that's great!' replied the young man. 'You'll be taking over my job then, for I've been called up. Going off into the Army next week. I say, would you like me to show you around the garage, the time it's quiet?'

'Why,' I said, 'that's very kind of you.'

'Come on then, put your bicycle down and come with me. I'll show you the downstairs first.'

'Downstairs?' I exclaimed.

'Oh yes,' said the young man. 'We can garage up to a hundred cars alone on the basement floor.' This indeed was a surprise to me; however, I followed him through the enormous selection of parked cars already parked on the top floor, until we reached a small wooden office, which I entered with the young man. At a glance I noticed that the office contained a slanting desk and two wooden stools, and sitting upon some kind of a structure was a till.

'By the way,' said the young man, 'I'm John Price.'

'And I'm Miss Quintin,' was my reply. Now formally introduced, we shook hands.

As we left the office, John locked the small door. 'We have to keep it locked, Miss, on account of the till.'

I then followed John down a flight of wooden stairs, finally reaching the lower deck. More cars were parked, and on my left John showed me a huge water-tank. Smiling at me, he said, 'If you get around to mending punctures this is the tank which you'll be testing the inner tubes in.' Then, pointing to the far corner, John said, 'Come meet the lads,' and before I knew where I was, I was being introduced to three motor mechanics, Freddy, Tommy, and Mick.

All I could say was, 'Hello.'

Then one of the three spoke; I think it was the one called Tommy. 'Like to shake your hand, Miss, but afraid my hands are too greasy.'

'That's quite all right,' I said. 'I understand.'

Then again Tommy spoke. 'Biss thee going to work here then? Taking John's place perhaps?'

'That's right,' I answered. 'And all being well, I start a week come Monday.'

'Well I be blowed.' This time it was Freddy speaking. 'As soon as we get girls coming to work beside us, we get our calling-up papers to go in the services. It just bain't fair!'

I could only smile, and say cheerio to them. So back up the wooden stairway I followed John, and by the time we reached the top someone was blasting their hooter for petrol.

'Some of these motorists have no patience,' said John. 'Wait till I've served the customer, Miss. Then I'll show you the petrol-pumps.' And so I became the onlooker, watching John carefully. I then glanced at the impatient motorist; why of course he was in a hurry, he had a taxi, and was carrying a passenger too. This taxi, I noticed, came from the taxi rank which parked outside the Bath Abbey, just up the road.

'Make it four gallon,' said the taxi-driver, and when giving John 8 shillings and 6 pence, he said, 'Here's a tanner for yourself.'

'Thanks, Guv,' said John. So as the taxi pulled away, John and I were left standing on the forecourt.

John slowly explained the workings of the petrol-pumps. Then, picking up the air-line, he gave me all the gen on tyre pressures. Finally he showed me how to jack up a car, saying, 'You'll find Mr Griffin a good boss, you know, and for myself I can only wish you the best of luck.'

I then thanked John for all his kindness in giving me valuable information which I knew would be of tremendous help in making a success of my new career. So, jumping on my bicycle, I gave a final wave to John and then started cycling up the road towards home.

On arriving home, only Rob was in, but he listened to me with much enthusiasm. 'Sounds good, our Paul, and four quid a week too! But don't forget you'll have the grease and dirt to contend with.'

'I know,' I answered. 'But I don't mind. And one thing, Rob, I'll be exempt from any of the services, because I'll be doing a man's job. And I'll be able to carry on with my Civil Defence duties.'

'Well, I suppose it makes sense. And it's what you wanted.'

'Where's our Mum?' I asked.

'Gone to meet Dad,' replied Rob. 'They shouldn't be long.' Now Rob looked in a studious mood. 'I say, Quinner, do they want anybody else at the garage?'

'Why?' I exclaimed.

'I dunno,' answered Rob. 'Perhaps I should have a change.'

'But Rob,' I said, 'you do well where you are. And I'm sure the Pitman family have been very kind to you.'

'I know, Paul. But since joining the Territorial Army, I've become restless. And besides, let's face it, our Paul, being a footman is no contribution to the war effort, is it?'

Of course I knew Rob was right, for if we were to win the war, ladies and gentlemen would have to open their own car doors.

Suddenly the front door opened, with Joey flying into the kitchen and Mum and Dad following, and in all excitability I shouted out, 'I've got the job at the Pierrepont Garage!' And with the same breath I blurted out, 'Start a week come Monday, at four pounds a week!'

'Good Lord!' said Dad. 'As much as that?'

Mum, on the other hand, was looking at me with perplexity. 'And in heaven's name,' she said, 'what will you be doing to earn that much money?'

'Well, Mum,' I answered, 'I'll only be on a month's trial. And there'll be so much to learn, like mending punctures, and testing inner tubes.'

'You'll be doing that sort of thing?' exclaimed Mum, now looking more surprised than ever. 'And what about your poor hands?' she said. 'They'll get so rough.' Then Mum looked at Dad, saying, 'Oh Pat, be our Paul doing the right thing?'

'It's what she wants,' answered Dad. 'And knowing Paul as we do, she has a determination all of her own.'

Mum just stood, and smiled.

Another Monday morning. I was ready to go off to work, but for one exception. I was feeling miserable, knowing perhaps that this was going to be my last week in the factory. After all, taking things into consideration, I was used to being a Hoffman presser, working amongst a happy lot of girls.

I expected things to be totally different this very morning, for would I not have to see Mr Gould, and give him a week's notice? And wondered, I did, how the man would take it. However, on arriving in the press room, I quickly told the girls about the Pierrepont Garage, and how I was going to start there a week come Monday. I knew they would be happy for me, and in all sincerity they wished me the best of luck.

The first opportunity I got, I went to see Mr Gould, and tapped boldly on his office door. I then heard Mr Gould's voice: 'Come in.'

I entered, and I could see Mr Gould was indeed surprised to see me. 'Why, it's Pauline Quintin. What can I do for you, lass?'

Suddenly a wave of apprehension swept over me, for I realised that I was in some difficulty as what to say. How the devil was I to explain that I wanted to leave, yet I didn't want to leave?

There was no doubt I was full of contemplation. Now I felt my cheeks getting hot, and I needed all my courage to speak. Yet I amazed myself with the quiet tone of voice in which I spoke. 'Please Mr Gould, may I leave on Saturday?'

I felt I had taken him unawares. 'You want to leave us, lass? But why?'

I then carefully explained to Mr Gould how it was regrettable, but that under the circumstances which had arisen, it was necessary for me to leave. 'You see, Mr Gould, for the sake of my parents, I just couldn't leave home.'

'I understand,' replied Mr Gould. There was silence, but Mr Gould broke it when he said, 'Are you going to do a man's job then?'

'Yes,' I replied. 'At the Pierrepont Garage, in the town.'

'Is it really what you want, lass?'

'I don't rightly know, Mr Gould. I only know it will stop me from going into the services, and leaving home.'

'Well young lady, if you are not happy at this new job, don't hesitate to come back and see me, and I will endeavour to help find something else for you. I'm sure I could pull a few strings somewhere.'

What a kind man, I thought.

'I know we'll all miss you,' went on Mr Gould. 'And I shall lose a good Hoffman presser, but this is the way it goes, I suppose. God knows it'll be for the best. And so, love, you'll be leaving us at the end of the week, then?'

At this point, I could only nod my head. I realised Mr Gould had been a good boss in every kind of way, and, relevant to the fact, I would miss all the girls, especially my dear good friends in the press room.

Returning to the press room, however, I quickly told the girls that I would definitely be leaving on Saturday. All went quiet, until Nancy spoke. 'We'll all miss you, you know.'

'I shall miss you all too,' I replied.

I must have sounded melancholy, for Edna spoke up. 'I say, cheer up. We can always pop into the garage and see you.'

'Why of course,' replied Nancy.

Breaking away from these girls I knew would not be easy, when the time came, for had they not always given me their loyalty and friendship?

One girl in particular, Evelyn Bird, a machinist, came into the press room often, to have small parts pressed, and often enough I was the one that did her little jobs, and I think we had something in common, for we could converse quite freely. Well, this very morning she came in to have the side of a pocket pressed, and when I told her I was leaving she didn't seem at all surprised. Instead she calmly said, 'Who will I get to do my bits of pressing?' Then she said, 'Have you heard the news about Mr Gould's son? It's rumoured he's missing.'

It was when Evelyn went out of the press room that I thought of my previous conversation with Mr Gould, and the odd way in which he said, 'This is the way it goes, I suppose. God knows it'll be for the best.' That was it — his own son was on his mind. And to think, this poor man had all this worry upon himself when he was discussing my situation, which I realised was only a trivial matter. Yet wasn't Mr Gould a typical example of being placable in such times of stress? Not every man would have this courage, so in my estimation he indeed was a fine man.

The 1 o'clock whistle blew, and on retrieving my bicycle from the pile I found my front tyre flat. Luckily I had got my pump, so I pumped as hard as I could, and was pleased when the air stayed in. Nevertheless, my journey home was interrupted many times by having to use the pump, for I had developed a small puncture all right; hence the loss of a precious five minutes. However, on arriving home, and through a quick lunch, I told Mum that I had seen Mr Gould, and it had been arranged that I should leave on Saturday. I mentioned to Mum also that Mr Gould's son had been reported missing. Mum gave a sigh and said, 'That's the human sacrifices of war.'

On the evening of the next day, we had a surprise visit from my second eldest brother, Tim. Immediately I saw him, I knew he was upset over something, and to our dismay Tim revealed the news that his wife Rene had been unfaithful; consequently she had left home, leaving behind their two children, Alfie, aged ten, and Iris, aged eight. I think we were all stunned at hearing this, because prior to the war they were one happy family. They hadn't an elaborate home, yet the house they had was nicely situated in a most delightful place in Batheaston, overlooking the lovely scenery of the Avon valley. So this was the result of husbands being away from home in the war. And how many did this happen to?

Well, Tim then asked my parents if they would look after the children, for the time being at any rate. Of course Mum and Dad were only too glad to come to the rescue. It was a blessing they were around to help out in this unexpected situation, although it has to be remembered that they were getting on in years; without me to help they might have found it difficult to cope for long. Anyway that very night I went with Tim to fetch the children home. It was very sad as we gathered bits of clothing up into a suitcase, for they wanted to bring so much with them. They kept saying to me, 'Can we take this and that, Auntie Paul?'

I think the worst part about it all was the very fact that they were old enough — at ten and eight — to understand all that which was happening, and why they were coming to live with us. It's true that war has so many ways of hurting people, and by this stage I knew my brother Tim was heart-broken.

Another Saturday morning was here, and it was to be my last time at the factory; and how like a book, the finish of another chapter. Let's say I was about to enter upon a new phase of my development.

It was not easy to say goodbye to everyone, and cycling home I had such a lump in my throat. But it was not until I reached Park Lane, where I had to push my bicycle uphill, that I let the tears flow freely down my cheeks. I must admit, my emotional feelings were soothed by my tears, and already I felt better for it.

Pushing my bicycle up the last little slope, who should fly around the bend but Alfie and Iris; they had come to meet me, bless them. I then suddenly remembered that I had promised to take them to the park, with hopes of catching some tiddlers or tadpoles in the park lake.

Already a great comradeship had formed between us, and I was just as excited at seeing them as they were with me. I let Alfie push my bicycle, while I held on to Iris's hand, and it appeared we · were quite three little chatterboxes, and were rather noisy when we entered home.

Dinner was awaiting us, so it wasn't long before we were ready to go to the park. Victoria Park was situated at the very bottom of the common; it was quite a large park, with all the amenities for children, including fishing in the lake, which Rob and I used to be so fond of doing. So, tying string securely around the tops of two jam-jars, we set off. First we had to go to Julian Road to buy twopenny fishing nets, at the hardware shop, but having bought them we were all set.

I noticed the delightful expressions on the children's faces as each held a fishing net, with myself being responsible for the jam-jars. So, with Joey at our heels, we almost ran into the park, and it gave me much pleasure at seeing the children so happy.

The lake was easily reached, and indeed it was a favourite place for the children, especially on weekends and holidays, so I wasn't surprised to see so many around; those who were not fishing were happily running barefoot around the sides of the lake, which sloped down to the water. How happy all these children looked on this lovely afternoon. There was a war on, but with so much happiness around it was easy to forget about all the troubles in the world.

Looking for a gap in which to fish, I heard a sudden splash. Oh no! But it had happened: Joey had decided to take himself for a swim. I was aghast, for it distinctly said on a notice-board, 'No swimming. No paddling. Entry in the water prohibited. By order.'

Well, shouts went up all round, along with laughter from lots of children. Iris, jumping up and down, was frantically shouting, 'Auntie Paul, look at Joey! Look at Joey!'

In desperation I called out Joey's name. 'Come, Joey! Come Joey!' Usually Joey was obedient, but at this very moment he didn't respond, for he was thoroughly enjoying his swim in the shallow water.

I did not panic, but on impulse I slipped off my shoes and then waded into the water, right amongst the tiddlers and tadpoles and frogs, hoping and even praying that there was not a park-keeper around watching me. I was now in the middle of the lake. Gosh, the water was now up to my knees, forcing me to hold my dress up with one hand, while the other hand grabbed at Joey's collar.

While attempting to drag Joey out it was evident we had caused a commotion, and being watched by so many caused me much embarrassment. As I struggled back to the edge of the lake, holding right on to Joey's collar, I couldn't help overhearing the different remarks passed by some adults. 'Dogs should be kept under control. Fancy allowing a dog to go in for a swim like that.'

Well, for Joey it was just a matter of a couple of shakes; he then made his escape into the long grass to dry off. But as for myself, was I not uncomfortably wet? However, I soon took off my stockings and hung them on a bush behind me to dry off.

Alfie, looking at me and almost understanding my predicament, exclaimed, 'Oh, Auntie Paul, wasn't Joey naughty?'

Then came a shout from Iris: 'Quick, Auntie Paul, a frog!' Whereupon I immediately investigated and found a little dark-brown creature, more like a toad I thought. Nevertheless, it had the actions of a frog, leaping on its hind legs in a disturbed manner, and finally slithering into the water.

'Let's put some water into the jam-jars then,' I said, and it was during this process that I was interrupted by a voice behind me.

'I say, Miss, I hope you're not thinking of going in for a paddle.'

I turned around, only to be confronted with an elderly park-keeper who now had his eyes upon my bare feet. With the stick in his hand he was gently tapping his trouser leg. No doubt I had aroused his suspicions; after all, I had taken off my shoes and stockings. But perhaps he hadn't noticed my stockings on the bush; if he had, he surely would have had the opportunity to reprimand me, and I was pleased when he walked away. Now to settle down with the children and show them the art of catching tadpoles.

The children's eyes watched me demonstrating. I pointed to the edge of the water, where there had accumulated a bunch of tadpoles; so, placing the net quietly in the water, I scooped up quickly the little black tails. Iris now started to jump up and down with excitement, while Alfie was fascinated to see them swimming around in the jam-jar.

I could see that both Iris and Alfie were anxious to have a go, and so I left then on the water's edge to go back to the bush and retrieve my stockings. They were perfectly dry, but it was impossible to join them with my suspenders because of too many onlookers; however, I did the next best thing, by rolling them below my knees.

I went back to the children, and I could see Iris was having a job with her net, so we both held on to it.

'It's the surprise attack that catches 'em,' I said. And so I left them for a while, busy with their nets. It was interesting for them. They laughed and I could see they were really having fun, yet I knew only too well that both would be missing their mother. I suppose it was good for them to have me around, and truly I enjoyed their company, but my guess was that deep down there was a certain amount of pining going on.

The next thing was, an ice-cream cart came on the scene, pulled by the loveliest of black ponies. Immediately a queue started forming. Everyone by now was so used to wartime queuing, and this occasion was no exception. I joined on at the end, and when my turn came I asked for three penny cornets. I then called to Alfie and Iris; they came running over and on the grass we sat, licking our ices.

There was laughter all around us, and just sitting there I could smell the fragrance from the flowers behind us. It indeed was a beautiful afternoon, for everything appeared so normal; yet I thought how many children's daddies would be away at the war. Then I decided that I mustn't be melancholy on this pleasant day.

I was aware of the presence of Joey, who lay in the grass a few yards off. I could see his coat was shining, and his swim had evidently done him good. Then Iris called out, 'Joey.' Her command was obeyed, for on all fours he actually crawled towards her, as if expecting a scolding.

'Who's been a naughty boy?' I said.

Then Alfie intervened. 'Oh, Auntie Paul, don't be cross with him. All little dogs like a swim.' He remembered, of course, that they had once had a little dog.

I smiled and said, 'Well, I suppose the water was a temptation for him.'

And so, after a successful catching of tiddlers and tadpoles, I decided it was time to go home. Up across the common we walked, the children each carrying their own little treasure in the jam-jars.

'How many you got, Iris?'

'Dunno,' was Iris's reply.

'I think I've got the most,' then answered Alfie.

So our afternoon in the park had turned out well, in spite of the ordeal with Joey. When we finally arrived home the children were full of laughter, especially when they told their Grandma about Joey being in the lake; in fact we all laughed, for I could see now that it had its funny side.

The next day was Sunday, and maybe a little different from usual; we had the children with us, so there were extras to do. One little job I could say goodbye to: it was no longer necessary to wash out my black overall. But that did remind me of one thing; I must try on my new boiler suit — so upstairs I went and put it on. It covered me from ankle to neck, and coming downstairs I was prepared for comments of any kind, for it was true that it was a far from feminine garment.

Dad was the first to greet me. 'Well I never!' Then he smiled with approval. 'You look OK in it, Paul, but don't forget to remove the ticket.'

Mum just looked on, then nodded; she was satisfied. This pleased me, but all the children did was just stare.

'This is my new uniform,' I said. 'Don't you children like it?'

'You look like a man, Auntie Paul,' said Alfie. The very truth only a child can give.

'Auntie Paul is going to do a real man's job,' exclaimed Iris.

'Well thank you,' I answered, bowing in fun as I spoke. All I needed now was Rob's remarks, and then I was through doing my dress parade. I knew Rob was somewhere in the garden, so out I went, with the children following me. I located Rob, who was cutting down some overgrown ivy which had grown in abundance over the wall. I called out, and when he looked around and saw me, he grinned. 'How do you like my new wearing apparel?' Hoping of course that he would be complimentary.

'I suppose, Quinner, you could go to a fancy-dress ball in it. But I doubt anyone asking you for a dance.' Then, smiling, he said, 'I think you look just dandy. But wait until you'll be up to the eyes in grease and oil.'

'Thank you kindly, Sir,' I said, bursting out laughing.

Well, back up in my bedroom, I looked at myself in the mirror. I definitely looked a bit odd, especially with my hair hanging over my shoulders; I must do something about that. So, clasping all my hair in my two hands, I held my hair in position at the back of my head. That's better, I thought, all I need now is a cap. But the thing was, I didn't possess one. One solution might be to wear a turban, a hat made out of a scarf; it was excellent for covering the head, and indeed the turban was popular amongst women, especially women working machines, for hair could be completely covered and protected.

That settled it then, I would make a turban out of Mum's old green scarf, the one she had no more use for. But where was it? When enquiring from Mum where it was, she appeared a little incognisant about it. 'Oh dear,' she exclaimed, 'I gave the scarf to Dad, to put on the scarecrow that's down the garden.'

I then made one dash down the garden to retrieve the precious scarf, hoping it was still there of course. However, on arriving at the tall archways of runner beans, I saw a sight that gladdened my heart: there stood Dad's scarecrow, looking so funny, for his head consisted of an old black bowler tied on with Mum's green scarf. It looked to me very much the worse for wear, for instead of being dark green, it had turned into many shades of lighter green, where the sun had given it a bleach. However, taking the scarf, I automatically said, 'Sorry, old man, but I need part of your headgear.'

Carefully examining it, I found it had not shrunk, but to make a turban I needed a mirror, so up the garden path I raced. I then called out to Mum, 'I've got it,' but when Mum saw the colour of it she gasped.

'Oh dear, it's gone many colours.'

I managed to make a turban which fitted my head, and then immediately I heard a clapping of hands. I turned around, and it was Rob. 'The pretty turban suits you, our Paul.' All I did then, was to wink at Mum.

The last thing that night, Dad said he would give me a call at around 5.15 a.m., giving me assurance that it would get me to the Pierrepont Garage in good time. 'Mustn't be late on your first morning, Paul.'

The next morning then I was up like a lark, with Dad making me tea and toast before I went off.

I actually arrived at the garage ten minutes before my time, that being if St John's church clock was right, of course. I was not surprised when I saw the two big garage doors still closed, but suddenly a small wicket-door opened, and out popped a head, a head belonging to a person I had not seen before.

'You must be Miss Quintin. Come in, please.'

I stepped through, and faced a young man with red hair.

'I'm Roger, usually nicknamed Ginger.'

Shyly I answered, 'How do you do.'

The young man then pointed to a small door on the right-hand side of the garage. 'That'll be the ladies' cloakroom over there, Miss.'

'Thank you,' I replied.

I then made my way through the parked cars to the door, and on opening it found a fair-sized cloakroom; there I quickly changed into my boiler suit, putting on my turban as neat as I could, and at the same time glancing around me. Everything was spotless, with two wash-basins and a toilet, with even a modern roller-towel.

Back in the garage, Roger came across to me, and I felt his eyes were upon me. 'Forgive me for staring Miss. It's just unusual to see a girl dressed up in a boiler suit.' I remembered what Alfie had said, that I looked more like a man, but then I comforted myself at the thought of what Rob had said, about me looking dandy, especially when I would be covered in grease and oil. I was sure that I would fit the role when I was mucked up a bit.

Roger then started sliding back one of the heavy doors. 'I'll help you,' I said, instantly pushing with him, and so, with the two doors wide open, we were ready for custom.

'The first thing I do, Miss, is to unlock the office, and then take the reading from the petrol pumps. The Guv'nor, he likes it done methodically. The petrol readings are checked and rechecked, before and after each shift. Important it be,' said Roger. 'Simple arithmetic really, Miss.'

I then followed Roger out on to the forecourt, where we both stepped up to one of the petrol pumps which stood a foot off the ground.

'See, Miss,' said Roger. 'Every gallon of petrol sold is registered on the clock.' I looked closely, and peered at the figures, which Roger noted down on paper. 'At the end of the shift, the amount of petrol sold should tally with the correct amount of petrol coupons you receive, plus the takings. And here's a tip, Miss — get the coupons first, before you gives petrol. And you must watch out for dud coupons or advanced coupons, and be more careful when it's dark, for some folk are up to all these tricks. Swindlers, I call 'em for they'll do anything if they are desperate for petrol. Even try bribery, Miss, so be cute, and watch 'em. Oh, one thing more, Miss, the Guv is hot on giving no credit, and our motto be, no coupons, no petrol.'

I appreciated the information Roger had given me, for I was inclined to be trusting to human nature, and if I had not been told such valuable information, how easily I could have been let down.

And so it came about that I was talking to Roger, in the little wooden office, when a car pulled up and stopped beside the petrol pumps; it was obvious we had a customer.

Eagerly I asked Roger if I could go out on the forecourt and serve petrol. 'Do you know what to do, Miss?'

'I think so,' I replied, giving Roger a smile of confidence. I hurried out, to serve my first customer, and there stood a most beautiful Bentley, with its owner beside it, a gentleman who looked most affable.

'Ah,' said he, 'a young lady to serve me. I require four gallons please.'

Remembering what Roger had told me, I still was timid when I asked for the coupons first, but I imagine the gentleman knew he had to convince me, and from his wallet he produced his petrol coupons. So all was well. At least that's what I thought, until, holding the nozzle of the pump in my hand, I looked everywhere for the entrance to the petrol tank.

'It's inside the bonnet, Miss.' And he kindly unlocked the bonnet and opened it up for me. To be honest, I was still in a state of perplexity, for I gazed upon a large assortment of wires and gadgets, plus the huge, fascinating engine. There was so much of it, but where on earth was the petrol tank?

I wonder if that's it, I thought, unscrewing a large screw top, which showed an arrow pointing to the right, clearly stating 'To open'.

Suddenly the gentleman gave out a sudden shriek. 'Not in there, Miss!'

Quickly screwing the top back on, I knew I had done something wrong. I blushed, and now the man was mopping his forehead with his handkerchief. Then he said, 'I'll show you where the petrol goes in.' Lifting the lid off a square box effect, he revealed the pipeline to the tank.

I felt relieved, yet stupid, at almost making a drastic mistake. It would have been a calamity indeed if I had mixed petrol with engine oil, possibly causing an explosion. A sudden wave of consternation swept over me; however, I served the man his petrol, and on withdrawing the gun I placed it back on the pump.

The gentleman by now had dropped the bonnet down, carefully fastening the attaching clips. He then gave me a 10 shilling note, remarking, 'Keep the change, young lady.' And while putting on his kid gloves, he said, 'You'll know next time where the petrol goes, won't you?' And I do believe the man chuckled to himself, as he jumped into the car and drove away.

I knew I didn't deserve such kindness, and especially his giving me a tip like that. After all, I had almost made a disastrous blunder, hadn't I? I went across to the little office, where Roger was, clasping in my hand the 10 shilling note and coupons. 'You managed all right then, Miss?'

'Only just,' I replied. I then told Roger all about the catastrophe that nearly was.

'Oh, don't worry, Miss. Come, I'll show you how to put it through the till.' After showing me, he gave me back three sixpenny pieces. 'Three tanners for you,' he said.

'For me?' I exclaimed.

'Yep, Miss, it be your tip.'

'Can't we go halves?' I said.

'Oh no, Miss, it's yours. We keeps our own, see.'

I placed the money in my pocket, and then asked Roger what I should do next.

'If you like,' said Roger, 'you can sweep the forecourt.'

I made myself busy. Then, back in the garage, I noticed the cars already parked; there was quite a selection, some very up to date. Roger then explained that they would nearly all be going out that morning, so the first ones out were parked in front. Then said Roger, 'This is where the mobile jack comes in handy.'

'Oh?'

'Come, I'll show you how it works.' The jack was alongside parked bicycles; Roger pulled it out on its four wheels and then demonstrated putting it under a Ford Prefect. 'Make sure it's under the axle, Miss. This be the strongest place. Then you ups and downs with the handle. It be easy to do — come, have a try.' And so, with the up-and-down movement of the handle, the jack soon hoisted up the little car; in fact the Ford had heightened a good foot off the ground. Then, with ease, Roger moved the car right around. 'See, it's easy, Miss. No need to drive 'em, when you've got this!' I quite agreed with him. Then, squeezing on a release handle, Roger let her down nice and easy, so now she was back on four wheels again.

In between serving petrol, Roger explained almost everything to me, and as one can imagine I was deeply grateful.

Well, 2 o'clock came before I knew where I was. I had in fact completed a whole shift, and finishing at such an hour seemed out of the ordinary. But there it was, home time.

I arrived home about 2.30. All appeared strange, especially as there was no one at home except Joey, and all he did was wag his tail and then close his eyes for more sleep. So for the remainder of the afternoon I made myself busy tidying up. I then glanced at the clock on the mantelpiece; it was just twenty minutes to four. I know, I thought, I'll meet the children from school. If I took the short cut across the fields I would just be in time for school coming out. I crept out, unknown to Joey, for he sure would have loved a run.

I hurried down the slope, past the farm, and then down the pathway that led to the fields. Through the iron swing-gate I went; then crossing the first field, I passed through the hairpin stile, which I could jump through when a child. I passed the cows, who were grazing and chewing their cud, but the poor things were absolutely tormented with flies that seemed to concentrate on their faces, almost crawling into their eyes.

Across the last field I came through the last swing-gate, and it squeaked for lack of lubrication; however, I finally reached the village of Weston. I then walked down a narrow road, with cottages on either side, until I came upon All Saints church, where I took a short cut through the churchyard; this brought me to the school.

As children, Rob and I would come this way, and some of the old headstones had been converted into pathways: hence the clatter when one ran across them. Anyway, I arrived just as the children were coming out of school and I soon spotted Iris and Alfie. I gave them a wave, and they came running towards me. I put my arms around them both, happy to think they were both settling down at my old school.

'Come on you kids, we'll take the road way home.'

'It's the longest way, Auntie Paul,' said Alfie.

'I know, love, but I want you to see something.'

'What is it?' exclaimed Alfie, with all the enthusiasm of a child.

'It's just a big house called The Gables. Belongs to an old Professor.' Now I sensed excitement in both the children, for they held tightly to each of my hands. 'It's Professor Musgrave, and if we are lucky we may see him.'

'Hooray!' shouts Iris.

The old Professor, who was easily in his seventies, lived alone apart from his ancient housekeeper, Nan, and her husband, who was responsible for all the odd jobs that wanted doing around the place. Professor Musgrave was a kind man, and very popular with children. Rob and I when younger often visited The Gables on our way home from school, like so many other children did. We never left The Gables without our pockets being full of apples or plums, which he always gave us when we left.

Now we were right outside The Gables, and so I went up to the big iron gate and peered through, and there I caught a glimpse of the Professor himself.

'Hello there!' I called out, but there was no answer. I then shouted louder. Ah, now he heard me, for he came across to open up one side of the gate. He looked at the children and myself standing there, and he seemed a little confused, as if his sight was failing him.

I was sure he did not recognise me or remember me, but he gave us a smile of welcome and said, 'I guess you've come to see my collection.'

'Only if it's convenient to you, Sir,' I answered.

'Oh yes, yes,' he replied. 'Come along in.' Now closer to me, he gave me a fleeting glance. 'Haven't I seen you somewhere before, young lady?'

'Indeed, Sir. My youngest brother and I often used to call in and see you, on our way home from school.'

'Ah,' said the Professor, 'that accounts for it. And now you've grown up, too.'

'Hope you didn't mind, Sir, my bringing along my nephew and niece.'

'It's my pleasure,' said the old Professor.

Slowly we followed him into the same old conservatory that I knew as a child, and after all these years I was still fascinated and impressed by the beauty of these gorgeous plants. The Professor had a name for each of these individual unique specimens of beauty, and always with great pride he could tell you exactly where the plants came from, and how he had come by them.

I glanced at the fine old gentleman, and I do declare it must have been the same old black velvet skull cap that he wore, which fitted him admirably on the top of his head. Funny, but I could never imagine the Professor without it. I dare say to a stranger he would appear ascetic, but to me he was the same sweet person, with the knowledge of a born naturalist.

I watched Alfie and Iris, who were now overwhelmed with curiosity as we approached the aquarium of tropical fish. I don't suppose they had seen the like of it before; there were so many tanks, all supplying homes for the most beautiful fish of extreme delicacy. But I knew that the big surprise was to come later, for on leaving the conservatory we entered into the house itself.

Passing the library, I could see that Nan was busy dusting books of some sort; however, we entered through another door, which led to the Professor's real treasure, for its contents consisted of butterflies and tapestry, such a marvellous selection of both.

The butterflies were indeed exquisite, their delicate little bodies lying in exotic manner underneath glass frames; just lying on view they were, and coming from all parts of the world. The sizes of them varied, of course; thus the assortment of frames.

Alfie gasped when he saw them, as if surprised at seeing such variation, while Iris remarked, 'Did they really fly, Auntie Paul?'

'Course they did,' said Alfie, 'They've got wings to fly.'

The next thing was the tapestries, those beautiful woven designs in colour, many of them so very old, yet hung down in a most dignified manner. I think the Chinese tapestry was the pride of the Professor's collection, and would always remain so while he lived.

And so our eventful visit had come to an end, and I know that the children, like myself, were most impressed. I thanked the Professor, and even the children timidly thanked him.

'Come again, any time you want,' said the Professor, with which he produced an old fruit basket, full of Victoria plums from last year's crop. 'Come, children, help yourself,' he said.

Shyly, the children took two each.

The old gentleman was now smiling. 'Come along, I'm sure you can do better than that. Fill up your pockets now.' This they did. These were the very same words he used to say to Rob and me.

We bade the Professor farewell, and then hurried through the big iron gates, closing them behind us. 'We'll have to hurry to be home before Grandma,' I said.

'Let's run,' said Alfie. We did, and must have made record time in getting home. Immediately I started preparing the tea, and had everything ready by the time Mum got home; this pleased Mum I could see, and so we had much to talk about over tea.

'How did you get on at the garage?' said Mum.

'Super,' I replied.

'Let me have a look at your hands.'

So, with outstretched hands, I remarked, 'See Mum, no different.'

Then the children talked incessantly of their visit to The Gables, and Mum had much to listen to. And when she heard my story of the Bentley, she looked so surprised, saying, 'Oh, I say!'

Mum as usual went across the common to meet Dad. Meanwhile I put the children to bed, and after finishing their prayers, little Iris spoke. 'Auntie Paul, when are we going to see Mummy?'

What answer could I possibly give, after such an unexpected question. 'I expect, love, you'll see Mummy shortly.' But I could not escape to see the tears that were in her little eyes. Evidently they were both missing their Mummy so very much.

Alfie, I was sure, overhead our conversation, but remained silent.

'You OK, Alfie?' I said.

'Yes, thank you, Auntie Paul.' I went over beside him to kiss him goodnight, but before I could do so he spoke. 'Auntie Paul, can we keep some fish like the Professor's?' I realised that Alfie's preoccupation was slightly different.

'Not exactly,' I said. 'You see, Alfie, the fish we were looking at today were tropical fish, and they can only survive in water that requires heating to a certain temperature. However, I dare say we could manage to keep some goldfish.'

'Really, Auntie Paul?'

'Really,' I answered. 'Now, be off to sleep. Pleasant dreams, God bless.'

Mum and Dad had returned home, with Joey panting, as if he had been running hard. 'Come on boy,' I said, giving him a bowl of fresh water, which he lapped up vigorously.

Dad was smiling at me. 'Mum says you had a good day at the garage. But what's this I heard about you nearly putting petrol in an engine?' Then Dad laughed out loud. 'My word,' he said, 'the perils of Pauline!' That was the name of a famous film serial, quite a few years earlier. I had to laugh myself, for after all I was the subject of which it might be said, ignorance was bliss.

Rommel had gone to the support of the Italians in North Africa, and had won back the gains made by General Wavell only a few months previous; and by the spring of 1941, British forces had been forced to withdaw from Greece and Crete, after a disastrous campaign.

The next outstanding event was that Hitler attacked Russia, and consequently they were brought into the war. It was not surprising that the Russian entry into the war was greeted with jubilation, for we were desperate for an ally. They needed our help too, and it was necessary for the British to make as many tanks as we could for the Russians; in fact they were in dire need, so it was in this September that Tanks for Russia week began.

At this period of the war, things appeared very much the same. We still had air raids on Bristol, London, and most home counties, with the result of much damage and loss of life. Nevertheless, the morale of the British people remained good. By now we were accustomed to rationing, coping with black-outs and air raids, and queuing for almost everything. Personally, I felt that the queue was more like a get-together, for we could converse quite freely, telling each other of our different whims, complaints or grouches maybe. Now then, if you were ever in the position of 'jumping the queue' the Lord help you, because you would be made to feel embarrassment to the full, by shouts of anger coming from everyone.

One thing the war had taught the majority of us was the art of being patient, and I reckon that on the Home Front the war had some good points to offer, for we could no longer afford to be extravagant. Our clothes had to be mended and re-mended; hence the saying 'make do and mend'. So indeed jumble-sales became popular. How well I remember sewing my stockings from toe to thigh, taking great pride in the darning of the heels. Patching, mending, and darning were priorities amongst the ladies of the day. So too was cooking, and to waste food was considered sinful, for were not our men on the high seas risking their lives for it? There were other sacrifices at home, for beautiful flower beds and lawns were churned over to make room for fresh vegetables. Our slogan for the day was 'Dig for Victory'. In my opinion the British people accepted the simplest way of living, and so we lived accordingly.

Every day at the Pierrepont Garage I worked with an increased interest, for now I was able to grease cars and mend punctures. I was mastering the art of using big heavy iron levers, which enabled me to remove the tyres off the wheels. I sold petrol and oil, topped up batteries, and was quite efficient with the air-line, giving correct pressures. I was also driving many types of cars, for businessmen would drive up on the forecourt and sometimes request you to take them to the railway station; afterwards you brought the car back for parking in the garage, and if you were around when they returned you were handsomely rewarded. On one such occasion, I had to take a Vauxhall and its owner to the GWR railway station, for the gentleman was going up to London for the day. He got out of the car, gave me a smile, and was off, and I was about to get in the driver's seat when I noticed he had left his brief-case on the seat.

Immediately it was action stations: I leapt out of the car, clutching the brief-case in my hand, and almost ran up the long flight of wooden stairs that led to the platform. The London train was in, and amidst the steam coming from the engine I caught a glimpse of the gentleman just climbing on to the train. As loud as I could, I shouted, 'Sir, Sir!' and frantically waved the brief-case. He immediately recognised me, and stepped quickly off the train.

I could see he was pleased to gain possession of his brief-case, exclaiming, 'How on earth did I forget that?' The next thing, we were showered with more steam, a warning that the train was about to pull away. The gentleman was now fumbling in his waistcoat pocket, and he then produced a 10 shilling note. 'Take this,' he said.

'That's all right, Sir,' I replied.

'I insist, for you have been most helpful. Without my brief-case, my journey would have been in vain.'

The carriages started jerking, he leapt on to the train, and from a carriage window he called out, 'I'll pick the car up at 6 p.m.'

'Righto, Sir,' I replied, pushing the 10 shilling note in my pocket.

I walked down the wooden stairs much slower than when I came up them, so I had time to glance at the posters on the wall: they were, of course, gentle reminders, such as: Is your journey really necessary? Keep Mum. Walls have ears. Save scrap. Let economy rule Britain. All being good common sense, I suppose.

Of course I didn't need the posters to remind me that the country was still at war. At this time my brother Pat remained on corvettes, and was well and truly involved in escorting convoys to Russia. Brother Tim, on the other hand, was still in England, at a regimental base at Yeovil in Somerset; as a result he was able to visit us quite often. It was natural, for he wanted to see his children, and I think he was content and happy to know they were staying with us. His preliminary proceedings for divorce had started, and it was arranged that a special hearing in court would take place on a certain date. We expected that without doubt Tim would win his case on the grounds of his wife's adultery. But something happened. Only two weeks prior to the hearing, and unbeknown to anyone, a secret reconciliation had taken place between Tim and Rene. This episode immediately cancelled out all divorce proceedings, and so they remained man and wife, each entitled to the custody of the children. However, after that they still lived apart, and from then onwards, I regret to say, Tim drifted his own way, Rene doing likewise, and both became forgetful of their responsibilities. For me, the dissolution of what might have been a very happy family was an unhappy situation.

I mentioned before that my Grandmother lived at White Whaltham, not far from Maidenhead. Well, one day we had a letter from her saying that she had heard that the RAF were going to build a temporary aerodrome very close to her cottage. In her many letters that followed we could tell that Grandma was getting anxious, so Mum decided she would go up to White Whaltham herself, and find out exactly what was happening. Dad suggested that Mum take the Black and White bus which would enable her to return the same day. This she did, and I remember going down into Bath to meet her. The bus was late arriving and I was pleased to see Mum when at last she appeared.

'Hello, duck,' she said. 'Guess you've had to wait a while.'

'Well Mum, did you have a good journey?'

'Not bad at all,' replied Mum.

'And how was Gran?'

'Your Grandma is well. But oh dear, everywhere around your Grandma's cottage is just one big upheaval, for all the surrounding fields have been dug up.'

So Gran hadn't exaggerated after all. As Mum and I walked home, Mum spoke of bulldozers and waggon loads of cement being used to make the runways.

'Oh no!' I gasped. For when Rob and I were children, we used to stay with Gran, especially during our summer holidays, and no mistake to say, it was a place of sheer beauty. At the bottom of the garden was a large field, where Gran's poultry took command, and I remembered how happy I used to be, with an old hat in my hand, picking up the scattered eggs which lay in the field. And what intelligent cocks and hens they were, for right on the dot they would come in for their feed, Gran of course being very punctual. Then, beyond the field, was a stream of beautiful clear water, which rippled over the smooth stones, and where some of the best salmon were caught. Being a child, I was skylarking about when I had the misfortune to fall into the stream, not once, but twice.

Many happy hours we had spent there, and once again war was responsible for the tribulation of quiet country folk like my Grandmother.

'Poor Gran,' I said. 'What will she do?' I knew full well that it could be dangerous living almost on top of an aerodrome, for would it not be a good target for any Jerry? Plus the noise from aircraft, flying around at all times. Dear Gran, I thought, always living a quiet sort of an existence, happy with only her garden and peaceful surroundings.

I sensed that Mum was worrying about Gran, and the discussion she had with Dad later on brought about only one conclusion: Gran would be better off staying with us for the duration of the war. I for one was more than delighted when Gran wrote back and said that she had made up her mind to come and stay with us.

Of course, many changes in the home had to be made in readiness for Gran coming. I was to move into the small box-room, where there was quite ample room really for a single bed and a chest of drawers, while the children took my room; it was decided that Gran would have the children's room, which overlooked the garden.

Dad suggested decorating. Wallpaper was out of the question in wartime; it would have to be pink distemper, which definitely would make it fresh and sweet looking, and this I felt sure would please Gran.

It was all arranged then, that Gran would let off her cottage, and I dare say any RAF personnel would be glad of it. So, when everything had been settled, and Gran was ready to come to us, Dad hired a car from the Bear Flat Garage, and taking me with him we made the journey to Maidenhead.

Dad and I saw exactly what Mum had described, and when going up Cherry-Tree Garden Lane, Dad said, 'Don't be surprised if Gran's a little sad.'

'It's only to be expected, Dad,' I replied.

Anyway, Gran was so pleased to see us that she hadn't time to think of her own feelings, and with a few belongings she made the return journey with us. Now our little family of four had increased to seven.

Although extremely busy myself, I helped Mum all I could, for as was expected she had lots to do in the home, and it was impossible for her to carry on with her job at the hospital; she gave it up temporarily, so as to devote her whole time to her family, caring for us with all the love and loyalty a mother could give.

Life just went on as usual. At the garage I did really work hard, and felt equally as good as any man. Mr Griffin agreed, and was pleased with the effort and adjustment I had made, so much so that my wages had been increased considerably. I was also getting very good tips. I enjoyed so much working in the garage, and life for me seemed full; all my spare time was taken up in driving for the Red Cross and the ARP, and coming into contact with so many different people was an education in itself. And with getting older, I realised that I was changing in more ways than one. I was losing my shyness rapidly, and therefore could discuss things more freely with people.

The garage offered me a variety of interests, like when the RAF lads used to come into Bath on Tuesdays and Thursdays to park their bicycles for twopence. Pierrepont Garage could offer a central parking place — that's why it was so popular — and at times they would just swarm in. I couldn't give them parking tickets quick enough, but they were always so full of good fun and humour, and one incident brings back memories.

A corporal had brought a jeep in for parking. He had, however, dropped off an official at his destination, and wanted parking space for the evening, so in the garage he came. Meanwhile I was busy underneath a car, greasing nipples and points etc., when suddenly I got such a kick on one of my shoes, and a voice said, 'Hey there, boy. Can I park the jeep?'

Still on my back I was, when I crawled out from underneath the car; then I jumped up on my feet. I think the corporal looked flabbergasted.

'Blimey!' he said. 'Didn't expect to see a girl! Please accept my apology.'

'That's OK,' I replied. 'How long do you wish to park the jeep?'

'All right if I pick it up just before 10 p.m.?'

Marking his parking ticket out, I requested that he leave his keys in the vehicle. He did this and then departed, and on his return to pick up the jeep he was still apologetic for his error in mistaking my identity.

Rob at this period was getting very restless with his job at the Pitmans and had become interested in doing a real man's job, so I promised to see Mr Griffin for him. An opportunity arose when Mr Griffin came into the garage. I approached him on the subject of Rob wanting to work with cars, on the mechanical side, of course, and I was pleasantly surprised when Mr Griffin appeared interested.

'Tell him to come down and see me,' he said, so Rob did exactly this, and gained so much of Mr Griffin's confidence that an agreement was made immediately that Rob should start at the Pierrepont Garage the following Monday, as an apprentice mechanic. This was wonderful news, for I could look forward to Rob's company at work.

The following Monday, Rob was put into the lower garage, and as time went on I would occasionally see him, and kept him supplied with cups of tea and cocoa. If I got a good tip before 9.30 a.m., I would send out for cream cakes for us all. Often enough it was those delicious cream slices for a penny each, but should my tips be small, we contented ourselves with ha'penny buns.

How the weeks flew by. Gran was now settled in, and it was my belief that the children were more settled too, for Alfie was now keen on football, and was put on the school football team.

We still had the occasional air raids. I recall one little incident, when one of our own Spitfires was in a dogfight with the enemy, and it appeared they were doing battle right above us. In the middle of all the other noise we distinctly heard a pattering sound on the corrugated roof of our outer shed. After the 'all clear' had gone, Dad investigated, and found what he expected, bullets from a machine-gun. But what we never found out was, did they belong to us, or Jerry?

And now I write about a mystery that was never solved. It was the month of September, 1941, with autumn in all its glory. It was a warm night too, so warm, I recall, that I found difficulty in going off to sleep. I lay in bed, just letting my thoughts drift I suppose, when suddenly I heard this strange, heavy thud. What it was I had no idea, and eventually, realising that it hadn't disturbed anyone else, I settled down to sleep.

At breakfast the following morning I spoke of the mysterious thud that I had heard, but no one else had heard it, so no comment was made of it. However, when I took up Gran's breakfast I discussed it with her, and she said, 'Now you come to speak of it, I did hear something, for it woke me up.'

I didn't start work until 2 o'clock that day, which gave me the opportunity of helping Mum with the washing. In those days we washed our clothes in a copper boiler which stood in the outhouse; the water was heated by a coal fire underneath, and I had just lit the fire when there was this knock on the front door. I went to see who our early visitor was, and lo and behold, standing on the doorstep was a special constable.

He spoke first. 'It's OK, Miss, nothing wrong. Just making a few enquiries about an incident that happened late last night.'

'Oh?' I exclaimed.

'Young girl it was, found dead she was, in a runaway car that hit a tree.'

'Oh dear,' I said. 'Where?'

'Across the first field, the road that runs off it.'

I knew it so well, for three very large houses stood back off this road; it was the very same road we took to Weston village, if it was too wet to cross the fields.

Now I was inquisitive. 'Has the girl been identified?'

'Don't rightly know, Miss. At the station, they suspect foul play. See, the poor wench was almost naked.'

'That's terrible,' I replied.

Now this story of a runaway car puzzled me. It's true the road is on a slight incline, but not sufficient, I thought, to gather enough momentum to reach a high speed, least of all hitting a tree and killing a girl. I came to the conclusion that the poor girl must have been murdered; this I was sure of, but kept my opinion to myself. However, I told the Constable that I had heard a thud at approximately 11.30 p.m. I mentioned too that my Grandmother had heard it.

'It must have been when the car hit the tree,' said the Constable.

And so it remained a mystery, never to be solved. The only evidence found was an army officer's button, but this alone did not give sufficient justification to make further enquiries. Finally the case was closed, with a verdict of accidental death. It's strange, but I could never accept that. To me it was not an accident, but instead a wilful premeditated murder, made to look like an accident. I reckon, had we been living under normal times, further investigations would have been carried out, whereby a different verdict would have been ascertained, I was sure.

That same late autumn, we lost Joey. Something had struck him down and he died peacefully in his own chair, curled up in a ball, just the way he used to sleep. As he lay dying, Dad spoke to him, but he did not stir. Then Dad touched his nose, and the only response Joey gave was a blink or two from his brown, bloodshot eyes.

'He's going peacefully,' whispered Dad. Tears rolled down my face, for we all loved Joey. He was only a mongrel dog, but a pal, and we gave him the best send-off we could. The children adorned his chair with some of the last autumn flowers, and placed some white curtain net all over him. Then Dad and Rob carried Joey and his chair to the bottom of the garden, Dad saying, 'We'll bury him in the corner, next to the artichokes.' We all looked on as Rob dug a hole — it had to be a big one to get the chair in — and then Dad gently lowered Joey into his last resting place. 'Goodbye, old pal,' he said. Rob then shovelled the good earth upon him. Finally Dad made a little wooden cross and placed it on top. The children wrote on it: 'To Joey, who is now in Heaven.'

It was during the start of my first winter in the garage that I was put in charge of the upper garage, and made responsible for the cars parked below. I had three persons under me, one an ex-Major in the Army who had unfortunately lost his right arm at the beginning of the war; he was a good worker, in spite of his handicap, and it really amazed me to see how well he could drive. There were also two young lads, both in their teens, who were keen and most willing. I shouldered the responsibility very well I thought, until one night I wished I had been a man, instead of a young girl.

I was on the 2 o'clock shift, with Freddie, the youngest of the two boys. The latter part of the evening was very quiet; in fact there were very few cars left to go out. I was sitting in the little office, sorting out some petrol coupons, when Freddie popped his head in the doorway and said, 'Like some fish and chips, Miss?'

'Yes please,' I answered. 'Get the usual, Freddie,' I said, giving him four pennies. (Three pennies were for the fish, one for chips.) 'Oh, and Freddie,' I said, 'plenty of salt and vinegar, please.'

While Freddie was up the street getting our supper, I put the kettle on, and when he returned we ate together, finishing off with our tea. Then, to my surprise, Freddie pulled out a twopenny packet of Woodbines, saying, 'Like a fag, Miss?'

'I don't smoke, Freddie. And Freddie, aren't you a bit too young to take up the habit?'

'I know,' replied Freddie. 'But all me mates smoke, and I enjoys a puff.'

'Well, make sure it's out when you've finished.'

'OK, Miss,' replied Freddie.

It was about 8.30 p.m., and I told Freddie that if he would like to go off early he could do so, as we were so very quiet.

Freddie now looked pleased. 'Will it be OK, Miss?'

'Of course, Freddie,' I replied. 'So off you go now, before I change my mind.' So putting on his cap, he bade me goodnight, and I did likewise.

Back in the little office, I settled down to some paperwork; in fact I was checking the takings. Suddenly I was aware of the silence — an undisturbed atmosphere; it was uncanny really, and I wondered if it was because I was on my own. Strange, but somehow I felt this premonition.

Then I heard a slight noise, but I couldn't make out exactly what it was. Must be from one of the cars, I thought, for often I heard weird noises coming from the engines cooling down, with the contraction of the metal surroundings. Now I definitely heard footsteps, which stopped right outside the office; then came two knocks. Ah, I thought, must be a customer for petrol, and I hadn't heard them drive on to the forecourt. On opening the door, I was surprised to see a soldier standing there. I noticed he was wearing a pair of rimless glasses. The light was poor in the garage — well it had to be really, for we were regulated to only a certain amount of lighting. It was impossible to see the soldier's eyes, yet I felt they were staring right at me. He spoke, and straight to the point he was. 'I need some money!'

I suddenly felt trapped, knowing what he was after. Being taken unawares like this, I felt my pulse beating quicker. I wasn't exactly afraid, and told myself to be sensible and not show affright, so as calmly as I could I spoke. 'You mean you want money from me?'

'That's right,' answered the soldier. 'I'm desperate for it. You have it, I want it.'

'But please understand, it's not mine to give.'

In the back of my mind, I remembered Rob's spanners lying on the floor, beside my feet. God forbid I would use them in violence, but if the worst came to the worst I knew I would have to use them to defend myself.

I spoke: 'You know, in all sincerity, I would like to help you.'

I wished, at that moment, that someone would walk into the garage, but alas, he and I were on our own. Then an idea struck me. The chance of it working was very slender indeed, but nevertheless it was worth a try.

'If you come back in a half-hour, I'll see what I can do for you.'

I felt the soldier was hesitant. Could he really trust me? He paused for a moment, and then, without a word, he walked away. I realised that he must have taken me at my word, trusting me to help him. And now I was feeling guilty, knowing perfectly well that I had no intentions of giving him any money at all: yet I had convinced him, and the very thought of having to betray someone did not give me justification for feeling proud of myself. On the other hand, I had to protect what was not mine, and I could not give away money which did not belong to me.

Stepping out of the office, I saw his shadow disappear through the big doorway. I stood aghast, and felt myself trembling. Then, realising that I must take a grip of myself, I went back into the office.

I needed help quickly. The police station was at the top of the road, so without any hesitation I picked up the phone and dialled the number required.

A voice spoke: 'CID — can I help you?'

'I'm Miss Quintin, working at the Pierrepont Garage, and I've reason to believe I'm about to be robbed by a soldier, who has demanded money from me, and who will be returning within the half-hour.'

The voice on the line replied, 'We'll be down, Miss.'

I replaced the receiver. Now it was my turn to put my trust in the police, and hope they would come to my rescue.

I suddenly felt doubtful. What if they let me down, or were too late in coming? And I felt guilty again. Here was a perfect stranger, in a desperate situation, who was going to put his trust in me, and I was going to crush that trust by betraying him. But on thinking it through I felt justified in doing what I had to do.

And so in the office I waited, for what seemed like eternity. Anyway, the half-hour was almost up, and there were no signs of the law; in fact I was now experiencing an uncanny silence again.

In the dim light I glanced at my watch. I could barely make out the time, yet I knew the half-hour was up. I felt myself fidgety, and on impulse I picked up one of Rob's spanners and placed it in one of the leg pockets of my boiler suit. Maybe it gave me a sense of protection, but I was hoping with all my heart that it would not be necessary to use it.

I stood outside the office. Then, looking up, I saw the outline of the soldier coming towards me.

But where were the police?

I suddenly felt trapped again, and almost sick inside. I stood rigid, by now almost frightened out of my wits.

Then, from nowhere, two detectives appeared, each making a grab for an arm of the soldier.

I just don't know what I felt at that precise moment. Relieved maybe, or ashamed of being guilty of a betrayal. I felt humiliation too, especially when they marched the soldier up to me, with one detective saying, 'Is this him?'

I shall never forget the look that soldier gave me. He had trusted me, hadn't he, and I had let him down. In me he saw a traitor, and with the detectives giving him a surprise ambuscade, it was no wonder he looked like he did. So they marched him away, and the very next day they sent for me to attend the police station. When I was seated in front of a police Superintendent, he commended me on my action on the matter.

'Yes,' said the Superintendent, 'he was really desperate for money. A Canadian deserter he was, with a wife and family living in Glasgow.'

I left the police station, knowing that the incident was closed and hoping I would never meet up with the same situation again; for it was most unpleasant, tricking a man, only to see him captured.

During this period of time, Gran was taken ill, and when Doctor Scott-White, our family doctor, came to see her, he immediately made arrangements for her to go into a hospital, St Martin's, which was situated on the other side of Bath. Doctor's diagnosis was that of pneumonia, so you can imagine how distressed we all were, especially when Gran was carried down the lane on a stretcher. Mum and I went with her in the ambulance, and it was sad having to leave her lying in a hospital bed, with her beautiful white hair almost covering the pillow.

I stooped over to kiss her before leaving. 'Don't worry, Gran,' I whispered. 'You'll be all right. And I'll be up to see you tomorrow.'

I could see Mum was upset, yet we both knew Gran was in the best place, for she would be given all the necessary care and attention.

In the weeks to follow, I was a frequent visitor to the hospital and I was so happy to know that Gran was making good progress. Gran, I knew, enjoyed an occasional tot of whisky, and once the immediate anxiety for her health was over, I took the liberty of taking her in a small miniature, with a screw top; covering the little bottle with my handkerchief, I would give it to Gran to take a sip. I must confess I was doing it illegally, but I knew there could be no ill effects. And what did it matter? Gran enjoyed it, like she did before her illness. Immediately she took a sip, bright roses came into her cheeks, and the smile on her face gave me extreme satisfaction. I could see that she really appreciated it. I also used to take her egg custards, which I made myself, using only the fresh eggs from our hens. We all wanted her back home, but on Doctor Scott-White's advice, Gran was to remain in hospital.

It was after I had been to visit Gran, on a Sunday, the 30th of November 1941, that one of the most important events in my life occurred. Gran and I had had a most enjoyable hour together, with myself feeling in high spirits. I think it was because I was wearing my new coat. It was the colour of air-force blue, with big lapels and a belt, and Gran remarked that I looked quite smart in it. 'It goes with your hair,' said Gran, meaning that it made a striking contrast, for my hair was red.

I left the hospital to catch the 3.30 bus into town, and on arriving at the Guildhall I got off the bus with all intentions of walking home up the Lansdown Road. But something very peculiar happened within me. I can only put it down to fatalism, the belief that everything is predetermined. Submission to fate perhaps? But whatever it was, it was stronger and more determined than I.

I wanted to start walking in the right direction, towards Broad Street, which led on to the Lansdown Road, but I just couldn't. It was as if some unknown power was insisting that I turn left, to go and catch the Lansdown bus. It appeared that I had suddenly lost the power of my own mind, for I started walking to the left, in the direction of the Parade Gardens, and at that moment it appeared to me that I was doing the right thing. I was aware too that I could not resist this strange power of guidance, wherever it was going to lead me; all I could do was catch the bus.

How ridiculous, I thought. Yet as strange as it all was, and I was in a state of perplexity, I realised that someone or something wanted me to catch the Lansdown bus, this I felt sure of.

When I finally arrived at the bus-stop, I found several other people waiting, amongst whom was an old schoolteacher of mine. She smiled at me, I smiled back, and then I took my place in the queue.

We appeared to have stood for ages, and someone remarked how late the bus was. Then, behind me, I heard laughter from some children. Curious, I glanced around me, and I was surprised to see two soldiers playing a game with the children; they were not part of the queue. Actually the soldiers were making paper aeroplanes. The children kept throwing them up into the air, and I wondered who was the most excited, the children or the soldiers, for they all appeared to be enjoying themselves hugely.

One thing I did notice was the vast difference in the stature of these soldiers. One was fairly tall and well built, with broad, square shoulders; he was wearing a khaki overcoat that nearly touched his ankles. The other soldier was short and podgy. Peculiar, I thought, they must be in a funny regiment. Then I recognised the RAOC badges, which explained everything. They were in fact from a regiment of non-skilled men; nevertheless they were useful men to the cause, and I couldn't help thinking they must be decent chaps to amuse the children like they were doing.

A cold wind blew, and standing there I was feeling chilled. I glanced at my watch. Gosh, I thought, we must have stood twenty minutes already and still no sign of the bus. I was just considering whether to start walking home when the Lansdown bus finally appeared.

I heard sighs of relief as we all hastened to climb on the bus, myself taking the very back seat. I was just about to sort out some small change for my fare when I noticed that the little soldier was getting on our bus, and lo and behold he came straight up to me.

'Excuse me, Miss, can we get to Corsham on this bus?'

'Oh dear no,' I answered. 'You want the bus-stop on the other side of the road.' I pointed in that direction.

He said, 'Thank you,' and then got off the bus. But it puzzled me why he should have come right to the back of the bus to ask me a question which could have easily been answered by anyone.

The bus remained stationary, for now the bus driver was missing. Gone for his tea-break perhaps. We'll move off sometime, I thought. And then, to my surprise, the other soldier came on the scene, walking up the gangway towards me. He stopped, and I looked at him, and without thinking I said, 'I think you are on the wrong bus.'

He did not speak, but smiled. Then he shyly produced a letter from his khaki jacket, saying, 'My address is on this envelope. Please write to me.'

I was dumbfounded to say the least. What could I say? Taken unawares like that, I had no time to recuperate. The soldier, smiling again, turned and then walked back down the gangway.

Suddenly I was all hot and bothered. The very impudence of this man, to ask me to write to him, not knowing who he was, or where he had come from!

The bus driver had now returned, and at last we were on our way.

After a few minutes, it came to my notice that the stranger's letter was still sitting on my lap. Curiosity overcame me, so I picked it up and read the address on the envelope:

J McCann   10561908
RAOC
Corsham
Wilts.

So, a member of the McCann family I thought. Rather a coincidence, it being St Andrew's day. There was a letter within the envelope, but I did not attempt to read it; I merely placed it into my handbag. Instead I tried to dismiss the thoughts about the stranger and his letter, but somehow I couldn't.

I smiled to myself. Even the idea of being romantically interested in someone did not appeal to me — especially a total stranger. Up until then, I had had no boy-friends, and actually I had no desire for the opposite sex. At that time I was very content with my life; busy without a doubt, but happy I was, doing what I had to do.

Small flakes of snow started to fall as I got off the bus. Must hurry home, I thought. Then I remembered the soldier's letter in my handbag. Curiosity and inquisitiveness overcame me, so I decided to have a quick peep at the letter. Now walking slowly, I pulled off one of my gloves, opened my bag and pulled out the letter.

126

It was an ordinary letter, not to me of course, but written from a brother to another brother, and signed Joe. Incidentally, my stranger's name was Jim. I placed the letter back in my bag, and as I hurried on, down came larger flakes of snow.

That very evening we had a surprise visit from brother Pat. He was just the same old Pat, forever wanting to tease me. However, the opportunity arose for me to be alone with him, and I just had to confide in him and tell him all about the soldier on the bus.

Pat now had a grin on his face when he said, 'You should write to him, our Paul. After all, he could be miles away from home.'

'I most certainly will not write to him,' I said.

'I somehow think you will,' replied Pat. 'Because I notice you are still hanging on to his letter. Anyway, even if it's only out of courtesy you must return his letter, for I dare say he'll be needing his brother's address.'

Well, I hadn't thought of that, which now put the situation differently.

'Go on, write to him,' said Pat. 'Make the poor devil happy.'

When the time came for Pat to go, I said I would walk along the top road with him. I always enjoyed a stroll, but I missed Joey's company, for it wasn't much fun walking back on your own. When Joey was at my heels, I somehow felt protected, and the little dog was always great company.

'Don't come too far,' said Pat, as we parted. 'I'll say so long to you now. And don't forget to write to your soldier.'

So, after kissing Pat goodnight, I strolled back home, thinking of all sorts really. What did our Pat say? The soldier could be a long way from his home.

I tried telling myself not to be sentimental, or get carried away with ridiculous thoughts, but even by the time I reached home I was still undecided. I just couldn't make up my own mind. Should I write, or ignore the letter? Perhaps I should tell Mum. No, better wait. After all, I did entrust my secret to Pat, and he did advise me to write. Anyway, it was entirely up to me now; the decision was upon my shoulders. I was going to have to use my own judgement in the matter.

Maybe I was just curious, rather than fascinated by this stranger who suddenly had come into my life. Anyway, whatever the reason, late that evening, I sat down beside the fire and wrote a letter to Jim McCann. And how well I remember that first sentence:

'I hesitate as to whether I should write to you or not.'

The rest of the letter remained short and brief, with the addition of a PS: 'On your next visit to Bath, will be pleased to show you around.' Then I signed myself off: 'Kindest regards, Miss Quintin.'

After addressing the envelope, I put a stamp on, and it was ready for posting. On my way to work the following morning, I dropped my letter in the wall post box. I had decided, and it had been done.

I continued walking down Sion Hill. The fall of snow the previous night had made the ground crisp with the early frost, and walking faster to keep warm I arrived at the Pierrepont Garage in good time. I had the big doors opened and everything unlocked by the time Freddie came, for he just flew into the garage on his bicycle, shouting, 'Sorry I'm late, Miss. Slept in!' Rob and the other mechanics didn't start until 8 a.m., and looking at the repair list for the day I knew they were in for a busy time.

It was during the course of the morning, while serving petrol, that I heard a girl's voice calling to me. I glanced behind me, and to my surprise I recognised two of the girls from Todd's, the clothing factory.

'See you in a minute,' I said, and after I had served my customer I went up to the girls. 'Hey,' I said, 'shouldn't you be at work?'

'Haven't you heard, Pauline? The conscription of women. Maggie and I have already got our calling-up papers, haven't we, Maggie? So the pair of us decided to have the remainder of the week to ourselves. That's why we're up in town. Only passing the garage, we just had to see you.'

'That's nice of you,' I replied. I enquired about my old pals in the press room. 'As far as I knows,' said Maggie, 'they are all OK. Oh, and by the way, Mr Gould's son is now a prisoner of war.'

Our conversation was interrupted by another car pulling up on the forecourt. 'Excuse me, girls,' I said.

'Oh, you just carry on, Pauline. We'll be getting on our way now.'

'Anyway,' I said, 'it's been nice seeing you both.'

'Same here,' said Maggie.

And as they walked away I called out, 'Best of luck, girls!'

'Same to you, Pauline. Keep the good work up.'

I gave the girls a wave and they waved back. I then concentrated on serving more petrol, my thoughts dwelling on the happy times I had spent with all the girls at Todd's.

This very same morning something happened in the garage which likely I was never to forget. All the punctures were repaired by us on the top floor, but imagine the surprise I got when an old Morris almost crawled into the garage with *every* tyre flat. I couldn't believe my eyes, and one could see that the flat tyres had been driven on.

A man of small stature got out. 'Can you help me, Miss?' he said. I detected at once he was a Yorkshireman.

'Oh dear,' I exclaimed. 'All your tyres are punctured.' Thinking to myself how very odd. I smiled at the poor distressed man. 'We'll do what we can, Sir. Should we need new inner tubes, can you provide us with the necessary vouchers?'

'Afraid not, love,' answered the man.

'Well, if you call back in an hour's time, it will enable us to see what we can do.'

'Righto,' said the man. 'I'll call back in an hour.'

I noticed that before he went, he examined the boot of the car, securing its safety by making sure it was locked. I thought it strange, because I couldn't recall a customer doing that before.

Even Freddie had noticed what he had done, for he remarked, 'Say, Miss, reckon he's got a dead body in there.'

I laughed. 'Come on, Freddie, we've got work to do.'

I helped Freddie to take the wheels off, and then out came the inner tubes. I examined them. No slits — so far, so good. Then Freddie, with the four inner tubes slung over his shoulder, made his way downstairs to test them in the water-tank.

Just minutes after, I heard Freddie almost running up the wooden stairs. 'Oh Miss, you'd better come down and have a look at 'em.'

I hurried down to the water-tank, and, testing each tube myself, I discovered that they were all riddled with tiny holes, making hundreds of bubbles. It would be impossible to do any repairs on them; what was needed now was four new inner tubes.

When Mr Griffin came into the garage, I approached him on the matter, explaining that the owner of the Morris had no vouchers for inner tubes.

'I best see the man myself when he comes in,' said Mr Griffin, which he did. Later I discovered that when the man returned, he signed an IOU for four new tubes. I could only think that he had convinced Mr Griffin to let him have the inner tubes on credit. Anyway, all was well, and Freddie and I could proceed with the job.

The Yorkshireman strolled away from his car which was better for us; we could get on with what we were doing. I jacked up the back axle higher, and had much difficulty in trying to get one of the back wheels on, so much so that I just had to see what was wrong. Crawling underneath, I came in contact with the boot of the car, and then I distinctly heard something drop to the ground. Fumbling around, I saw something lying in the dirt and oil. Flabbergasted, I picked up two rings, and putting two and two together I came to the conclusion that they had fallen out of the rusty old boot of the car, which, without doubt, was rotten with age.

129

I crawled out from underneath the car, clutching the rings in my hand. I then told Freddie that I was going next door to see Mr Griffin and if in the meantime the man should return, Freddie should tell him that I was having bother with the back wheel.

Freddie looked at me puzzled.

'I'll explain later, Freddie,' I said, with which I dashed to the big house next door. I rang the bell, still holding on tightly to the rings I had found. My mind was in a whirl. It was all so very suspicious. Rings such as these just don't fall out of the boots of old cars. I came to the conclusion that there was the possibility of stolen property being in that boot. If I was right in suspecting that the man was a thief, that would explain his having no vouchers for his inner tubes because the car might well be stolen too. I imagined the man must have driven over barbed wire or something, in a hurry maybe to get away.

Quickly I told Mr Griffin all. 'Damn funny,' he remarked. 'I'll phone the police. And Miss Quintin, I'll depend on you to delay the job as long as possible.' So, giving Mr Griffin the rings, I returned into the garage, and there the man was talking to Freddie.

I went up to the man and said, 'I'm extremely sorry for the delay but I'm having trouble putting on the back wheel, and I'll have to fetch up a mechanic from downstairs.' Normally I would have sent Freddie down, so it was no surprise when Freddie said, 'I'll go down, Miss, and fetch one of the lads up.'

'Thank you, Freddie, but I have to go down.' Hurrying downstairs, I got hold of Rob, and almost in one breath I told him all I knew.

'Just leave it to me,' said Rob. So up came Rob to the top floor, carrying in his hand a few spanners. 'What's the trouble then?' said Rob, giving me a wink.

'It's the back wheel, just can't get it on,' I replied.

Rob, now on his back, was underneath the old Morris. 'Blast it,' I heard Rob say. He then crawled out from underneath the car, remarking, 'No wonder you can't get the wheel on. I'll have to file down a piece of old rust. It's stopping the wheel from going into position.' Rob now went back downstairs, exclaiming, 'Won't be a minute.'

The act of delaying the repair was coming up to expectations, and minutes were passing over quickly. However, I observed that the man was becoming restless, for now he was walking up and down. Then he spoke: 'Do you think it'll take long?'

'I don't think so,' I replied. 'Ah, here's the mechanic now.'

Rob once again began crawling underneath the car, and strangely enough he actually was filing at something.

Time continued to pass, and Rob was just about to put the wheel on properly when in walked Mr Griffin with a policeman.

I noticed a panic-stricken look on the Yorkshireman's face, and he immediately made a dash out towards the big door. Rob, acting quickly, put his foot out, thus tripping the man, who fell flat on the floor; and before he could gather himself up, the policeman had grabbed hold of the collar of his coat.

'All right,' said the policeman. 'Would you mind opening up the boot?'

I could see the man was shaking; it could have been the shock of the fall he had had, or the fear of having been found out. I only know he looked ghastly, for he was now fumbling in his pocket for his keys. He eventually unlocked the boot, which sprang up quickly. All eyes stared at the contents.

I looked in utter bewilderment at the haul we had uncovered. There was a collection of silver, paintings, and various antiques, plus a small brown paper bag in the corner; this had obviously contained the rings.

So I was right, the man was guilty of burglary. I could have been wrong, of course. After all, I had very little evidence to go on. But I did find those rings, and it was a sudden impulse which had resulted in me going for Mr Griffin. I only knew that if I had been mistaken, I would have admitted it apologetically to all those concerned.

My story ends with another policeman coming on the scene, and they marched the man away, taking him into custody for robbery. Meanwhile we parked the old Morris in the corner of the garage. She stood there with four new inner tubes in her wheels; all our efforts to make her roadworthy had been wasted.

At home that evening, I was telling Mum and Dad of the day's events at the garage, and were they surprised. Even Alfie, with his face beaming, remarked, 'Oh, Auntie Paul, did you really catch a robber?'

On the Wednesday morning of that week, I was busy on the forecourt serving petrol when Rob arrived, and in his hand he carried a letter. 'For you, Quinner,' he said. 'Post was early.'

I pushed the letter into my pocket, but after serving my customer I went to the office to open it. I did not recognise the handwriting, but I guessed who it was from, especially when I looked at the postmark: Corsham, Wilts.

I quickly opened the letter and read: 'Dear Miss Quintin, Delighted to hear from you. . . .' His letter suggested that I meet him one evening outside the Abbey. Then, finally, he said, 'I just knew you would write to me,' signing himself off with 'Jim'.

At the age of nineteen then, this would be my first date ever, provided I actually desired to meet this stranger again. But to do just that appeared to be the right thing to do, so writing back I arranged to see him the following Saturday night outside the Abbey.

I decided to tell Mum, and she was very surprised, yet smiling she said, 'I'm sure you are old enough to understand. But just the same, be careful, duck.' Good advice from Mum, as always.

So Saturday night arrived, and funny as it seemed, I was looking forward to meeting the soldier. I dressed neatly, finally dabbing myself with Yardley's Lavender Water.

Rob I felt sure could smell the scent, for he said, 'Aha! Somebody seeing someone special tonight?'

I guess I blushed, and hence it gave me away.

'Who is he, Quinner, someone I know?'

'Complete stranger,' I replied. 'Anyway, none of your business, our Rob.'

He chuckled. 'Would Madam like a chaperon? Could oblige.'

Mum interrupted. 'Time is getting on, and you'd better be going if you want to catch the bus to town.' Actually I was in plenty of time. I caught the bus and got off at the Parade Gardens. Now it was just a few minutes to walk to the Abbey, so I had time to look in a few shop windows. Knowing I was early, I just strolled around the corner to the Abbey, and as I did so, my eyes focused on my stranger already waiting for me.

When I got up to him, he was smiling, and very timidly I said, 'Hello.'

'Pleased you made it,' he answered.

The affinity between us seemed easy, as if we had known each other for a very long time. I suggested we go to The Saracen's Head for a drink, myself having no desire to drink, yet I sensed that my stranger would maybe like a pint of beer. Anyway it was a bitterly cold night, and the refuge of a nice warm pub would be appealing for the both of us.

My stranger then asked me what I would like to drink, and he was taken aback when I asked for a grapefruit juice.

In the weeks to follow, I met him several times. By this time I was getting to know a bit more about him, and likewise he was getting to know me. I think I gained considerable trust in him, for not once did he take advantage of me; we merely participated in friendliness, and so it was as if we had created a great companionship.

It was Christmas, and Dad suggested that Jim come up home, which he did, and spent a most enjoyable time with us all.

I think the only concern Dad had about Jim was the fact that he was much older than I, nineteen years older to be precise. Of course this accounted for Jim's steadfastness, which, I suppose, attracted me to him. And it was a good Christmas, apart from the absence of Gran, who was still in hospital.

That very same December of 1941 brought America into the war, for the Japanese had attacked Pearl Harbour, a base out in the Pacific. The onslaught was a bombardment from the air, killing Americans and sinking many boats, and quite imprudently Germany and Italy also declared war on the United States, while Britain declared war on Japan. And so the struggle had become world-wide.

A few days later, the Japanese bombed two of our battleships, the *Prince of Wales* and the *Repulse*. The loss of these great ships had an appalling effect on morale at home.

In the following February of 1942 two German battleships, the *Scharnhorst* and the *Gneisenau*, sailed calmly through the English Channel, despite attempts to sink them. The humiliation was keenly felt, and still more disaster followed in the same month, when Singapore fell to the Japanese.

Winston Churchill tried to lift everyone's spirits when he reminded us that, with the USA on our side, we were no longer alone.

About this time came a shortage of flour, bringing to its end the white loaf. The pre-war extraction rate of wheat had been seventy per cent; thirty per cent had been discarded. Now, however, we could not afford to be so profligate, and the 'National Wheatmeal Loaf', based on flour of eighty-five per cent extraction, was introduced; many people hated it. The Government, however, subsidised British Restaurants, making cheaper nutritious meals available. Soap, too, went on the ration.

In this very same month, February 1942, Mrs White, of No. 7 Lansdown Place West, passed peacefully away. I knew I would miss her, for I had often visited her after I ceased to sleep in her house. To me she was a dear and sweet old lady, and it was always a pleasure to be in her company.

Then came the spring of 1942, and war or no war the natural beauty of spring was just the same, with the budding of the trees, and the first spring flowers, along with the song of the cuckoo. Mr Chubb, the farmer on Primrose Hill, had some new-born lambs which were quite frisky in the fields below our house, while all the gardeners were busy preparing soil for planting.

How well I remember one Sunday morning. Bill Harding, our next-door neighbour, was busy putting in his seed-potatoes, while Dad and I were also in the garden, when the warning siren went. Dad shouted to Bill, 'Better make tracks for the shelter!' To which Bill answered, 'Oh, to hell with Jerry. Gunna put my spuds in first, Pat!' Often the warning sirens would be a false alarm, whereupon nothing happened, so you couldn't blame Bill.

My brother Tim was still at a training base, instructing new recruits; Pat, on the other hand, was still on convoys to Russia; and Tom's regiment, currently stationed in the north of England, was preparing for service overseas.

I myself was always very busy in the garage, and much of what spare time I did have was devoted to Civil Defence duties. However, any evening I did have free I would meet Jim in town, and together we would go into some nice quiet pub for a drink and a chat, and where Jim could enjoy his pipe.

It was during one of our meetings that Jim told me he was going to be transferred to a little village called Wem, in Shropshire, where there was the only military railway in the country.

'I should have told you before,' said Jim, 'that I was once a driver on the LNER. But unfortunately I was dismissed for assaulting a guard, while under the influence of drink.'

As I listened to his story, I must have been showing signs of dismay, but to my surprise he beamed into a smile and said, 'In a way I'm pleased it all happened. For had it not been for my dismissal from the railway, I would never have met you. I was called up with my age group, and put in the Army. Mind you,' went on Jim, 'I was given the choice of what I wanted to do. I said I would do anything, and that's why I became attached to the RAOC. But now they have found out about my train-driving credentials, and I'm to be transferred to the RE (Royal Engineers).'

I listened to Jim. Had he more to tell me?

'First,' then said Jim, 'I'll be going home on ten days' leave, and from there I will be going straight on to Shrewsbury.' He paused. 'Telling you about myself, Pauline, has shocked you, hasn't it?' He was staring at me with his big blue eyes. 'I think I've told you everything, and I couldn't blame you if you gave me the cold shoulder. Another thing,' said Jim. 'I'm much older than you. So we must not become involved with one another unless we are absolutely sure of one another. Anyway, we'll wait until after my leave, and see how things go.'

Tears came into my eyes. Was this then going to be the end of our friendship? Yet Jim held my hands in his, as if determined never to let them go.

'I'm going to miss you Pauline,' he said.

I did not tell him, but I knew I was going to miss him too.

It wasn't easy that night to say goodbye to each other, but the parting did come when he finally saw me off on the bus.

'Take good care of yourself,' he whispered.

I waved to him as the Lansdown bus pulled out, and then when I could no longer see him I suddenly felt so utterly forlorn, a true indication that I was in love with him.

The days that followed seemed empty, and it was a blessing that I had plenty of work to occupy my mind. Then, almost a week after, I received a letter from Jim, saying that on his way back to Shrewsbury he would break his journey at Bath, and come and see me.

The news made me hilariously happy, for I never expected to see Jim so soon, and his letter contained another surprise when I read his PS: 'We'll not meet in town. I'll see you up home.'

It was one evening then, just as I was putting the children to bed, when there was a knock on the door. I flew downstairs and opened wide the door, and there was Jim, standing with his kitbag and all his equipment.

My emotions overcame me. I couldn't help it, I just flung my arms around his neck.

'Oh Jim,' I whispered, and now tears of joy were rolling down my cheeks.

'Hey!' said Jim. 'What's all this about?'

'Sorry,' I answered. 'Just got carried away, that's all.'

'Guess so,' replied Jim. 'It's funny, but I just feel the same way too. And oh, it's so good to see you.' With which he hugged me, and in all sincerity I felt his deep affection for me.

So, after gathering ourselves together, we got back to normal over a cup of tea, with Mum and Dad for company. Later, after a light meal, I helped Mum with the washing-up, leaving Jim with Dad.

Then the time came for Jim to go. 'I'll come down to the station, and see you off,' I said.

'Oh no you won't, young lady. You're staying right here at home,' said Jim.

'But I — I'd like to,' I blurted out.

'It's far too late,' replied Jim. 'You can see me off at the bottom of the lane. How will that do?'

Side by side, we walked slowly down the lane, each silent, and each feeling the same way I suppose.

Then, at the bottom of the lane, Jim put his kitbag down against the wall, held me in his arms and kissed me. Then he said, 'I do love you, Paul. So take good care of yourself.'

I could not speak. My heart was full. Almost immediately he disappeared into the darkness, but I did manage to call out, 'So long, Jim.' Then I walked slowly back up the lane. He had called me Paul, so I knew he was much closer to me now.

Although I didn't know it at the time, Jim had used the opportunity to make it clear to Dad that his intentions were honourable; but before proposing to me he had wanted to talk with Dad first about our future.

The next letter from Jim came from Shrewsbury, telling me all about his new base. He said it was right out in the heart of the country, and about five miles from Shrewsbury itself. He appeared to be happy, telling me how good it was to be back on steam-engines. Most of the troops were Americans, and black too, a swell bunch of lads, he quoted. I was happy for him, and pleased that the Army had accepted him as an engine-driver.

My next meeting with Jim was in town. It was short, but there was sufficient time for Jim to take me into a jeweller's shop, and buy me the sweetest engagement ring. And so it was we became engaged, although we did not as yet set a date for our marriage.

In April of that year (1942) Jim's mother was taken ill, so on a 48-hour leave he went home to Gateshead to see her. On his way back, he stopped off at Bath to see me, before proceeding on to Shrewsbury.

We only had a couple of hours together, and must have practically spent the whole time in a little café around the corner from the railway station; over cups of tea, Jim had much to tell me.

He talked of the bridges that crossed the river Tyne, separating Gateshead from Newcastle, and explained to me about the High Level Bridge.

'Imagine, Paul,' he said, 'trains on the top **of** it, with tramcars and traffic underneath. Then below that, the river itself, where large boats pass through.'

'Must be a marvellous bridge,' I said.

'It is,' exclaimed Jim. 'And last night Jerry tried to blow it up. I was on the bridge at the time and I thought I'd had it.'

'Oh no!' I murmured. 'What happened, Jim?'

'Well,' said Jim. 'I had to catch the 10.45 out of Newcastle station. In fact I had just left home, when the warning siren went, and being a good mile to the High Level Bridge, I hastened my steps and caught up with a young sailor, also going to the Central station to catch a train. Well, we must have been about twenty yards on the bridge, when it all started. Enemy aircraft were right overhead, and so our searchlights went up, and then Jerry must have dropped hundreds of flares, so much so, the night had turned into day. I told the young sailor to put his helmet on, and I did likewise. Then the sudden whistling of bombs coming through the air made me shout to the sailor, "We'll have to bloody well run for it, mate!" '

'Oh Jim,' I gasped, 'what a terrifying experience you both must have had.'

'We both ran like hell,' said Jim, 'for I had visions of us both landing in the Tyne. And when we finally reached the other side of the bridge, we were both saturated in perspiration. And I'm sure it wasn't through running, but the damn fright Jerry gave us. I shuddered to think,' said Jim, 'of being trapped on any bridge during a bombardment.' He was quiet for a few minutes and then said, 'It'll be a good thing when it's all over, Paul.' I agreed in silent acquiescence. So, after seeing Jim off on the train, I made my way home.

I knew that I was going to be on the 6 to 2 shift the following day and I had decided that during the afternoon I would go up to St Martin's Hospital and see Gran; then from there I would take up duty with the Civil Defence until midnight. So, with all intended purposes, I was in for an early night in bed. But when I did arrive home, I found that Dolly, my brother Tom's wife, was there.

A very nice person was Dolly; their only son Jimmy was staying with his maternal grandparents, thus enabling Dolly to do war work in a factory. We were always pleased to see each other, and she told me news of Tom. Rumour had it that his regiment was going to be drafted to Burma. When she told me this, her facial expressions were those of anxiety.

I then told her about Jim and me, and I think listening to my story lightened her own worries.

'Oh, Paul,' she said. 'I'm so happy for you.'

It was a usual procedure of mine to walk her half-way back home, the distance of a good two miles. We were good company for each other, so after leaving home at 10 p.m. we talked incessantly. We reached the Royal United Hospital, and usually this was my point of turning back, but it was such a lovely night, and we still had so much to talk about, that I decided to walk a little further.

Eventually Dolly said, 'I think you had better go back now, Paul.'

'OK, Doll,' I said, so kissing her goodnight, I retraced my steps. Passing the hospital once again, I turned the corner into Weston Lane. It was nicknamed 'the dip'. Everywhere appeared so quiet, and romantically my thoughts were with Jim, so I felt happy within myself, but after I had gone some way, the beam from my torch suddenly spotted something shining. At first I thought it looked like silver paper. I then investigated a little closer, and was startled to find that it was the nose of a bomb, the rest of which was buried in the ground. I thought it strange it hadn't been detected before, but then I could see why: long blades of grass and bracken had camouflaged it.

I realised that I must immediately notify someone about this, so back I hurried to the villas in the dip. At the first villa I came to, I pressed the modern electric bell. A dog barked. I waited. Then the door was opened by a man in a dressing-gown, who looked very surprised to see me. However, I spoke first. 'Sorry to bother you at this late hour, but I've located an unexploded bomb up the lane. Thought perhaps I should warn you.'

'Come in, come in,' said the man. I detected his nervousness, for he almost shouted a lady's name: 'Susan!'

He picked up the phone in the hallway, dialled a number, then waited. Meanwhile a lady appeared, also in her dressing-gown, and who looked quite bewildered. I wanted to speak to her, but I was afraid I would interrupt the man's conversation on the phone.

'Ah, Mr Malcolm speaking. It has come to my notice that a bomb has been located in a hedgerow up Weston Lane.' Pause. 'Yes, a young lady came across it.... Ah, righto, thank you.' After giving his address Mr Malcolm replaced the receiver, looked at me and spoke: 'They are sending a bomb-disposal squad right away. And would you please hang on until they arrive.'

'Certainly,' I answered.

By this time Susan was aware of all the facts. 'Everything all right, Jeff?' she said.

'Not exactly, Susan, we may have to make an evacuation. For an hour or so maybe. So I suggest you dress, and put a warm coat on, dear. Then we must let our neighbours know what's happening. Excuse me, Miss, I must dress too.'

So I was alone in the hallway when the bell rang. I opened the door and came face to face with two special constables.

'Mr Malcolm live here?'

'That's right,' I answered. I then explained to the two gentlemen that I had come across the bomb while walking up the lane, and if they came with me I could show them exactly where it was. Meanwhile Mr Malcolm had dressed and was now in the hallway with us. He seemed eager to help.

'Best you evacuate, Sir,' said one of the specials. 'Can I leave that to you then, Sir?'

'You can depend on me,' said Mr Malcolm.

So the two constables and myself left the Malcolms' villa and proceeded up the lane. Then, shining my torch near the spot, I located the evil thing.

138

'Blimey,' remarked one of the specials, 'it's a big 'un, Joe. Best you go back down to the villas, make sure everyone is evacuated.'

In no time at all, a jeep came on the scene, and out jumped four military men, equipped with bomb-disposal apparatus. They glanced at the bomb, and orders were given to dismantle it. Then the officer looked at me and said, 'You best be getting on your way, Miss. Oh, and by the way, thanks for the tip-off.'

So, making hurried steps, I finally made my way home. My early night in bed had turned out to be a late one. However, I found out later that the bomb was a live one, so it could have gone off at any time. It was a bit of luck I had spotted it before it did any damage.

In spite of everything, I was up with the larks the next morning and arrived at the garage in good time. The morning just flew over, and I did well with tips — 15 shillings in all — so with this extra money I could buy Gran a nice big bunch of flowers, seeing I intended visiting her that very afternoon. On my way up to the hospital I called in the cake shop for an egg custard, and then into the snug of a public house for a miniature whisky.

The bus then took me up to St Martin's Hospital, and I was very much looking forward to seeing Gran, for I had so much to tell her. I tiptoed into the ward. Gran, bless her, was sleeping, but she must have sensed my presence for she awoke with a smile. So kissing her I said, 'Hello, Gran.'

We soon settled down into conversation, and I talked of Jim and I becoming engaged. 'I'm so happy for you,' said Gran. 'May you both be blessed with everything that is good.'

I then gave Gran a wink. 'I say, Gran, how about a sip of your favourite medicine?' I noticed Gran's eyes lit up, so out came the small bottle of whisky, camouflaged by my pocket handkerchief. 'Take little sips,' I whispered.

Gran's lily-white hands held tightly around the bottle. Then she said, 'Here's to you, darling, and your intended.'

Her little sips began to make her cheeks go rosy, as I knew they would. I don't know for sure, but I felt my happiness was within Gran, for although bedfast, she looked a picture of contentment.

It was time for me to go, and as always I felt reluctant to leave my Gran. But time was getting on, and I had to be on duty with Civil Defence at 4 p.m., so, giving Gran more kisses, I left her waving to me.

I hadn't to wait long before the bus arrived to take me to town, and it was only five minutes' walk to our depot in James Street, so I arrived in plenty of time. When I did arrive I had quite a chat with

Flo, the telephonist, who was well married by now, and expecting her first child.

I looked on the duty board and saw that I hadn't to drive that evening. Instead I was to be an attendant on the ambulance driven by a lady I will call Mrs Wilson (not her real name); usually this happened when there was a surplus of drivers. Mrs Wilson and I had yet to meet. However, I found her in one of the cubicles which contained two bunk-beds, each with a blanket; also in each of the cubicles was a small table, for writing purposes.

When I introduced myself, Mrs Wilson answered with a 'Hello' in what I thought was a slurred kind of voice; and there was no doubt about it, she was slightly intoxicated, for now she was giving off an occasional hiccup. Then, to my surprise she produced a bottle from her bag. 'Come along, do have a drink with me.'

I was quite shocked. 'Thank you, Madam, but I do not drink.' It was obvious Mrs Wilson was in no fit state to drive any vehicle, let alone an ambulance. I did not want to be animadvert, yet for her own good, and that of her reputation, I was forced to speak to her abruptly; this I knew would not be easy, and so I had to brace myself. 'Excuse me, Madam, I know it is none of my business, but don't you think you have had sufficient to drink? You know it's not allowed on duty.'

Her reaction came as rather a surprise to me, for she was now looking at me pathetically. 'I'm sorry,' she said. 'I'm not a good example, especially to a young girl like you.'

She then made her way to the nearest bunk-bed, and I was more than relieved when she just flopped on it. I then took the liberty of hiding her bottle; a strong smell of gin came from the cork.

I then went to the other bunk, picked up a book and started reading. I sincerely hoped we wouldn't be called out, but a call did come, at approximately at 5.30 p.m., when the little red light in our cubicle started flashing. This was the signal that all personnel were required in the assembly room.

I switched off the flasher, which had not disturbed Mrs Wilson, for she lay there fast asleep, and I must say I was thankful. Quietly I tiptoed out of the cubicle and hurried down to assembly. I wondered what kind of an assignment we had on, for as yet we had not received an alert.

Superintendent Wright greeted me. 'Hello, Miss Quintin. Where's Mrs Wilson then?'

'I left her resting, Sir.'

'Not ill, I hope?'

'Oh no, Sir.' Now I had to tell a little white lie. 'She has a headache, Sir.'

'Oh, very well. Dare say you can manage the job on your own. It's just to pick up a load of blankets from the Isolation Hospital. They've to be put into quarantine. They'll have protective coverings on them, so you'll not be unduly concerned.'

'I'll go immediately, Sir.'

'Yes, carry on, Miss Quintin.'

I gave a sigh of relief. Checking what ambulance I could take out, I soon had the keys in my hand and was on my way to the Isolation Hospital.

When I reached the hospital, the porters soon loaded me up. Although it was late afternoon, the sky remained bright and sunny, and in the hospital grounds I noticed all the spring plants coming through. I thought it was a pity that Mrs Wilson should be missing all this, but I knew she was better off, under the circumstances, staying at the depot; at least she would have time to recuperate.

I arrived back at the depot prompt at 6.30. If we were on duty at this time a little snack was prepared for us, and really I was ready for something to eat. I sat with others at the long narrow table and noticed the continued absence of Mrs Wilson, so directly I had finished I asked for a cup of tea to take to her; I guessed she would need some refreshment by now. Reaching the cubicle, I found Mrs Wilson full of remorse, and noticed that she had been crying. However, I presented her with the cup of tea, whereupon, timidly, she thanked me.

I did not converse with her, merely gave her the chance to drink her tea, which I knew would do her good. I myself picked up my book; I wasn't reading, but just thinking. Mrs Wilson, without doubt, was a lady of good upbringing, with a background of a good education and breeding. So why the desire to indulge in drinking, especially when on duty? I came to the conclusion that she had a worry of some sort, and the only way of drowning her sorrows was to drink her way out of it. There just had to be a logical reason for her behaviour that afternoon.

I sensed that Mrs Wilson had finished her tea, so peeping over the top of my book I said, 'All right, Mrs Wilson?'

I could see her eyelids were still red and swollen from crying, but she forced a smile and said, 'It's Miss Quintin, isn't it?' I smiled at her, and then she spoke. 'I must apologise, for I know I have disgraced myself in your presence. Please forgive me.'

Placing my book down, I went over and sat beside her. I just had to give my assurance and trust to this lady. 'I do understand,' I said. 'And if you would like to talk, I'm sure it will help.'

My last sentence must have astounded her, especially coming

141

from a young girl like myself. Maybe I was too young for her to confide in; possibly we were not on the same wavelength, for this same Mrs Wilson could give me many more years of life, and had no doubt had experiences that perhaps would even astonish me. But Mrs Wilson knew that I knew that something was wrong, and realising that I was willing to share her unhappiness, she decided to take me into her confidence, and talk. 'Well,' she sighed, 'it's a long story. Could be boring for you to hear.'

'We have nothing to lose,' I replied. 'We could be here until midnight, providing Jerry gives us some peace.'

And so it was that I just sat and listened. One thing I observed, she did look a lot brighter.

'Well,' she said, 'before the war started, my husband and I were extremely happy, living in almost a mansion of a house, with servants and a gardener. Oh, life was just adorable. We enjoyed parties, and entertained quite a lot, giving our social life an added zest. We had wealth, my husband even directed his own factory in Wales, and often I would accompany him, for we were seldom separated.'

Then came this pause when she said, 'Oh the felicity of it all.' Without any interruption on my part, I waited for her to continue talking, and I realised it was helping her immensely.

'My husband knew I was unable to bear any children, but he was just wonderful over it. He fully accepted the situation, and that was more reason why I loved him so, and I never ever doubted his love for me. Then, of course, the war came, and he received a commission in the RAF.' Then, suddenly, she stopped talking, and with her eyes filling up with tears, she spluttered out, 'Ted's met this girl, who is now having his baby.' Sobbing now, she whimpered, 'He wants a divorce, so that he can marry her.'

I was flabbergasted. 'Oh, Mrs Wilson, I am so sorry.' By this time I had my arm around her shoulder. 'Try not to cry.'

This damn war, I thought, bringing so many heart-breaks. How could one blame the likes of Mrs Wilson for indulging in something like alcoholism? After all, it had the power to lessen her anxiety. This poor woman must have been heart-broken, for now she was sobbing in both hands. I did not console her immediately, knowing that a good cry would relieve all those bottled-up feelings.

Eventually she wiped her eyes, and then gave me a little smile.

'That's better, Madam,' I said 'Now powder your nose while I fetch us some more tea.'

Over our cups of tea, our conversation moved on, enabling our friendship to develop. 'Oh,' I said, 'I nearly forgot. I hid your bottle.' So down on my hands and knees I got, and crawled underneath the bunk to retrieve it.

Then something happened which gladdened my heart. Mrs Wilson took the bottle and poured the remainder of its contents down the small wash-basin. So today was not the end of the world for her after all, and we had accomplished something together: it was laughter, and common sense had prevailed.

It was almost midnight when our flasher went, and it was action stations for us all, for although we had not yet received a warning siren, we got the alert flashes which told us that enemy aircraft were approaching our coastline.

I glanced at Mrs Wilson. 'You all right, Madam?'

She looked at me, quite composed, and said, 'I'm all right now, Miss Quintin.'

I knew, of course, which ambulance we would have to take out if necessary, for I had enjoyed driving her that very afternoon, and indeed the vehicle was a great pleasure to drive, for just pressing a button to start her was simplicity itself — a great advancement from the likes of Old Jane, on which one had to swing the handle to get her started. Nevertheless, Old Jane was still doing a fine job with learner-drivers, not forgetting Mr Penny, of course, who tutored brilliantly.

After checking on everything, Mrs Wilson and I returned to assembly, there to await any calls. We sat amongst other colleagues waiting for news. Then we heard the loud siren of Stothert and Pitt, the big engineering firm, and it sounded as if it was even louder than usual.

It stopped. Then, only minutes later, we heard the drone of enemy aircraft overhead; then more enemy planes, all of which passed over.

'It'll be Bristol again,' said someone.

With the door ajar, I could just see Flo, waiting in anticipation. Then a light started blinking on the switchboard. She picked up the receiver, and our first call had come through. We looked on while Superintendent Wright stood by.

Flo then looked up at him. 'It's Bristol, Sir. They may need our assistance, going to ring back later.' So all of us could do nothing but wait in anticipation.

Again the blinker went on the switchboard, and Flo quickly put the receiver to her ear. 'Right,' she answered. 'Message understood. It's Filton Aerodrome, Sir. Require at least two ambulances.'

Superintendent Wright looked at us all. 'We need two ambulances to go to Filton.' He had no problem in asking for volunteers, for we were all of the same mind. We were all volunteers in the Civil Defence, dedicated to help our fellow men, and each of us knew that someone would have to make the trip to

Bristol, while others had to stop behind, and so the choice was left to the officer.

He did not call out ambulance personnel, but quoted instead two registration numbers. Our number was FB101, and of the two ambulances to be selected, we were one. We were given detailed instructions, and before long we were speeding down the road, 'hell for leather' as you might say. And I might add that Mrs Wilson was an excellent driver. We talked as we went along, myself giving our first-aid equipment a final check. All was in order.

Going through Keynsham, 6 miles from Bath and 6 miles from Bristol, our ambulance went into a wobble, so Mrs Wilson pulled into the side of the road and stopped.

We must have jumped out together to investigate, and to our dismay we were both looking at a front-wheel puncture.

'Oh dear,' said Mrs Wilson, 'this is going to hold us up.'

'Not for long,' I remarked quite cheerfully. 'I'll have the spare on in no time.'

One thing I was pleased about, the spare was accessible, for it was attached to the side of the ambulance, securely fixed with two leather straps.

I was just about to jack up the ambulance, when our other ambulance came on the scene, and Mr Smith the driver got out. 'Need any help?'

'Thank you,' I replied, 'but I think we can manage.' Sometimes I hated this independence of mine, but Mr Smith insisted he help me jack her up, so I let him help. I don't suppose he would know that I was used to this kind of work, so it was no problem to me.

'Will you be OK now?' he said.

'Yes thank you,' I replied. And so the other ambulance crew left us, proceeding on their way. With the nuts tightened on the wheel, I released the jack, and secured the other wheel, and we were mobile once again.

We arrived at Filton all behind, like a donkey's tail, but nevertheless we were ready for any kind of action. Actually the raid was over, but amongst the rubble there was always the culmination of a tragedy. People were hurt and we had to help them as best we could, and when we saw the amount of damage done we expected more casualties than there actually were. It wasn't long before we had completed our mission, finally doctoring up those that required attention.

I observed Mrs Wilson: deeply engrossed she was, in attending to others. In one way, I was pleased for her — she was forgetting about her own trouble — yet on coming to this aerodrome her thoughts would be nearer to her husband, who was himself in the RAF. And perhaps they were entangled thoughts? Who knows?

144

However, she appeared none the worse for it, and accepted some hot cocoa, as I did, from some air-force lads.

Later the pair of us started back, grubby of course, yet relieved to think we were on our way home and that the raid on Filton Aerodrome hadn't been as heavy as we expected. What we did not realise at the time was that before very long the beautiful city of Bath was to suffer much heavier bombing raids, with far larger numbers of casualties.

PART FOUR

IN THE spring of 1942, Churchill agreed to launch a new bomber offensive against Germany: this led to our attack on Lübeck during March of 1942, which destroyed half the town, so the Germans decided to respond with the so-called Baedeker raids on our cities of historic interest. (Baedeker was the name of a famous series of tourist guidebooks.)

I remember vividly a Monday morning in the April of 1942. Although I was on the 2 to 10 shift at the garage, I got up early as usual, and while dressing I heard the cuckoo, for we were now truly starting the lovely weather. This particular morning was beautiful: the sun, already well up, was streaming through the trees, and what made the morning nice was we were all at home.

At breakfast Mum and I decided to do the washing, so while Mum was getting the children ready for school I set about putting on the fire underneath the copper boiler, making sure that the boiler was half full of water. The fire burned brightly, so the water heated quickly, and Mum and I set to in the outhouse.

How well I remember Mum scrubbing on the washboard, getting the dirt out of the collars and cuffs; the only things we used were brown soft soap, soda, starch, and a product called Dolly's blue bag, which whitened the whites. Surprisingly enough, we had finished by 11 o'clock, and all pegged out too.

Mum then suggested we have a cup of cocoa, so sitting down for five minutes in the kitchen I switched on the wireless, which stood on the sideboard. I had not intended to listen to Lord Haw Haw, but strange as it was we got him at the start.

The old familiar traitor's voice spoke. 'Germany calling. Germany calling. Today I'm going to talk about a little place called Bath, in Somerset. You know it, of course, the West of England's beauty spot. Are any of you Bathonians listening?'

By now Mum and I were all ears. I looked at Mum, and Mum looked at me. This indeed was a surprise we hadn't expected. This man was talking about our own dear place, and he seemed so very convincing that we were almost obliged to listen to him; and so we did exactly this, as he continued speaking.

149

'We are coming to bomb your beautiful city. Why, you may ask. I will give you an answer, dear people. For surely you know by now that you have almost flattened our beautiful city of Lübeck. So let us say it is tit for tat. We shall visit you with a reprisal raid . . . . To conclude, you will want to know when we shall be coming. Alas, we cannot give you a definite date. But be well assured, we shall visit you, dear people. I hope you have listened carefully, and remember, I always speak the truth.'

His voice was so full of sarcasm, especially when he said, 'Look forward to our coming then, and how sad it is for me to have to tell you, but your lovely Georgian city will be exterminated. So, my friends, gaze upon your beautiful city one last time, for when we have finished with it, it will be no more.'

I switched off the wireless in disgust, while Mum referred to him as a swine. 'So insolent,' she remarked.

Whether I should believe Lord Haw Haw or not I wasn't sure, but I must admit his speech got me thinking. The threat of a reprisal raid was real enough. After all, we had bombed their beautiful cities, and it wouldn't surprise me at all if a reprisal raid should be made in dudgeon. God forbid it, but there was the possibility. However, I did not discuss it any further with Mum, keeping my opinion to myself.

At 2 p.m. I was on duty at the Pierrepont Garage, and it was an assortment of a shift really, for a mixture of people came and went. I did have one pleasant surprise though: a car pulled up on the forecourt for petrol, and who should it be but my cousin Jack from London. I think he was more surprised to see me in a boiler suit than I was to see him. It had been many years since I last saw him, so the reunion was great, as one can imagine.

But one thing puzzled me — how come he wasn't in one of the services? He looked fit and strong, as he always was. Anyway, he told me he was a commercial traveller. Somehow this was difficult for me to grasp, for if anybody should have been in uniform it was he. Still, it was none of my business I suppose, and who was I to judge him? There could be some logical reason for his being a civilian. However, he convinced me that he was really a commercial traveller when from his car he produced two pairs of silk stockings, saying, 'Here you are, Pauline. Something to remember me by.'

'Oh, thank you very much!' I replied. 'But, er — '

'Don't ask any questions,' he said.

Such occurrences went on everywhere, of course, for many things were had without coupons: it is undeniable that there was a flourishing black market.

Then cousin Jack gave me a kiss on my cheek and said, 'Well, I'd better be off. Don't forget to remember me to everyone.'

'I won't,' I answered. He then got in his car, and drove away.

On the Thursday of that week, I finished working at 10 p.m. It was indeed a beautiful night, with a full moon shining, and the slight breeze that was blowing was making the small white clouds dance across the sky.

I looked up at the moon. So bright it was, it was as if it were daylight, and knew I would enjoy walking home without the light from my torch. Up the Lansdown Road I went, and I was about to pass the Lansdown Grove Hotel, which was then accommodating American soldiers. Several of them were sitting out on the porch, and one of them even gave me a whistle. I smiled to myself and walked faster, remembering that I was engaged to Jim, so I had no time for any hanky-panky.

My thoughts then wandered to the both of us, Jim and I. How would it all turn out, I wondered. One thing I was sure about, we had confidence and trust in each other. Walking home seemed to remind me of everyone, and when I reached Lansdown Place West I thought of my dear old lady, her words forever haunting me: 'My child, you'll never want for anything in this life.' And how very true.

Now I was walking up the steepest hill of all, Sion Hill, and on reaching the top it was just a matter of walking along the top road and into the lane. I was walking quite briskly now. Then, looking ahead, I could hardly believe what I saw, for parked against the wall was a single-decker bus, and getting closer I could see it was green. Crumbs, I thought. What on earth is a bus doing up here?

Arriving home, and before taking off my coat, I blurted out to Dad, 'There's a bus, Dad, parked along the top road.'

'I know,' answered Dad. 'It's mine.'

'Your bus, Dad?'

'Suggestion of the Bath bus company, to take our buses home with us. Precautionary measures, of course,' said Dad. 'Avoiding 'em all being together in the depot, should there be a direct hit.'

This made sense, of course, but why now, of all times? I was curious. 'Do you expect a big raid, Dad?'

'Well, I don't know, Paul. It's a job to tell. I think maybe it's Lord Haw Haw — reckon he's put the wind up a few folk. I suppose we must observe, and take precautions.'

We sat down to supper — meat oven pie it was, most delicious. We talked a while, and were just about to prepare for bed, when the warning siren went.

'Oh no!' said Mum.

'Must be going to give us a midnight rendezvous,' said Dad. 'We'd best get the children up.' I went upstairs for them, though I thought it was a shame to awaken them out of their sleep.

'Wakey wakey. Who's for a tiddy-back to the shelter?'

Iris, still half asleep and now rubbing her eyes, climbed on my back. Then, downstairs, she slid off my back on to the mattress in the Morrison shelter, where Mum, Dad and Rob were busy sorting themselves out. I went upstairs again to fetch Alfie. Poor kid, he was already standing on the bed, waiting for me to carry him down; a bit more awake than Iris, he gave one jump on to my back.

'Come on, my lad,' I said. Then, going down the stairs, I started singing 'A-hunting we will go'. We were almost to the bottom of the stairs when to my horror I distinctly heard the whistle of a bomb.

My reaction was one of shock, for I knew I would never make it along the passageway to the shelter in the sitting-room. For a fleeting moment I was seized by panic, and I cried out, 'Oh God!'

The coal-house underneath the stairs was our only retreat, so in a split second I swung the small door open with all velocity and threw the pair of us on to the hard knobs of coal, with Alfie getting the worse of it because my weight was on top of him.

A moment later came this loud explosion, followed by vibrations which I felt within our cottage, and the noise of shattering glass.

Then Dad yelled out, 'Where are you, Paul?'

'We're in here!' I shouted. 'In the coal-house!'

Dad shone his torch on us, and Alfie and I must have looked not a pretty sight, just lying there on the black coal. Dad pulled me up first, saying, 'You all right, Paul?'

I turned around to lift Alfie up, and now he was crying, for it must have given him such a fright as I threw him down, but I had no other choice; the small coal-house offered us protection, and I just had to take it under the circumstances.

I put my arms around Alfie, to comfort him. 'Don't cry, love. Be a brave little man for Auntie Paul.' In the beam of Dad's torch, I saw his little face, black with coal-dust, with two white streams of tears rolling down his cheeks.

'Quickly,' said Dad. 'Best all get into the shelter until the all clear goes.'

The 'all clear' went sooner than we expected, so we all crawled out of the shelter. How weird it all was, for now the moon was actually shining down upon us: we had lost most of our windows, and the scullery ceiling had fallen down.

'Can't put any lights on,' said Dad.

'I'll get my torch,' I said, knowing it was still in my pocket and that my coat was hanging behind the kitchen door. Then, shining my torch around, I could see nothing but splintered glass lying everywhere.

We then heard voices, loud voices, lots of them. 'Something is up,' exclaimed Dad. 'Rob, come with me. We'll see what's wrong.'

Dad and Rob had a struggle to open the front door, crunching through more glass that had come from the window above the door. I lit a candle in the kitchen, while Mum put the kettle on the gas, for what we all needed now was a good cup of tea. Then Rob appeared.

'Hey Quinner, you'd better come quickly with me. Bring that first-aid kit you've got.'

I grabbed my ARP bag, a blanket that was airing on the line, and my tin helmet; evidently there was someone hurt. Rob and I almost ran up the lane towards the little cottages where Billy Biss and his family lived, and to my dismay and horror I saw that the cottages were almost flattened.

'Oh no!' I gasped. I hurried over the rubble with Rob, and found Dad and others working desperately to free people from the debris, all our friends and neighbours. Knowing that The Retreat had a telephone, I shouted to someone to go down and ring the Civil Defence, quoting the number required. 'Tell them if it's possible, to send two ambulances.'

The moon was giving us light, no doubt a blessing in disguise, for I was able to see what I was doing in helping those that were hurt. I looked up at the long lengths of timber hanging vertically and ready to fall. 'Watch out for falling debris!' I shouted.

Someone handed me a sheet, which when torn up made excellent bandages, and I was just about to bind up the lacerations on a man's head when I noticed a woman coming from behind a shattered front door. Her clothes were almost in rags, and she stumbled, as if dazed.

I immediately left the man, saying, 'I'll be back.' Then I hurried to the aid of this poor woman. I held both her hands in mine; she was trembling, and spoke in a feeble voice: 'Little girl, trapped she be.'

Looking over the woman's shoulder, I observed a caved-in cottage, and I knew that no human being could possibly survive under such an amount of fallen stonework.

I called out to Dad and Rob, and told them what I knew. 'God Almighty,' exclaimed Dad. 'You say a little girl is under all that lot?' Then said Dad, 'Rob, let's see what we can do.'

And so it was, that with bare hands they made an opening into the rubble, by shifting big stones, one by one. Then I heard Rob say that he was going in.

'Rob,' I shouted, 'take my helmet.' Rob, now crawling on his stomach, disappeared through the opening.

With the others, I could only stand and stare. I remember saying to Dad, 'Will our Rob be all right?' Knowing that it was a most heroic move on Rob's part.

Time passed, and I was now becoming anxious for Rob's safety; the suspense was keenly felt by us all. But relief came when first we saw the soles of Rob's shoes, then his legs and body appeared, and finally, with both arms fully stretched, he came wriggling out. His hands were grasping a little girl's feet.

When both of them were clear of the opening, Rob laid the little girl gently down on a coat. Then he said, 'Will she be all right?'

At first, I thought she was just unconscious. But when I knelt beside her, and clasped her hands in mine, they felt so icy cold. I then felt her pulse, and there was no response. This dear little girl was dead. She had been a victim of bomb blast, for apart from dirt there was no sign of injury.

'Who is this little girl?' I cried out.

A man came forward. 'It be little Jean, Miss. Evacuee from Wales. A young couple be looking after her.'

Then a man and woman, greatly shocked themselves, came on the scene. The woman almost collapsed when she saw the little girl lying there. 'Be she dead?' she said.

'I'm sorry,' I answered, and the woman began sobbing on the man's shoulder.

I suddenly began to wonder — if this man and woman were foster parents to Jean, then who was the mysterious woman who had come from the cottage, telling me that a little girl was trapped? I was puzzled, but at that moment I had no time to ask anyone.

One had to see, in order to believe, the results of bomb-blasting. The effect on the features of this man and woman was astonishing, almost frightening, for both had old, wizened faces, twisted in torment. I began to hate this war even more, especially when I looked upon the body of such an innocent child.

Then, looking around at all our neighbours, amidst all this turmoil, my eye fell on Mr and Mrs Biss. Mrs Biss was holding on to her little terrier. 'I say, are you both all right?'

'Me and Ma's all right,' replied Mr Biss. 'Anyhow, we'll be going over to the daughter's at Weston.'

'Look,' I said, 'call and see Mother. She'll give you a hot drink.'

They went down towards my home, followed by some others, for knowing Mum they realised that everyone who called would get some refreshment, and some of them were in dire need.

By this time, air-raid wardens, special constables, and personnel from the Civil Defence, were all on the scene. I helped as much as I could, transporting the injured down the lane. Then I overheard a special constable say, 'So they had to drop a bloody bomb right in front of these cottages. What was the point of that?'

This was a good question. In fact I thought I knew what had attracted Jerry. I mentioned previously that there was a gardeners' nursery on Primrose Hill, and, without a doubt, it was the moon shining on so much glass that had indicated a prospective target for a German bomber above; the crew probably thought it was a factory.

Could I blame the beautiful big moon for our night of horror? I just don't know. Anyway, we were all thankful that there were not more killed that night, and our own little cottage might well have copped it too.

It must have been around 4 a.m. when we were all back home again. It was still a long time off dawn, and we still had much to do. Dad suggested that we should block up the windows and have some light on the place, and so with torches, a hammer, nails, and cardboard, we all helped; and when the last window was finally boarded up, Mum switched on the lights.

'Now I can see to cook some breakfast,' she said.

The kitchenette was not a pretty sight, for amongst the lime and dust were a lot of dirty cups, together with all the smashed jars of jams and pickles lying in heaps on the floor. However, Mum did not complain, but got on with frying the bacon and eggs. We all tucked in; I reckon we were hungry.

After breakfast Mum and Dad decided to go up to bed. 'Just an hour will do me,' said Dad.

Now Rob and I were alone, so I took the opportunity of saying to Rob, 'You know something, our Rob. I was real proud of you tonight, crawling under all that debris.'

'Quinner,' he answered, 'you did well yourself.' Then suddenly he burst out laughing. 'Oh boy, if your Jim could see you now. Just look at your knees!'

I glanced down at them. They were in a bit of a mess: there were big holes in the knees of my stockings, plus the fact that I still had splinters of coal-dust embedded in my skin.

Rob then decided to go up to bed. 'Might catch up on some sleep. Goodnight, Quinner.'

'Don't you mean good morning?' I replied.

'Oh yes, I am a bit mixed up. Anyway, so long. You try and get some rest too, our Paul.'

I was alone. The fire was almost out, and I felt tired; yet I did not want to go to bed, so I made up my mind that I would stop up. I banked up the fire, and looking around I could see so much that wanted doing. I made up my mind to get stuck in, and I thought that if I moved around quietly I would not disturb anyone. Anyway, I managed to get a lot of tidying-up done, and with a pair of Dad's gardening gloves on I endeavoured to pick up the pieces of glass.

The soft brush came in handy for sweeping up the dry cement dust, which had made so much mess in the kitchenette when the ceiling came down.

After completing my task, I had a good wash down in front of the fire, which was most refreshing. Then, placing a couple more knobs of coal on the fire, I settled back in the armchair.

I must have dropped off to sleep, for I knew no more until Dad awoke me with a cup of tea. Sitting beside me, he started rolling his own cigarettes, made only with St Julien tobacco. Then he spoke: 'We were darn lucky last night, Paul. And living on Primrose Hill, I thought it was the last place in the world to drop a bomb.'

'Dad,' I replied, 'it's a strange and entangled war. The enemy, they are intent when dropping bombs to have no mercy on those they kill.'

'But you know, Paul,' replied Dad, 'we are just as guilty as they are.'

'What has happened to the world, Dad?'

'Same old story,' replied Dad. 'It's got greedy and powerful. Well, at least mankind has.'

I would have been happy to talk longer with Dad, but I knew he would soon be off to work. Anyway, there was one thing to be said: this particular morning he would have his very own transport to get to work.

'I'll walk along the top road with you, Dad.' I felt I needed some fresh air; anyway, I wanted to know if Dad's bus was OK. And there she stood, the old Regal bus. Apart from a few cracked windows she was all intact; the old stone wall had evidently protected her. Dad then kissed me, jumped up in the cab, and drove off.

Strolling back, it suddenly dawned on me that we hadn't thought about our poultry. I wondered if they had survived. I walked quicker, and soon was in the lane. I went in through the back gate which led into the garden and approached the chicken-run. It was daylight now, and as I opened the little gate that led into the chicken-run, the young cockerels were already strutting about. Next I peeped into the large hut which accommodated the poultry at night. What I expected seeing I really didn't know, but to my surprise and delight they were all alive; even the hens were quietly laying their eggs. Now it was I who was really intruding on their privacy. I came to the conclusion that they must have all been huddled up together when the bomb dropped, so each must have protected the others, with their feathers.

I helped Mum that morning to get the children off to school. Alfie had to have a bath, and of course they were very tired; yet at breakfast they were so full of curiosity, asking so many questions about the bomb dropping. Alfie then said to Iris, 'Auntie Paul dropped me in the coal-house. We nearly got killed, you know.' Such was the talk between children, but how very true.

After breakfast Mum went off to work. Now that my Gran was a long-term patient in St. Martin's Hospital, Mum had resumed her job at the Royal United; and after the children had gone off to school I decided to go to bed for an hour. And how heavenly was just to crawl between the sheets; it was no wonder I slept until midday. However, after rousing myself, I was soon downstairs.

The kitchenette was still in a dusty mess, so I thought I would make myself busy before going off to work, and I was in the midst of washing shelves down when I was interrupted by a knock on the front door. I dried my hands on my pinny, then went to the front door and opened it. Standing there was Billy Biss, looking very smart in his air-force uniform.

'Hello, Pauline,' he said, and before I could reply he spoke again. 'Mum and Dad, are they all right?'

'They are both OK. Saw them last night after the bomb had dropped, and they were going over to your sister's at Weston.'

'I've been up home,' said Billy. 'Couldn't believe what I saw. And everything is in such a mess.'

I could see Billy was at sixes and sevens. 'Do come in, Billy. I'll make you a cup of tea.' So it was over tea and biscuits that I told him all about what had happened.

Then Billy, looking at me, said, 'This rotten war. Remember when we were kids? Carefree and happy, weren't we?' I couldn't agree more.

I could see that Billy was anxious to go to Weston village to see his parents, while I was wanting to finish off the job I was doing.

'I'll not hold you back,' said Billy. 'I can see you are busy. Anyway thanks for the tea and chat. Hoping to see you again soon.'

He left, and I really felt sorry for him, for apart from the shock at seeing his home he was faced with problems concerning the welfare of his parents.

As I washed down more shelves, I couldn't help but think of the waste of it all. Mankind could only blame himself for all the misery and suffering, and yet we camouflage it with just three letters: WAR.

I had almost finished my job now. I was down on my knees, scrubbing away at the large flat stones on the floor until they were almost white. The kitchenette almost looked back to normal. I looked around, admiring my own work, and hoping that what I had done would please Mum. Then I remembered. I had one more job to do before getting myself ready: it was to feed the chickens. So I made a bran mash for them, which consisted of bran and boiled potatoes.

157

I was almost ready to go off to work when I heard a letter being pushed through the letter-box. I immediately recognised Jim's handwriting, so I opened the letter quickly and read it. He was well, kept busy he said. He couldn't tell me exactly what he was doing, but if I guessed rightly he would be driving military trains.

That day, on my way to catch a bus to work, I was hurrying along Sion Road when I came across a familiar figure. It was an elderly woman. Mum knew her well; she did daily charring for almost everybody. She was seated on an old wooden seat, and in her lap were at least a dozen pieces of paper.

'Hello,' I said.

'Good afternoon,' she answered. Then, looking at me more closely, she said, 'You be Mrs Quintin's daughter. Could you help me, my dear?'

I looked at her, and then glanced down at the bits of paper. Apparently she was trying to sort out what job she was to do next. I sat beside her, and glanced through the bits of paper, thinking to myself that the old char had plenty of work on. 'Ah, here it is,' I said. 'Friday afternoon, a Mrs La Touche.'

'So it be the Spanish lady I goes to this afternoon. See, my dear, haven't got my proper glasses on. Can't read in these. Bought 'em at Woolworths for sixpence — thought they were a bargain. Anyway my dear, thank you kindly. Blowed if I knew where I had to go next.'

I looked down upon this elderly lady, who was at least in her seventies, and I couldn't help but think that she was too old for scrubbing and cleaning. Yet my heart was full of admiration for her, knowing she had the will-power that enabled her to still scrub and clean. Of course the domestic situation was desperate; servants were becoming scarce, so many more people needed daily helps, which was the next best thing. Anybody who could do cleaning and use a scrubbing-brush was very much appreciated.

I said farewell to the old lady and then walked briskly on, arriving at the Pierrepont Garage prompt at 2 p.m.

The change of shifts was quickly accomplished, and it emerged that Mr Griffin's nephew was going to help out, which he often did. He was another young man who in my opinion should have been in the services. It was strange but I could never find out much about him. He was a bit of a dark horse, I thought, although I did know he used to go up to London quite a lot. And imagine how surprised I was, when he told me, of his own free will, that his visits to London were because he was keeping company with a lady much older than himself. Quite boldly he said, 'It's not love, Miss

Quintin, but her lovely wealth that attracts me.' Immediately I somehow despised this young man, but knowing that I occasionally had to work with him I was almost forced to show some response to his sociability.

This young man was very sure of himself, but in private the rest of us nicknamed him Hoppy, because he gave us all the impression that he was forever hopping around, so full of his own importance. However, this particular afternoon I witnessed embarrassment on his face. I never imagined he could blush, but he did. He was about to jack up a car, and while bending over, it suddenly happened. I clearly heard the rip of the back seam in his trousers, which gave way from waistband to crutch, revealing to me his underwear, for I was standing right behind him.

The situation I saw Hoppy in made me burst out into laughter. I couldn't help myself; it was all so funny, especially when he turned around, and made an attempt to walk backwards.

'Damn utility trousers,' he said.

Of course I didn't improve matters by laughing at him, and when he did return, he was wearing a pair of white cricket flannels.

'I know it's ridiculous,' he said. 'But at the moment I've no other trousers to wear.' I could have told him that there was a spare boiler suit below, but then it would have been beneath Hoppy's dignity to wear anything like that. I could tell that Hoppy was cross, but every time I thought of him walking backwards, and in such a predicament, it only made me want to giggle all the more.

The afternoon and evening passed over quickly, with Hoppy not getting his cricket flannels too dirty, and so came 10 p.m.; it was time to close the big garage doors.

'Goodnight, Miss,' said Hoppy.

'Oh, goodnight,' I answered.

When I finally left the garage it was another lovely night, with the bright white moon shining. I couldn't resist it; I would walk home. So up Lansdown Road I went, and nearing the Lansdown Hotel I caught up with two American soldiers who had two girls with them. By their performance, it was clear that all were intoxicated. They were singing and laughing, and were even a little unsteady on their feet, so it was not surprising that they were blocking the pavement. I had to step out into the road to pass, and as I did so one of the soldiers spoke: 'Hi gorgeous.' I smiled to myself and walked on, wondering who was seeing who home. I could only think that for their own particular purposes the girls were escorting the soldiers back to the American billet in the hotel.

With America now in the war, we had quite a large number of their servicemen over here in England, many of whom were in training. To me they were far superior dressed than our lads, but this alone did not impress me. Maybe it was their style; almost all of them chewed gum. The thing was, they always had this extra money to spend. It attracted our girls, of course, and in consequence good times came out of it. So, as the saying goes, the Yanks had the money, and our girls helped to spend it.

Americans formed the vast majority of the allied servicemen who swelled our population by almost one and a half million during the war. The Americans were to be known later as GIs, and they became an important feature of wartime Britain. They seemed to have plenty of everything the civilian population was short of: razor-blades, cheap cigarettes, and the new nylon stockings. The plea of children following any American was, 'Got any gum chum?' And often they had.

I arrived at the top road to find Dad's bus standing in the usual place again, alongside the stone wall. I felt the bonnet: it was still warm, which told me that Dad was only a little ahead of me. When I got in, Dad greeted me with, 'Hello, Paul. We've been waiting for you to come in. It's much nicer having our supper together.'

Mum had made an excellent meal, with pork chops and apple sauce, and we had just about finished when the wobble-siren started.

'Looks like we're going to have unwelcome visitors again tonight,' said Dad. 'And best we all go down into the Pitmans' cellars for shelter. For if the raid is prolonged, as well it might be, we'll have the comfort of the heating and lighting.'

'Dad,' I said, 'I'm on call tonight, so I'll have to reach the depot as soon as possible.'

'Oh dear,' remarked Mum.

'I'll come with you tonight,' said Rob.

'Oh, I'll be all right,' I answered. 'Anyway, if I run most of the way I can be down at the depot within fifteen minutes.'

'You'll have to run blinking hard to do it in fifteen minutes,' remarked Rob.

'Anyway,' I said, 'I'll see you all settled at the Pitmans before I go on my way. And Rob, I'd rather you stopped behind, and help look after things.'

'OK,' said Rob. 'You win.'

I brought the children down and dressed them. 'Where are we going, Auntie Paul?'

'Just to the Pitmans' shelter, love.'

I picked up a couple of dolls for Iris, while Alfie had his toy engine and comics tucked underneath his arm.

'Can I bring Topsy, Auntie Paul?'

'Why of course,' I said. Topsy was a little black dolly which Iris idolised; her Daddy had bought it for her.

I noticed Mum had her bag full with odds and ends, and soon we were all ready to leave home. I had my ARP bag and helmet swinging from my shoulder, while Alfie and Iris each held on to my hands.

'Come on,' I said, 'we'll race to the Pitmans.' So down the slope we ran, then into the driveway of the Pitman estate. The drive was flanked by an avenue of trees, and the moon shining through them made it all a somewhat peaceful, romantic scene. It was ideal for courting couples, but not for growing children. However, the night air had given the children a remarkable stimulus, producing a temporary increase of energy, for both of them suddenly let go of my hands, and started running through the trees.

'Come back!' I shouted. No response. Next I tried whistling. I then shouted their names, and this time they obeyed my call and came running towards me, with Alfie now holding something up in his hand.

'Look what I've found, Auntie Paul.'

'Goodness me, whatever is it?' Iris was now giggling at my reaction. I looked closer at some small creature in Alfie's hand; it reminded me of a stoat, or some kind of a weasel. 'It's dead,' I exclaimed.

'Not really, Auntie Paul, because it moved when I picked it up.'

By this time Mum, Dad, and Rob had caught up with us.

'What's all the commotion then?' said Dad. Then, looking at Alfie, he said, 'What the devil have you got in your hand?'

'Just a little animal, Grandad, and it'll die if I don't look after it.'

Suddenly we heard the drone of enemy aircraft approaching. 'Quick everyone, into the shelter!' shouted Dad. We all hurried down the steps that led to the vaults. Then, opening the door, we all disappeared inside.

Already we had company, and amongst the people trying to make themselves comfortable were Bill Harding and his wife.

'Hello, Pop,' said Bill. 'Guess we are all of the same mind tonight.'

'Yes,' replied Dad, 'it would be taking chances staying back up home. And it's safer here for us all.'

The domestic staff of the Pitman family had now joined us, and we gathered that Mr and Mrs Pitman were away. I saw our Rob talking and laughing with one of the maids; it was evident they had worked together when Rob was a footman. Then we all heard a couple of thuds; some distance away maybe, but close enough.

After seeing everyone settled, I decided that it was time for me to go, so kissing my family goodnight, I made my way to the door.

'Half a mo,' said Dad. 'I'll be taking a liberty I know, but I'll take you down in the bus.'

'Oh no. No Dad, you stop right here. Then I know you are all together.'

Now Mum was frowning. 'Do you have to go, duck?'

'Yes, Mum, but don't you get worrying now. I'll be all right.'

Then Dad said, 'Don't like you going off like this. It's a good ways to town, and it would only take me five minutes to drive you down.'

'Please stay with everyone, Dad. They look upon you for guidance. Anyway, if I can't make it to town, I'll come back, I promise.' So, calling out, 'Cheerio,' I made my exit.

All appeared quiet outside, so I decided to hurry while I had the chance. I ran up the slope, and then along the top road. I started panting a bit, but I continued on, running down the road that led across the common.

I glanced at the moon: it seemed to be shining that much brighter. There was no one about, and it was extraordinary, but I suddenly felt this uncanny melancholy feeling. I think it was due to the quietness that surrounded me. I was almost to the common when the silence was broken by the sounds of aircraft getting nearer. Now they were right above me.

Then came the whistling of bombs coming through the air, and in a fleeting moment I was suddenly pulled to the ground, and felt my arm rubbing against someone else in uniform.

A voice echoed in my ears. 'OK, Miss, wait for it.'

The explosions that followed were in my judgement approximately two miles away, I would say in the vicinity of Twerton. However, I got up on my feet and started brushing my trouser legs, while at the same time being curious to look at my rescuer.

A middle-aged man he was, wearing a warden's arm-band. 'I say,' he said. 'Bain't you Pat Quintin's daughter?'

'I am,' I answered.

'Thought so,' he replied. 'What be you doing out this time of night then?'

I explained that I was attached to the Ambulance Section, and was on my way down to the depot.

'You can't do that, Miss. I mean walk all that way to town. There's bombs dropping, and you might get yourself killed. I'll tell 'ee what I'll do. I'll ring up the Civil Defence, ask 'em to send up transport for you.'

'I don't know if they will do that,' I replied.

'Won't be a jiffy.' Then he vanished.

Having no other choice, I stood and waited. After all, the man's suggestion was sensible if not logical — I could just as easily be killed in a vehicle as on foot, but if a car came for me I would at least be saving my energy for more important matters.

The man then joined me again. 'They be going to send up a vehicle for 'ee.'

'Thank you,' I said. 'It's kind of you to have taken all this trouble.'

'It bain't no trouble, Miss. Happy to oblige.'

While the man and I stood, more aircraft came over, and they were the enemy, for more bombs dropped in the distance, on the other side of Bath I shouldn't wonder. Possibly Bristol. What was Jerry up to? Warming us up gently for something big, by the sound of it.

Anyway, I was pleased to see a Mr Smith arrive with an Austin ambulance; he was an old colleague of mine, and he had come to pick me up.

'Sorry to give you all this bother,' I said. 'It seems I'm putting everyone out tonight.'

'It's all right, Miss. All in a course of duty.'

Saying goodbye to the ARP man, I jumped up beside Mr Smith, and after reversing up the road we were soon on our way. 'Looks like we're in for it tonight,' he said. 'Best get to the depot as quick as possible. Things could get rough.'

I suddenly remembered what Lord Haw Haw had said, but I did not speak of it to Mr Smith. I remained silent while he concentrated on his driving. I decided I would be optimistic about Lord Haw Haw, and not believe his threats of bombing Bath to the ground.

We reached the depot, and found much activity going on; a number of bombs had already been dropped over a wide area around the city.

Mr Wright assembled us all together. 'Ladies and gentlemen,' he said. 'It appears we may be the target for Jerry tonight. You know the usual procedure, of course. But under the different circumstances tonight, in which enemy aircraft are dropping bombs at random, we'll have to use new tactics. I have decided to detail each ambulance and its crew to a confined area. By this method we will be covering a wide area of Bath, and so be ready on the spot. I suggest,' went on Mr Wright, 'that you take up positions, north, south, east, and west. Of course it will be necessary to have some ambulances standing by, here at the depot, for emergencies. Everybody happy about this arrangement?'

We all agreed that this was the best thing to do, and the arrangements were made quickly. The majority of our fleet of ambulances were split up into four sections, with each crew allotted to a particular position in one sector.

'One last thing,' said Mr Wright. 'We must stick by the rules. Our job will be to transport casualties only, to the nearest hospital available, administering first aid as best we can. May I conclude by saying that if things get out of control, it will be left entirely to each individual to act according to his best judgement. Best of luck everyone.'

Now we were organised. I was one of the crew to stand by at the depot, alongside Mr Smith, while the remainder of the crews were already on their way.

While waiting, we heard more aircraft coming over, together with the occasional thud of bombs dropping. Behopes, I thought, they would all drop in the River Avon.

Then calls started coming in to the depot. Our first call was to proceed to the York House Hotel, which was situated at the top of Broad Street. Part of the hotel had received a direct hit, and when we arrived we found people coming out of the hotel in a dazed condition, plus the fact that there was glass and debris everywhere. I noticed that the bomb responsible had sliced off a third of the gable end.

'Damn fools,' said Mr Smith, referring to the wounded. 'Should have been in the shelter.' Nevertheless, we rendered first aid, and transported casualties to hospital. Some had lost their lives, and were victims without any identification. I'm a sentimentalist at heart, moved by feelings rather than by reason, so this episode tugged away at my heart strings.

On one of our visits to the hospital, we met up with other crews coming from different areas of Bath. All through the night we were busy, and at odd moments I would silently pray that all my family were unharmed, knowing that Mum would be praying for my safety in return. I heard one man call out, 'Murderous pigs!' He had cause to voice this opinion, for we had nothing to defend ourselves with, not a gun or a searchlight even. Undefended, that's what we were, an open city and an easy target. If our planes had intercepted the enemy maybe it would have been worse — I just wouldn't know. I only know that it was all so terrible and frustrating, and I don't mind saying that there were times when I was frightened myself.

Our struggle through the night seemed unavailing. Of course the moonlight helped the German bombers, but it also gave us light to see with. Jerry certainly had us all on our toes, and to me it was the most nerve-racking raid ever. But it was, of course, as nothing compared with the two nights which were to come. The main target that night was the city of Exeter, and the full force of the enemy attack had yet to be experienced.

The 'all clear' finally went around about 5.45 a.m., but we still had much to do, so it must have been nearly 8 a.m. when Mr Smith and I arrived back at the depot, after we had finished our last assignment.

We were all assembled. Three of our colleagues had been injured, and not one of us escaped being very tired and weary, for the night's activities had taken their toll. Before we left the depot we all appreciated the hot tea that was made for us.

All I wanted to do now was to go home, for my anxiety about my family was intense, so when Mr Smith suggested that he should drive me home I gladly accepted.

Mr Smith and I were too tired for any conversation as he drove me up to Primrose Hill, and when he pulled up alongside Dad's bus I just thanked him and jumped out of the cab. Then my eyes caught sight of the Regal bus, and to my dismay I saw that nearly all the windows were shattered. Immediately I started running, as fast as my legs could carry me, and when I did reach the lane I found part of the wall down. It made me realise that bombs must have dropped near my home. I couldn't wait, and almost flew up the lane, but then a sudden wave of relief came over me when I saw that our little cottage was all intact.

I opened the door quickly, shouting out, 'Coo-ee!' and as I did so there was Dad standing in the passageway. 'Are you all OK?' I gasped.

'Yes, we're all right, Paul. I phoned up your depot, they told me you were on your way home. And Mum's got a good breakfast for you.'

Dear Mum, she was almost in tears at seeing me, and I felt the same way. Tears did flow from my eyes, the result of a mixture of feelings I suppose. We put our arms around each other, and between sniffs, I said, 'You see Mum, I am quite safe.'

'Thank God,' murmured Mum, 'for it's been a dreadful night.'

I made an attempt to eat up the breakfast Mum had cooked for me. 'Aren't we lucky?' I said. 'Still eating fresh eggs.'

Mum was now smiling. 'Eat it all up now,' she said.

Crunching away at the fried bread I tried talking to Dad in between, our conversation dealing with the night's events, of course.

'Oh,' I said. 'You've lost a lot of windows in your bus.'

Dad was now smiling. 'They'll be easily replaced, Paul.'

I suddenly was aware of Dad's eyes upon me. I don't suppose he would ever have dreamed of seeing me in such a state, for I knew I must have looked like something dragged out of a bush backwards. I was now beginning to feel the scratches on my face and hands, and I was still covered in dust and dirt, and Dad was smiling at me.

I knew at that very moment that all his love and understanding were concentrated upon me. I suppose in one way he was proud of me. After all, I was his daughter, and he knew that I had taken a hiding.

The children came in to see me, and Alfie, full of excitement, said, 'I got the little ermine better, Auntie Paul.'

'Little ermine?' I replied.

'Oh yes, Auntie Paul, a man in the shelter told me what it was.'

'And where is it now?' I exclaimed.

'Well,' said Alfie, 'when we came out of the shelter, Grandma said I must let it go free, for it was no use as a pet, because it belonged to the wild life. So when I put it down, it scampered off into the trees.'

Poor little Alfie, he looked so disappointed. 'Never mind love,' I said. 'You were a good boy to make him get better.'

Alfie soon got over his disappointment, and I was relieved that the kids were none the worse for the ordeal they had gone through during last night's raid. Then Mum placed her arm around my shoulder. 'I think you had better go up to bed, duck. For you haven't a lot of time, if you want to be at the garage for two o'clock.'

'I should have a wash first, Mum.'

'Skip it, darling, for it's sleep you need most.'

I knew Mum was right, of course, so into bed I crawled, and was soon in a different world of peaceful sleep, and knew no more until Mum gave me a gentle nudge.

'It's one o'clock, Paul, and I've brought you up a cup of tea.'

'Thanks, Mum.' I was trying now to rouse myself, which was difficult. However, I was soon downstairs, enjoying a bowl of Mum's thick vegetable soup. Already I felt refreshed. True, I hadn't had my usual eight hours' sleep, yet what sleep I did have was sufficient to build me up again.

In between getting ready for work, and talking with Mum, I mentioned that I was on duty again that night, and also the following night. I now sensed that Mum was getting concerned over me, for she frowned and said, 'Let's hope we have two quiet nights. We could all do with a rest.' In fact, during the next two nights Bath was to experience its heaviest bombing of the war.

As usual Mum came to the door to see me off. She kissed me and then said, 'Cheerio, my darling, take care.'

Hurrying down the lane, I turned the corner and waved. I was still in my Civil Defence uniform, and it was still in a bit of a mess. Good job it was dark in colour, it hid all the stains and creases; anyway, the clean white blouse I was wearing made me feel respectable.

166

I enjoyed walking to town. The sun was shining, and the buds on the trees were almost ready for bursting out into leaf. The air was fresh and clean at first, but as I got nearer to town new smells hit my nose. Not very pleasant ones either, but the smells of smouldering timber mingled with that of decaying matter. Gangs of men were toiling away at the debris of some buildings that had been hit.

I turned into Pierrepont Street, which led down to the garage, and what I saw was a scene that was almost unbelievable. Queues of cars were lined up one behind the other, all waiting in turn to be served with petrol, and to my astonishment I saw Mr Griffin himself serving at the pumps. With him was Miss Clarke, his secretary, who was busy taking the money and petrol coupons.

As I came on to the forecourt, Mr Griffin's face beamed, and he remarked, 'Am I glad to see you Miss. It's been like this all the morning. It was the raid last night — panic has seized the people. Most want to get the hell out of it.'

I immediately detected a bitterness in Mr Griffin's statement; evidently he didn't agree with people who wanted to run away from a crisis. I realised, however, that these people had quite a logical reason for wanting to escape. The previous night's episode was a warning of worse that might be to come, and one could hardly accuse these people of cowardice. Yet I suppose they were acting rather selfishly; after all, some of us just had to stay behind and face up to things.

I hurried and changed into my boiler suit, and was still fastening my belt when coming out on to the forecourt. I then took over from Mr Griffin.

'Oh, by the way, Miss,' said Mr Griffin, 'we've had notification from the Ministry that the situation being what it is, next month's petrol-rationing coupons have been made valid. Gives folk the opportunity of obtaining extra petrol, and so to vacate Bath, if they so desire.'

I suppose in a way it made sense. People could evacuate the city and travel to a safer zone. On the other hand it could well be idiotic. Some folk with no intentions of leaving Bath could fill up their tanks in advance, using up petrol which was needed else- where. Racketeers could become involved, selling these unexpectedly valid coupons, at an exorbitant price, no doubt. However, I knew I must disperse these thoughts from my mind, and concentrate on the job.

In the hours to follow, Freddie and I worked jolly hard, and we were never off the pumps. However, at mid-afternoon, Miss Clarke kindly brought us out cups of tea, which we placed on the wall, taking the occasional sip when we could.

All kinds of vehicles came rolling up, some new, others old, and many of them packed with luggage. It reminded me of a stream of folk going off on holiday, but with a difference, for these people did not look happy, more was the pity. Quite honestly, I was pleased when we had sold out of petrol, and I was able to put up the sign saying, 'Sorry, no petrol available.'

Freddie and I went over to our little office, and I almost flopped on the stool, slipping off my shoes at the same time. It was heavenly just to relax for a while. I looked at Freddie, who was now sitting at the top of the wooden stairs. 'You all right Freddie?'

'I'm OK, Miss,' he answered.

'Be a good lad, and make us both some tea.' He was a most willing young man, and when he brought the tea I was able to give him one of my egg sandwiches, which Mum had put up for me.

Our takings for that day were very high indeed, so I welcomed Miss Clarke when she came into the garage to help me check the money and coupons. And, as was to be expected, dud coupons had slipped through.

When we had almost finished, Mr Griffin popped his head in the doorway, saying, 'Managing all right, you two?' Then he said, 'I've been on to the Petroleum, and they are going to send us a tanker of BP as soon as possible, so it could arrive at any time, Miss. And if you require my help, I'll be next door, for I'll be staying at home this evening.'

It must have been around 7 o'clock when a tanker pulled up on the forecourt. The driver said, 'How do,' then climbed on top of his waggon, holding in his hand a dip-stick, which he put down into the container. Then he called out to me, 'Like to check this, Miss?' This I did, and the dip-stick showed 500 gallons of best BP petrol. I re-checked it when the tanker was empty, signed the delivery note, and in minutes the big tanker moved out.

I was reluctant to do so, but I had to take the sign down, and so it was back to business as usual. Within minutes we were selling the petrol as fast as we could, Freddie remaining on the pumps while I supervised, taking the money and coupons.

It was remarkable the different types of people who turned up requiring petrol. One old Vauxhall, for instance, was pushed on to the forecourt by three Polish airmen, the fourth airman being at the wheel. They stopped pushing when alongside the pumps, and one airman mopped his forehead with his handkerchief. I could only assume that they must have conked out quite a distance away, for they all looked exhausted with pushing.

The driver then got out. He didn't speak, but instead handed me a four-gallon petrol coupon.

'Put four gallons in, Freddie,' I said.

Then another Polish airman smiled at me, and spoke in broken English. 'Bad night, last night.' I nodded, and very slowly the man spoke again. 'We wanted to intercept. We wanted to help. But orders, stay grounded, very bad.'

I now smiled back at the man, acknowledging what he had said. At least it was good to know that these Polish lads were ready to help us, and it wasn't their fault that they remained grounded, for they had their orders, which had to be obeyed. Later I heard a rumour that these Polish airmen hadn't had sufficient training, and as yet were not qualified for flying. Another rumour was that they had no fighter-planes to intercept with. Well, whatever the reason, one could hardly expect such a small air-force base as Colerne to do wonders, for in my own opinion I don't suppose they would have stood a chance, even if they had intercepted Jerry.

It had crossed my mind that Lord Haw Haw would now have something to crow about, and I wondered if that wretched man had a conscience, knowing that his own fellow-countrymen were in peril. I suppose we were to blame for listening in to him on the wireless, but he was so damned convincing, and how right he had been about Bath so far. Remembering that he said that our lovely Georgian city would be ruins, it was my guess that Jerry was about to visit us again.

Eventually we had a lull in customers, whereupon I sent Freddie up to the fish-and-chip shop for two pennyworth of fish and a pennyworth of chips. One thing, we did have peace in which to eat them. Normally I sent Freddie home sooner, but this particular night I hung on to him until the very last, in case we suddenly became busy. But by the time 10 o'clock came we hadn't disturbed Mr Griffin and it was time for us to go.

The Civil Defence depot wasn't far from the garage, a mere five minutes' walk, so I arrived there before 10.15 p.m., and was soon looking at the duty board: my eyes were fixed on my name, and I was to be in attendance that night with Mr Penny. This made me happy, because I had that much more confidence when I was with him. So, after reporting to Mr Penny, I had a few words with Flo, the telephonist, and then went into a cubicle and just flopped with exhaustion on top of the bunk bed.

I must have dropped off to sleep, for I awoke with a start to find that the warning flasher was going on and off. I glanced at my watch: it was 11.15 p.m., so gathering myself together, I slipped on my shoes, and hurried to assembly. I met Mr Penny on the way, and in his hand he held a cup of tea. 'You have this, Miss. I'll get another.'

'Thank you,' I replied, grateful for a refreshing cuppa.

Now I was sitting beside Mr Penny in assembly, while Mr Wright addressed us all. His face looked grim as he spoke. 'It is my opinion that we are in for a much bigger raid than last night's episode. And I must be frank with you all, we must be prepared for the worst. Last night, as many of you will know, we were detailed to separate assignments. This indeed proved a valuable asset. In other words,' said Mr Wright, 'by spreading out to different areas, it enabled us to be on the job, and to cope quicker. So we shall do the same tonight.' He gave us our detailed instructions, finally saying, 'The best of luck to you all.'

'Come on, Miss,' said Mr Penny. 'I'll explain the situation as we go along. Our destination is on the north side of Bath. That's where you live, isn't it, Miss?'

'That's correct,' I replied. 'I'll be on home territory.'

So up the Lansdown Road we went, passing Kingswood School, once the famous school for the sons of Methodist clergymen and now accommodating the personnel of the Admiralty. Further up the road we reached the Admiralty huts, situated in a large field, surrounded by barbed wire and mesh and guarded too, by special constables. At the start of the war, the Admiralty was dispersed from London, scattering their various sections all over England. The Bath departments consisted of DNA (Director of Naval Accounts) and CEC (Civil Engineering in Chief).

We passed the main gate and then Mr Penny pulled in to the side of the road, saying, 'Let's take five,' meaning, of course, that we should stop for five minutes. From the position we were now in we got a good view of the valley and the very centre of Bath. With such a powerful moon shining on the scene, it all had a ghostly appearance.

The next thing we heard was aircraft approaching.

'Here they come,' remarked Mr Penny.

Then came the thuds, followed by more thuds. Then we caught sight of dotted glows, right in the centre of the city, and it seemed within minutes that those little glows had developed into fires that were rapidly spreading; and while Mr Penny and I watched it was as if Bath in its valley was burning from end to end.

Looking on, I experienced a terrible sinking feeling, for the buildings that were ablaze now were actually glowing, like the fire one would see on a bonfire night.

'So, Jerry has concentrated on the valley itself,' said Mr Penny. 'Must be hell down there.'

So helpless we were, but there was nothing we could do. Like sitting ducks, we had to take what Jerry handed out to us.

'You live up here somewhere, don't you, Miss?'

'It's about five minutes' walk away,' I replied.

'Would you like to see your folks before we move on to Swainswick?' This was the next stop on our planned route.

Suddenly I was uplifted. 'Oh, rather!' I answered.

Immediately the engine in the ambulance started up, and we were moving down towards Sion Road, which led eventually to Primrose Hill. Then, suddenly, it happened. There was a tremendous explosion. Our ambulance shook, as if in a tornado, and it took all of Mr Penny's concentration to apply the brakes and stop.

'My God!' said Mr Penny. 'That was close.'

We both looked out each side, knowing that the blast had come from behind us.

'Oh no!' gasped Mr Penny, and I myself couldn't believe it, for the spot where we had been parked had suddenly become obliterated, apart from the cloudy mass of suspended particles which was still rising from the bomb crater. In my innermost thoughts at that moment I could only give thanks to our guardian angels, for we had just experienced a narrow escape indeed.

'We'll turn back,' said Mr Penny. 'Make sure no one has been hurt.'

We got out of the ambulance and were confronted with a nasty big crater, with barbed wire and mess sticking out of it. Amongst the onlookers were the local special constables, who were now estimating the damage.

I heard one man say, 'Bloody lucky it fell on the road.'

Then Mr Penny shouted out, 'Everybody OK?'

A voice answered, 'Everybody is OK, no one hurt.'

We left the constables blocking off the road, while we made a second attempt to proceed down Sion Road.

'In one way, Miss, that was a convenient bomb. Jerry wasted it with no harm to any life.'

Making our way along the top road, Mr Penny to my surprise stopped outside a public telephone box. 'I'm ringing in, Miss. They could be needing us back at the depot.' From the ambulance, I watched Mr Penny dialling, and there must have been no reply, for he immediately replaced the receiver. When he returned to the driver's seat he looked bewildered and said, 'The line is dead.'

He remained quiet, as if studying up what to do next, and I think I shared the problem with him. We both knew that we were assigned to patrol a certain area, but what if our services were more urgently required in the city? I decided to let Mr Penny use his own discretion, and act accordingly.

'You might as well see your folks while you're up here,' he said.

I got out at the top of the lane, telling Mr Penny that I wouldn't be a minute. Then, running as fast as I could down the slope, I reached the door of the Pitmans' shelter, and as I banged on the door I could hear music coming from within. It got much louder when the door was opened by a Mrs Billett, an old neighbour of ours, who lived at the bottom of Primrose Hill.

She looked almost stunned when she saw me. 'I be blowed,' she said. 'If it bain't be Polly Quintin.'

As I entered the music stopped, and I sensed all eyes upon me. However, I went in pursuit of Mum and Dad and the children, who were so pleased to see me. Someone handed me some cocoa, and between sips I blurted out what news I had to tell.

I then suddenly missed Rob, and enquired where he was.

'He's fire-watching in the Pitmans' house,' said Dad. 'He's all right.'

Satisfied that everybody was OK, I decided it was time I leave them. 'Must hurry back,' I said. 'On our way to Swainswick.' Thinking to myself, that's if we keep to routine. I looked at Mum and Dad and said, 'I was so near, I just had to see you all.'

I glanced around: everyone appeared in high spirits, and at that moment I even heard laughter.

I kissed Mum and Dad, and then looked down upon Iris and Alfie, who were still awake and were intrigued at trying to put a jigsaw puzzle together. I just patted the tops of their little heads. After saying cheerio to everyone I made my way to the door, and then disappeared into the night.

Again enemy aircraft were above me, so I started running as hard as I could up the slope, and indeed I was panting by the time I reached the ambulance. Mr Penny already had the engine running as I jumped up into the cab. 'Hope I haven't been too long, Mr Penny.'

'Not at all,' he replied. 'Anyway, I hope you found your folk OK.'

'They are all down in the Pitmans' cellars, you know.'

'Best for 'em, on a night like this,' replied Mr Penny. 'I think we'll make our way over to Swainswick, as planned, Miss. Like to take the wheel, Miss? Give me a chance to have a puff at the old pipe.'

Exchanging seats, I waited until Mr Penny had lit his pipe and then we were on our way over the hills to Swainswick. The aroma of the pipe tobacco reminded me of someone else. Dear Jim, I thought, I wonder what you are doing now? And although I was concentrating on my driving, my mind was apt to dwell on other things. I was now thinking of my brother, Tom, who I knew was on the high seas, on his way out to Burma or somewhere, and in fact I was thinking of Pat and Tim also.

In the interim, however, our drive to Swainswick was not interrupted, so we arrived in good time. It was here that we got another view of Bath, from an entirely new angle. But what we did gaze upon only caused us consternation, for our city had now developed into a blazing inferno.

I sensed that Mr Penny would make a quick decision, and when he said, 'We're going in, Miss,' I was not surprised. Both of us were aware of a sense of supererogation: we wanted to do more for our fellow men than duty strictly required. So down the hill we sped, this time with Mr Penny driving.

When we reached the London Road, we were almost into the city, and as we approached we met up with the scars of the onslaught, which were all of a similar pattern. Buildings which were completely gutted and piled high with debris made an ugly scene; firemen were struggling desperately to put out the fires, and every pair of hands available was helping out in some way or other. And the glass — there was so much of it lying around everywhere that we felt there couldn't possibly be a window left intact.

We came across another ambulance, its crew busy with the injured. Mr Penny leaned out of his side of the cab, calling out as he did so, 'Do you need any help?'

A voice answered, 'Managing OK, but they'll be glad of your help at Walcot Street.'

Walcot Street! Suddenly I felt sick inside, for that was where Pat's home was. Now my concern was for my sister-in-law Violet and little Patricia; also for Gran Quintin, who lived with an aunt and uncle of mine.

We moved off again, and I was tormented with suspense. When we reached the top of Walcot Street, it was tricky for Mr Penny to drive over the debris and broken glass, and we discovered it was the top end that had been hit. Pat's home was at the bottom of the street, which hadn't been touched, thank God. That was where Gran lived, too, so I felt a little happier. Nevertheless, our findings were heart-breaking; three big stone houses had been hit, and people were just lying around waiting for help or transport to hospital.

There were children too who needed comforting, along with house-pets. I recall seeing this old cockatoo, who was still in his cage but had been rescued, and amidst all the turmoil he was calling out, 'I love you! I love you!'

I worked beside Mr Penny, administering what first aid we could; as for those who needed further medical treatment, we transported them up to St Martin's Hospital.

After our second run up to the hospital, a porter in Casualty gave us a cup of tea, which we appreciated.

'Tell me,' I said to the porter. 'The hospital, it is OK, isn't it? Only it's my Grandma, she's a patient up here.'

'Don't you be worrying, me dear. The blessed St Martin will look after his own.' It indeed was a comforting thought.

Then Mr Penny glanced at me. 'We best be on our way, Miss. Thanks for the tea, mate.' I too thanked the porter, knowing that his tea had had a reviving effect.

On leaving the hospital, Mr Penny suggested that we make our way to the depot. We went through many streets and saw gangs of men everywhere, sweeping piles of glass into heaps with their big brushes. At this period, all was quiet in the air, but as the 'all clear' had not gone yet we could expect Jerry to return at any time.

We turned into James Street, and I was pleased to see that our depot was still standing. There were of course windows missing, but much activity was going on inside, and already other crews from the outskirts had come back to the depot, so we weren't the only ones to have made that decision.

Looking at the switchboard, I expected to see Flo, but instead a man was sitting in her place. I immediately enquired after Flo.

'They had to rush her to the Royal United Hospital.'

'Whatever for?' I gasped.

'Shock, Miss. Must have brought on a miscarriage.'

'Shock?' I said. 'From what?'

The man then pointed to the ceiling above him. 'Look up there, Miss.'

I looked up and saw a nasty big hole.

'A miracle it was,' the man continued. 'The bomb came through the ceiling and settled itself in Flo's waste-paper basket. And lucky for us it didn't go off, or we would all have been blown to kingdom come.'

I just flopped into a nearby chair, and almost muttered to myself, 'A miracle indeed.' But to have this happen to poor Flo. My gaze then fell upon her knitting, which was still on the top of the switchboard: a baby's garment almost completed.

I felt like crying. I couldn't understand why this should have happened to such an authentic person as Flo. This then was the spoils of war: too many innocent people were getting hurt, not only physically, but mentally as well. I began to understand why we had conscientious objectors, for were they not right to object to this kind of warfare? My mind was full of animosity for all this so-called war, but I had volunteered to help; so, remembering that I was still on duty, I rejoined Mr Penny.

'Call just come through for us, Miss. We've to proceed to Kingsmead Street.'

As we left the depot, we heard the drone of more enemy aircraft overhead, followed by more thuds, which shook the ambulance as we drove along. As we got nearer to our destination, my heart gave a leap, for I was born at No. 4 Kingsmead Street, and was always proud of the fact, for in earlier times it was known as the King's Meadows.

I glanced at my watch. It was just 5 a.m., and for all that the night had been fully occupied with events, the time had dragged; and still the enemy persisted in dropping bombs.

Being matutinal, the bright moon was declining; it settled beneath rolling clouds, making it a shade darker, which enhanced the brightness of the smouldering fires.

We passed Kingsmead Square, sheltered by the very large oak tree. All these features were a part of me, because I had spent my early childhood in the area.

Turning into Kingsmead Street, I could smell the thick scent of smouldering timber, and to my horror I saw my old school in one mass of flames, shooting high, and coming out from every direction. A lump came into my throat as I remembered my happy junior-school days. I suppose in a way I should have expected such a blaze, for I recalled all our wooden desks and seats. And the books — all those beautiful books which I read as a child. And then there was Rocker, for I'm sure he was still there: Rocker was a huge rocking-horse, all made of wood. I suddenly shivered at the very thought of it all burning.

As we arrived, so did one of the fire-engines. The firemen quickly went into action, concentrating on controlling the blaze. How I admired these men, who fought gallantly against all odds, sedulous to achieve results.

We continued driving up Kingsmead Street, but very slowly now, for the road surface was strewn with all sorts of rubble, and so I had time to glance at the fine old house where I was born. It had taken a hiding too, but nevertheless it still stood there in all its stately charm, as if in defiance of Jerry's determination to destroy.

In the middle of Kingsmead Street was a little lane, known to everyone as Cross Lane. It was a short cut up through to Monmouth Street, and very popular too. The lane consisted of little houses and two tiny shops, one of which was kept by a general dealer, open at all times. The other shop was always my favourite, especially when I was a child. Its owners were middle-aged, and a most devoted couple they appeared to be. They didn't sell a lot, but as a girl I had often bought their second-hand comics and books. The little shop window was kept stacked high with bundles of firewood and jars of pickled onions — an unusual combination I know, yet I was sure the elderly couple made a living from their own resources.

It was this little lane that had taken the brunt of yet another attack; later we were told that 23 people had died in the Kingsmead area.

Parking the ambulance outside The Red Lion pub, we started making our way up the lane, and as we did so we were met with choking dust that seemed to linger in our nostrils; in fact the atmosphere was stifled with it. There wasn't a pathway — it had disappeared — and we could only pick our way over heavy stones and rubble. With the moon disappearing, we were obliged to use our torches.

Suddenly I heard voices — excitable voices. Then I heard a child crying, along with the bark from a dog. And now we were amongst these poor stunned people, and all trying to help each other.

Blankets from somewhere had been laid on a flat piece of ground and on these the injured were placed. Mr Penny and I went into action immediately, and with the light from our torches we administered first aid. We had to give priority to the more serious injuries by arresting haemorrhages, tending to broken limbs, and of course helping the unconscious.

I think I would have needed a dozen pair of hands to cope with a situation like that. However, we managed to struggle back down the lane with the injured, and we had to make several runs to the Royal United Hospital, which was about three miles away. Mr Penny drove admirably, with myself travelling with the casualties in the back of the ambulance.

I vividly remember one of these runs. We had four patients strapped to the bunks, and two lying on stretchers on the floor of the ambulance. All were greatly shocked, and I did my best to comfort those who were still conscious. But what answer could I give to one poor man, when he asked about his wife, and with tears streaming down his face he said, 'I feel sure she's dead.' I held his hand in mine, and maybe it was a blessing that he drifted into unconsciousness.

The Casualty department was on alert, and so on our arrival we were dealt with promptly. Then, when dawn came, glittering in its first light, I, like so many more, was deeply thankful.

I can recall our last journey to the hospital that early morning. Mr Penny, like myself, was all in, and three little words could sum it all up: tired, dirty and hungry. And how grateful we were to the little nurse who brought us mugs of tea. We sat in the reception area. Smoking was prohibited, of course, yet an exception was made when the Casualty Sister said, 'You may have a smoke if you wish.' Being a non-smoker, I was content to sip my tea, while Mr Penny relished the fact that he was able to have a few puffs on his pipe.

To watch him resting back in his seat, inhaling the fragrant tobacco, gave me some kind of stimulation, which gave an added sense of accomplishment to our night's duty. While we sat there we heard the 'all clear' go, and I don't know exactly what came over me, but my eyes filled up with tears of emotion. It was a reaction, most probably. Whatever my feelings, our night's work was over, and we had survived, thank God.

Mr Penny, recognising my uneasiness, placed his pipe in his pocket and said, 'Time I took you home, young lady.'

I looked at him, and saw how very tired he was. 'Should I not report back at the depot first?'

'This time you have an excuse for not doing so,' he replied. 'Anyway, don't worry. I'll attend to things.'

I was pleased, and was glad when he drove me home. And when I jumped down off the ambulance, he said, 'For a young girl you did remarkably well.'

I smiled back at him and replied, 'I did well, Mr Penny, only because I was under your supervision and guidance.'

I walked slowly up the lane. Don't suppose I could have hurried even if I had tried. However, I was at least home.

The broken windows of our cottage were still covered with plywood, which had replaced the cardboard we used earlier, and when I opened the front door there to my surprise stood Alfie, holding up a lighted candle. When he saw me, he hysterically shouted out, 'Auntie Paul's home! Auntie Paul's home!'

The next thing was, Dad appeared, holding up yet another lighted candle, and when he saw me his face gladdened into a smile. 'You all right, Paul?'

I could see, even in the half-light, his expression of relief. 'I'm OK, Dad. Just tired.'

'It's been a rough night then,' said Dad.

Mum came out of the scullery. 'Oh, duck,' she said, 'I'm so glad to see you. We've only just come up from the Pitmans. There's no electricity, so I'm trying to cook breakfast on the gas stove.' Normally Mum did all her cooking by electric, so it was strange to see her at the gas stove. She was managing nicely, but I guessed she needed help, so slipping off my jacket I rolled up my sleeves and then washed my hands and arms under the cold tap; and sweet was the carbolic soap.

The bacon sizzled in the pan, and so it was, with candles flickering on the mantelpiece, we all sat down to breakfast. Had we not lost the windows previously, the daylight filtering through would have been most welcome. As it was, it was not until after breakfast that Dad took the plywood down, and how lovely it was when daylight streamed through, and with it the refreshing morning air.

Then Mum looked at me. 'Goodness gracious, duck, what a mess you are in.'

I knew only too well the state I was in, for one of my trouser legs had been ripped off at the bottom.

'Nell,' said Dad, 'what Paul needs now is a good bath.'

'I know,' exclaimed Mum. 'But what are we going to do for hot water?'

177

'No problem,' replied Dad. 'I'll put the copper fire on. The water will heat up in no time.'

So out came the tin bath, and with plenty of hot water and carbolic soap I enjoyed a luxurious dip in front of the fire. Mum, always interested in our well-being, saw to it that a clean nightie was airing at the fireside.

Then came a knock on the kitchen door, with Rob calling out, 'Will you be long, Quinner?'

'Won't be a minute,' I answered.

How refreshed I felt. It was as if all my tiredness had left me, but I had to be sensible and go to bed, for it was necessary that I should get a good sleep. I had a long day yet ahead of me, and I would be on duty again that very night.

Dad, being on a late turn, was pottering about in the garden, but just as I was about to go upstairs, he came into the kitchen.

'Not in bed yet, our Paul?'

'Just making tracks,' I replied.

'Did you have many casualties last night?'

'Afraid so,' I answered. 'Kingsmead School has had it, Dad, and so has little Cross Lane too.'

'Damn shame,' exclaimed Dad.

Now it was Mum who intervened. 'Time you were up in bed, duck.'

I kissed them both tenderly, knowing that I had the best folk in the world to love and care for me, as they both did. I crawled into my feather bed, and to me it was heaven. How snug I was. I said my prayers, remembering all those who suffered through the perils of war.

Witnessing so much suffering, I was already feeling much older than I really was; and suddenly I connected my feelings and thoughts together. I just thought, what a wonderful way it would be to die, just as I was feeling at that moment: comfortable, relaxed, and at peace.

I knew no more until I was awakened by the sound of someone whistling as they came up the lane, and the next thing I heard was something coming through the letter-box. The whistler must obviously have been the postman.

Slipping on my dressing-gown and slippers I went downstairs, and there amongst other letters was a letter from Jim. Quickly I opened up the envelope and read; by this time, I was sitting on the stairs.

Jim said he was well, and hoped I was the same. Maybe, I thought, I could write him a few lines before going off to work, but alas, the clock in the kitchen told me that it was almost 1 p.m.

Straightaway I went upstairs to dress, and when I returned downstairs there was Mum in the scullery, busy pressing my uniform. The children were elsewhere with Dad.

'Hello,' she said. 'Had a good sleep?'

'Rather,' I replied. 'Feel as fit as a fiddle now, Mum. Oh Mum, you shouldn't have bothered with ironing.'

'It needed doing,' said Mum, and in fact she was right. I really appreciated what she had done, for even my tunic had been pressed, and with it came another clean white blouse.

I gave Mum a quick kiss on the forehead. 'Thanks, Mum.'

'Well I knew you hadn't time, so I just got on with it. Anyway, love, put a light underneath the pan, we'll have some dinner together.'

Our meal had already been cooked and only needed warming up, hence the delicious aroma coming from it, and my salivary glands came into action immediately. 'Mmm,' I said. 'Something smells good.'

'Just a shank of ham, plus the trimmings,' said Mum.

I was hungry, so I enjoyed my dinner, but said no to a second helping. Soon it was time for me to go, and I reminded Mum that I would again be on Civil Defence duty after 10 p.m. 'But it'll be my last night for the week,' I told her.

'I hope then, please God, you have a quiet night.'

So, kissing Mum, I ran down to the corner of the lane, waved, and then hurried along the top road.

That particular afternoon was simply gorgeous: well it was April, and the sun had some warmth in it. I felt fit, and walking briskly I overtook others walking down the hill. But, as I got nearer to the town centre, everything started to change. I saw fine old buildings and houses which had crumbled to the ground, and people were still trying to salvage what they could. There were numerous gangs of men trying hard to tidy up the mess, but the scars of the blitz were prominent, the war showing its ugliness everywhere.

I noticed too, many members of the Women's Voluntary Service in action. I called them the ladies in green, for their basic outfit was dark green in colour, and they often wore attractive lime-green blouses. Their task was providing for the needs of the blitzed, organising soup kitchens, and distributing wearing apparel to the needy. In a few simple words, they fed and clothed all who required their help. Such an organisation was always more than welcome, and really they did a superb job.

Opposite the Pierrepont Garage was St John's church, where Jim would go when he was in Bath, and when I looked up at the big clock, which always kept accurate time, it told me it was only

17 minutes to 2 o'clock. As a result I had time to go into this very fine old church. I opened the big wooden door and stepped inside. I was a little hesitant. After all, it was my first visit to a Catholic church, so walking a little way up the middle aisle, I stopped and then knelt in prayer. I was aware of the peace and serenity that surrounded me.

The soft candles flickered on the altar. Then I saw the light penetrating the colourful glass windows. I felt alone with God. I felt as if my soul needed something like this, to overcome the anxieties that still remained within me. And I was thankful too, thankful that my family and I had come through the past two nights without any harm. I remembered also those unfortunate people who had undergone suffering. I now got off my knees and sat on the seat behind me. I gazed once again on the beautiful altar, which gave me an authentic feeling of repose and assurance.

Getting up, I moved slowly towards the door, and there I met a very young nun, who gave me a most beautiful smile; it was almost a smile from an angel.

Once again I was out in the street, amongst the hustle and bustle, whereupon I hurried over to the garage, and on approaching the forecourt I noticed that the little wall that divided us from the public footpath was completely flattened. And that wasn't all, for part of the back of the garage was missing, the result most probably of the blast from a bomb. Subsequently someone had worked hard, tidying up the big stones that had fallen, and the rubble had been swept up into neat piles.

It was then that I noticed all the cars. Not one had escaped from a thick covering of lime dust, and I could see I was in for a busy time, for we couldn't possibly let the cars go out in such a state.

Mr Griffin then came on the scene, and trying hard to brave a smile, he said, 'We are in a bit of a mess, Miss.'

'Yes, I can see,' I answered. 'Still, I'm sure we'll have the cars cleaned up in no time.' Optimistic as I was, I knew we had quite a job on.

Young Freddie, like myself, started at 2 p.m., so I kept him on serving petrol while I tackled the job of cleaning the cars. I managed to get hold of a soft-haired hand brush, which I used to sweep the thick dust off the cars, one by one; some, of course, were worse than others. Getting through about fifty cars was no picnic; I succeeded, but I must admit that when it came to the last one I was pleased.

I must have been a glutton for work, for I suggested to Mr Griffin that I should take the cars one at a time on to the forecourt, and give them a quick hose down.

'Good thinking,' said Mr Griffin. 'But I insist I help you.' So, as fast as Mr Griffin came out with each car, I went into action with the hose-pipe.

At times I got mixed up with the cars coming in for petrol, and I overheard one customer remark, 'Must you really give car washes now?'

I had no time to explain to anyone exactly what I was doing, and I just kept on hosing down as fast as I could. Neither was I a pretty sight, wearing a pair of men's wellington boots which were almost three sizes too big for me. When Mr Griffin finally brought the last car on to the forecourt I wasn't sorry, and I was glad to take off those very heavy boots. Meanwhile Miss Clarke kindly brought us out tea and biscuits. So all went well. The cars looked splendid, all shining from the dampness of the water.

Later on, well past tea-time, we again became extremely busy on the petrol pumps, and I wondered if folk could be thinking that there would be yet another blitz on Bath. I suppose people wanted to take precautionary measures, enabling them to make a quick exit, should it be necessary.

Myself, I thought it impossible that we should have another night of severe bombing; yet who was I to predict what might or might not happen? Being optimistically minded, I thought no more about it.

The petrol sales then declined a bit, so I took the opportunity of sending Freddie up to the fish-and-chip shop, and when he came back we sat eating our meal out of the newspapers. I observed that Freddie looked tired. Well, the poor lad worked hard on the pumps, and deserved all the tips he got. Actually I could still smell petrol lingering on his clothes.

I too was feeling a bit tired, but as it was coming up to 9 p.m. I knew we hadn't long to go before finishing. Almost prompt at 9 o'clock many of the customers came in for their cars, and nearly all remarked how clean they were; so much so that I was given many good tips, and in appreciation I gladly shared them with Freddie, who had worked equally as hard as myself.

It was 15 minutes to 10 o'clock when I sent Freddie home, and I'm sure he was happy at the thought of the many silver coins jingling in his pockets.

All was quiet, so, quickly taking off my boiler suit, I was soon in my Civil Defence uniform. And it was a strange thing — I was so tired, yet I was ready for whatever the night had in store for me.

Closing the big garage doors, I stepped out into the brilliant moonlight, and looking up at the clear sky I thought how peaceful it all looked, with the twinkling of the stars making a serene setting. How could anyone possibly disturb such a beautiful night?

I intended just strolling around to the depot, but to my surprise the warning siren went, so I immediately hurried my steps. Once again Jerry was coming, and sooner than ever tonight, I thought.

Immediately I was engaged in meditation, this time of home. Dad would have reached home by now, and if he was lucky he might just have finished his supper. My concern was that everyone would make their way to the Pitmans, where there was adequate safety.

Reaching the depot, I found the usual activity going on, but, in spite of it all, hot cups of tea were being passed around; with a cup in my hand, I looked at the duty board.

Ah, here it was. Driver Miss Quintin — Attendant Mr Penny. How lucky could I be? I sipped my tea quicker, delighted to think that I would be on duty with Mr Penny once again, and when I did find him, he was busy checking first-aid equipment. He told me that the ambulance we were supposed to take out had developed a nasty leak in its radiator, so we had no alternative but to take Old Jane. This I didn't mind, for I knew Old Jane, in spite of her characteristic features. Anyway I was confident I could drive her well, for once her ancient engine got started she was capable of doing her stuff. I knew too that she would splutter and vibrate, but one could easily adapt oneself to the situation, and so drive accordingly.

'We'll need plenty of blankets, Miss,' said Mr Penny.

'OK, Mr Penny, I'll fetch some.' So up the wooden ladder into the loft I went, where all surplus stock was kept. I picked up the blankets at random until my arms were full. I carried them back down the ladder, and on reaching Mr Penny, I said, 'Might as well put these blankets straightaway in the back of the ambulance.'

'Righto,' he replied.

I came outside, where all the ambulances were parked in herring-bone positions, ready for moving out. And there she stood, Old Jane herself, at the very end of the fleet of ambulances.

I looked upon her with respect. True, there was nothing modern about her at all, and yet she stood out from the rest. Oh yes, she was quite different. She had in fact the look of a most dignified old lady, with all her brasses shining in the moonlight, and to me she was something very special, for had I not learnt to drive with her? Knowing that she had done more service than the rest, I felt privileged just to ride in her.

I placed the blankets on the floor of the ambulance, and was just about to close the tail-doors when I heard above me the old familiar drone of enemy aircraft approaching. Our unwelcome visitors had arrived.

Usually on instinct I would have hurried inside, but instead I stayed put, looking up into the sky. Maybe I felt defiant, or curious as to what I might see; certainly I was far from feeling brave, because my spine felt chilled.

It was through the white clouds that I caught a glimpse of them. I counted three in all. They were right above me now, and I wondered what they would do next. Curiosity overcame me, and I willed myself into waiting and watching. Must be reconnaissance planes, I thought, or else by now they would have dropped bombs. But there were no bombs. Instead, lots and lots of pinky coloured flares came floating down from the heavens, burning even brighter than the moonlight.

Then came the drone of more aircraft. These would be the blighters who meant business, and I began to feel my heart beating. I knew now I must take cover inside, whereupon I rejoined Mr Penny and the others.

'They've already dropped flares on us,' I gasped.

A man nearby spoke. 'Damned Huns. I suppose we'll be in for the grand finale tonight.'

No sooner had he spoken than we heard thuds, which vibrated around us.

I looked at Mr Penny and said, 'Shall I go up for the remainder of the blankets?'

'I would,' he answered.

I almost raced up the wooden stairs, gathering up another armful of blankets, and then deposited them beside Mr Penny.

'Just leave 'em here, Miss, till we goes out.'

Meanwhile, as was expected, calls started coming in, and so, crew by crew, our colleagues were now disappearing. Soon we were the only ones remaining, and we stood and waited, myself feeling a little apprehensive.

Then came a light flashing on the switchboard. 'This will be for us,' remarked Mr Penny.

We then heard our male operator reply with, 'Yes, yes,' and at the same time he was writing something down on the pad in front of him. He then swung around on his swivel chair.

'There's been a direct hit on a shelter, Mr Penny.' And he handed him a note of the location.

'Right,' answered Mr Penny, 'we're on our way.' He picked up the blankets and almost flew out of the door, with me following, and run we did across to Old Jane, who looked quite forlorn just standing there on her own.

'Jump in, Miss, I'll give her the handle.' This way I knew was a sure start, and with my foot slightly touching the throttle Mr Penny immediately got her going, with her engine as fresh as a daisy.

I drove slowly out of the depot, but gained more speed on my journey. The only traffic we met were fire-engines, special vans, and of course our own ambulances. But everywhere, even in so short a time, we registered only appalling conditions.

Finally we reached our destination, only to find wardens struggling to pull bodies out of the crumbling debris; in fact there was very little of the shelter left, and I noticed that many of the bodies were wearing the uniform of special constables.

Mr Penny jumped down from the ambulance and I went to follow him, but he told me to remain in the cab.

He returned, saying, 'I'm afraid we can't do anything here.' I knew what Mr Penny meant: we had no casualties, only bodies, and many mutilated at that. It was tragic. No one had survived, and we wondered why on earth all these special constables were together. No doubt some sort of inquiry would be set up later, but that was outside our line of duty. All we could do was to make our way back to the depot.

I was driving through streets littered with rubble, broken glass and choking dust, which was coming up through the cracks in Old Jane. As we approached the depot, we were flagged down by one of our colleagues. 'Can you help us out here? We need your help badly.' Two houses had been hit together, and the majority of people that were pulled out needed medical attention. And, in the midst of all the upheaval, more planes came over, and more bombs were dropped on us. It was a nightmare, but we concentrated on those who were badly hurt, getting them to hospital as quickly as possible.

One of our journeys was distinctly out of the ordinary, for our patient was an expectant mother who had already started labour. Mr Penny gave me three taps at the back of the cab: this was the signal for an emergency stop, so pulling in to the side of the road I jumped out and hurried to the rear of the ambulance. When I opened up one of the tail-doors I realised why I had had to make an emergency stop, for it was obvious that a baby was going to be born in the ambulance. But I could see that Mr Penny had everything under control.

'Miss,' he said, 'in the cab, on the upper shelf, just above the driver's seat, you'll find a box marked "Sterile". I'll be needing it.'

Quickly I found the box, and gently I handed it to Mr Penny. Now inside Old Jane, I was watching something miraculous. A supernatural event, or that's what it appeared to me, at that particular time. For here was Mr Penny, who with great confidence was bringing a little baby into the world, with all the practical ability that he possessed. I felt honoured indeed to be a witness to this remarkable event.

Mr Penny's dexterity led to a happy ending, when the cries from a little baby girl echoed inside Old Jane. Then Mr Penny handed me a blanket saying, 'Put the little nipper into it, Miss.'

Carefully I wrapped the new-born infant into the blanket, and caressed it close to me; then, with Mr Penny's help, I got into a sitting position alongside the mother, who I noticed was perspiring heavily.

'Stay where you be, Miss, I'll make for Maternity.'

On arrival at Maternity, almost everyone came to help. The mother of the child was taken to a special cubicle, and I handed over my little gem to a nurse.

Sister then called Mr Penny and me into her office. 'Splendid delivery! I congratulate you both.'

'Oh, um, it's Mr Penny here who should have the praise, ' I said, 'for I've never experienced seeing a birth before.'

A smile came over the Sister's face. 'You are young,' she said. 'But quite capable, I'm sure, should a similar situation arise.' After she had spoken, she summoned a maid to bring us a cup of tea.

'You'll excuse us if we appear to be in a hurry, Sister,' said Mr Penny, and so the understanding Sister added more milk to our tea. We drank up quickly, and then departed from Sister's office.

On the way back to town, there was still no ease-up from Jerry, who persisted in tormenting us. The bombs being dropped were many, for we experienced constant thudding and vibrations. Maybe they really did intend to flatten us to the ground, as Lord Haw Haw had said. If only there could be a pause, but alas, there wasn't.

The constant bombardments were clearly generating chaos, and when we got back to the depot Mr Wright conveyed to us — that is, those of us who still remained at the depot — that we remained on duty only of our own free will. But it was evident that we were all volunteers, and all of us were for the same cause; our vocation was making sure that casualties received transportation for further medical treatment. The amazing thing was, no one panicked; everyone was perhaps frightened, like I was at times, but we could do no more except soldier on.

More and more calls just poured in from everywhere. The thing was, how could we possibly cope with so many? The only solution was to combine the calls together, and have one ambulance deal with several cases in succession, for we had no means of contacting crews once they left the depot. So it wasn't easy, and we were up against all odds.

We faced many interruptions when trying to reach a destination, giving rise to bustle and confusion, and I'm afraid it wasn't only problems of transport that we became involved with; we had to face the task of keeping control and giving assurance and consolation to all kinds of people. For instance, one dear old lady we came upon was very stubborn, and insisted that she was going to stay put and remain in her little house, which had been made very unsafe by explosions.

'Do what you like,' she stammered, 'but I'll not budge.'

I tried hard to convince the dear old soul. I told her that her evacuation would merely be on a temporary basis, and that she would return to her home in the near future. I don't really know how I succeeded in convincing her, but, in this case, I did win. Mark you, she only agreed to be evacuated on certain conditions, namely if her cat and budgerigar could go with her. And so we put this dear old lady in the care of welfare, plus of course the cat and the bird.

I must say that, on the whole, the morale of the people stood up well in spite of everything. After all, there could be nothing more heart-breaking than seeing one's home destroyed, unless of course it was to lose someone close. If it was only material things that were destroyed, it wouldn't much matter, but it was the extinction of life itself which, to innocent folk, made war so horrible.

And so through the long night, Mr Penny and I, like so many more, toiled away, administering of our very best. It's strange, too, how fate that night stepped in for us, and pulled us through.

We were proceeding to a call from Twerton when we got a puncture. We had to stop, jack up Old Jane, and put the spare on; this delay cost us five minutes at least, but it surely saved our lives. Had we not stopped, we would have been on a stretch of road that was hit by a land-mine. We had to make a detour to arrive at our destination because of damage to the road.

Myself I was getting accustomed to the unfamilar noises and explosions. We were issued with ear-plugs, but I would never use them; I preferred to hear what was going on.

Once again we found ourselves back at St Martin's Hospital with more casualties. Someone gave us each a mug of cocoa, which Mr Penny and I appreciated and enjoyed. Then, when we were almost ready to leave the hospital, one of the porters called out, 'I say there. Be you the ones that delivered the little 'un?'

'That's right,' replied Mr Penny.

'Well 'ee've to go to Maternity.'

'Nothing wrong, I hope?' said Mr Penny.

'Nothing bain't wrong. It's just the mother, she be wanting to see you both!'

'Well, I suppose we best pop in for a minute,' said Mr Penny. 'Come on, Miss.'

We walked along to the Maternity wing. It wasn't necessary for any introduction, for the cries from newly born babies echoed in our ears. To me, it certainly eased this night of frustration. When we reached the swing doors of the ward itself, we were confronted with a Staff Nurse, who gave us rather a suspicious look. After all, we both looked in a mess, and arriving in the early hours of the morning was not appropriate for visitors. However, Sister herself came on the scene. She smiled and said, 'Hello. Have you come to see Mrs Marsden? She's just in the side ward. Please follow me.'

Sister almost marched us up to Mrs Marsden's bedside. The dear lady looked astonishingly well, and when she saw us her face broadened into a smile of gratitude. 'So pleased you came,' she said.

As one could imagine, we were not very presentable, our uniforms being dirty and torn — hardly a credit for the Civil Defence.

Mrs Marsden spoke: 'I just want to thank you both for what you did. And I appreciate all the help you gave me.'

'A little girl, wasn't it?' I said.

'Yes dear,' she replied. 'Now then, how would you like to give my daughter a name?'

I think I was astonished at this request, yet I replied quite freely. 'I would like that very much.'

By this time, Mr Penny was just looking on, intrigued perhaps with our conversation. Then, smiling at him, I remarked, 'Shall we call her Jane?'

'Why that's a lovely name,' said Mrs Marsden. So Jane Marsden it was, named truly after her birthplace, even if it was only the inside of an old ambulance. But let's say a special ambulance, for she was beyond the usual to me.

Sister then popped her head in the doorway, a slight reminder that it was time for us to go. So, saying farewell to Mrs Marsden, we left Maternity, and on approaching Old Jane, a flood of emotion came over me, for what better combination than a dignified old lady of an ambulance and the sweet newly born.

Tears moistened my eyes. The tiredness was prevailing; however, the aroma from Mr Penny's pipe was giving me a new kind of refreshment, so as we made our way back to the depot the stimulus that was within me gave rise to calm.

I drove round the corner into James Street, and what we saw greatly shocked us both. I myself applied the brakes abruptly, for our own depot was on fire, with flames almost leaping through what remained of the window frames.

'Oh my God!' were Mr Penny's words.

Almost together, we both jumped down from the ambulance and then automatically started running towards the depot, but we were soon stopped by a fireman shouting, 'It's no good! You can't get through!'

Again I saw these brave men, working so hard, desperately trying to control the blaze.

Then Mr Penny spoke to another fireman. 'Anyone hurt?'

'Nothing serious,' replied the fireman. 'Just a few sustained minor injuries.' The same fireman, his helmet lifted, was scratching his head. 'Can't understand this bloody blaze,' he said. 'No known report of a bomb being dropped here. So it's a damn mystery how it's got alight.'

I knew, of course, that there would have to be some explanation, but it was a relief to both Mr Penny and myself to know that there were no serious injuries sustained to any of our colleagues.

Then yet another voice shouted at us, this time from a special constable. 'Be you Mr Penny?'

'Yes.'

'I got a message for you.' With this, Mr Penny was handed a dirty old piece of paper, which he read and then handed over to me. It read as follows:

To Bill Penny
Sending me up to hospital for check-up.
Take over Bill. Best of luck —
A. Wright

I knew, like Mr Penny did, that we were in fact in one hell of a catastrophe, for to start with, we had no base to operate from. So our first problem was how to get reorganised.

There was one thing — I had great faith in Mr Penny, and if anyone could find a way through, he would. His calmness in the face of our predicament gave him power to operate immediately.

'Miss, fetch me some white chalk out of the cab.'

I obeyed immediately, running back to Old Jane, and shining my torch inside the cab. I came across some chalk, and hurried back with it. Meanwhile, in my absence, Mr Penny had retrieved a large piece of slate. I guessed what he would do next: he was going to write a message on the slate, and so it was. In large block letters he wrote:

'To all personnel — please report to police station.'

Then Mr Penny secured the slate by packing it with stones, so that it was made visible to all. 'Now we'll make our own way up to the police station,' he said. Evidently he had ideas of organising an operation from the main police station, so that was where we went next.

The police headquarters were in a large building situated opposite the Abbey. Beside it stood an archway, which we found closed with two wrought-iron gates; these in turn led to a massive courtyard, ideal for parking our ambulances.

But first it was necessary to see the Police Superintendent. He could grant us the necessary permission, that was if it went through the proper channels. An introductory procedure was inevitable, and hence we were now standing in front of a Sergeant's desk.

The Sergeant came forward, as was expected. Then, looking at Mr Penny, he said, 'What can I do for you?' He was eyeing us up most carefully, for to say the least we both looked in a state of untidiness.

'If it's convenient, I would like to see the Superintendent, please.'

'Um,' said the Sergeant. 'He's a very busy man at the moment. But I'll try and find him for you. It's been a damn rough night for us all.'

I could never agree more.

The Sergeant went away, and after several minutes he returned saying, 'Follow me, please.'

'Shall I come with you, Mr Penny?'

'Might as well,' he replied.

So, with the Sergeant leading the way, we were ushered into a large office, and there seated at a desk was the man we wanted to see, the prominent figure of the Superintendent. I noticed that the poor man looked awfully tired, yet his eyes were fixed upon us, and I was surprised when Mr Penny spoke first.

'Personnel of the Civil Defence, Sir. I'm here to see if you can help us.'

'Do be seated,' said the Superindentent, and I could tell he was somewhat agitated. I dare say the activities of the night had brought him problems too. 'In what way do you require my help?'

'In detail, Sir, our depot has been gutted by fire, and what we desperately need now is some sort of a base from which to operate.'

'Well now,' said the Superintendent, who was rubbing his chin. 'As you know, a request such as this should be dealt with well above my level. Presuming, of course, you need our station to operate from.'

Mr Penny then nodded.

'Well now,' said the Superintendent, 'I cannot refuse to give you assistance. And under the circumstances, and in view of the importance of your job, which is so vital to the community, I don't see why you shouldn't park your ambulances in the courtyard. And also, you'll be given an office, where you'll take up assignment.'

'I'm very grateful to you, Sir,' said Mr Penny.

'You must understand that I can only grant your request on condition that it remains on an emergency temporary basis.'

This was certainly a circumlocution, but in all the services there is always the old familiar red tape. However, we had got what we wanted, a base to operate from, even if it was only temporary.

The Superintendent then rang a bell on his desk, and on doing so he looked at me and smiled. Meanwhile, Mr Penny once again thanked the man for his help.

The next thing, the Sergeant appeared.

'Sergeant,' said the Superintendent, 'be good enough to arrange some refreshment for our visitors' — meaning us, of course. 'Also, show them office number eight. Our friends here will occupy it until further notice.'

'Yes, Sir,' replied the Sergeant.

We then left the Superintendent at his desk and followed the Sergeant to a canteen, where a few policemen were dining and drinking cups of tea. We proceeded up to the counter, where the Sergeant spoke to a waitress. 'Guv'nor's request — two good breakfasts, Ada, and a pot of tea.' He turned to us. 'I'll leave you then. And when you have finished, come back and see me at the desk.'

All this hospitality was unexpected, but appreciated just the same. So Mr Penny thanked him, and then he left us.

It was while we waited at the table that I suddenly felt like an interloper and imagined that all eyes were upon us. However, Ada soon arrived with a pot of tea, and a breakfast that was most appetising. We both must have been hungry, for we left nothing on our plates.

'Feel better now, Miss?'

'Yes, thank you, Mr Penny.'

'Come on then.' We saw the Sergeant, who when confronted was busy writing at his desk, but he called out to a young policeman, who escorted us to No. 8 office.

Quite a large office it was, with two desks in it, having two separate outside phones. I could see Mr Penny was pleased with his findings, for he remarked, 'This will do us nicely. Thank you, Constable.'

Immediately Mr Penny started making telephone calls, trying to locate colleagues and telling them of our new location, so it was not surprising when we started to receive calls from personnel of the Civil Defence. We were able to give them careful instructions regarding the parking of their vehicles, and a reminder that we were operating from No. 8 office in the main police station. The repeated instruction we gave was, 'Pass the information around.'

I was amazed at the speed of our organising. Our only concern was that we were giving the police switchboard operator extra work to do, but he was a cheerful fellow and under the circumstances I'm sure he didn't mind.

I remained with Mr Penny, receiving and answering calls. Then, at 20 minutes past 6 o'clock, the 'all clear' went. Mr Penny looked across from his desk. 'It's all over, Miss.' The poor man, how tired he looked, and if any man deserved gratitude from us all, it was him.

I knew that everyone in Bath must have been relieved to hear the sirens blowing, for the night had been long and arduous. Those of us who escaped injury had something to be thankful for.

I held my head in my hands, and silently prayed; and my prayers must have got mixed up with my tiredness, for quite innocently I dozed into sleep, due purely to exhaustion, I suppose. I was awakened by the aroma coming from Mr Penny's pipe, and I suddenly realised what had happened to me and felt somewhat embarrassed. 'Oh dear,' I gasped. 'Must have dozed over.'

'Not to worry,' said Mr Penny. 'Anyway, it'll have done you good to have closed your eyes for five minutes.'

Another policeman then entered our office, carrying a tray with two mugs of tea on it. 'Good morning,' he said. 'Sarge asked me to bring you in some tea.'

'Thank you,' said Mr Penny. 'And thank the Sergeant too.'

I thought the tea that morning was the very essence of life, for it suddenly gave me a new kind of vigour; all I needed now was to splash my face in cold water, which I did, reviving me to the full.

Back in the office, Mr Penny decided it was time we went home. 'I'll run you up home, Miss,' he said. This gladdened me, for now I was anxious about my family.

Mr Penny dropped me off along the top road, and I then started hurrying towards home. I first noticed Dad's bus parked in its usual place, alongside the wall. It was OK. So far, so good. But when I turned the corner into the lane, I'm sure my heart missed a beat, for there outside our cottage stood Dad talking to a special constable. I immediately knew there was something wrong. Then, as I got closer, the reality of things gave me an answer. I trembled at what I saw, for our home had been hit badly by a bomb. The adjoining cottage had escaped a little, but the scars of blasting were visible there too.

I ran into Dad's arms. 'Oh Dad!' I spluttered out. 'Are you all OK?'

'We are all safe, Paul. And thank God you are all right.'

Getting the initial shock over, I looked through the iron bars of the basement window. It appeared that the whole inside of our little cottage was nothing else but a shambles. I could see that part of the upstairs had fallen through, conglomerating together our bedding, clothing, the lot.

Quietly I spoke. 'Has Mum seen all this?'

'Afraid so. We all came up from the Pitmans together. It was lucky, Paul, that we had their sanctuary to go to in the night. Unfortunately at the moment we cannot do anything,' said Dad. 'So Mum and the children have returned to the Pitmans.'

'And Rob?' I said.

'He's managed to go to work. Anyway, Paul, you go down to the Pitmans, see Mum and the children. They'll be so pleased to see you. You might even get a cup of tea.'

'I'll go down later, Dad, but for the moment I'm staying with you.'

The special constable left us. Dad and I were alone, and my heart was heavy at seeing our home in such a state. I wondered to myself how on earth we were going to cope in sorting everything out — but all this sorting out was precisely what Dad and I had in mind.

We went into the house, stepping over this and that, and we reached what remained of the kitchen.

Then we heard something.

It was if someone was brushing past the nut bushes, which were to the right of the window. Dad's reaction was to place his finger to his lips.

I wanted to speak, but dare not.

'Stay where you are,' whispered Dad, with which he cautiously climbed out through the broken window-frame, the back door being blocked. I stood rigid, expecting anything to happen.

I then caught a glimpse of a man in grey, a grey-coloured uniform, which just slumped forward.

Then the startled cry of Dad's voice echoed in my ears. 'Paul, quick!'

I almost leapt through the window-frame after him, and there, lying at Dad's feet, was the figure in grey of a German airman.

'Poor devil,' exclaimed Dad, for now the airman was lying on his back, unconscious, with blood oozing out of his mouth.

'Golly!' I said. 'He looks in a bad way. Dad, help me turn him on his side.' I looked closer at him, and noticed how young he was; he was almost a boy, with blond curls falling over his forehead and a blood-stained uniform.

'He must have bailed out,' said Dad. 'But funny, no signs of a parachute, and he couldn't have walked far in his state. What we going to go with him, Paul?'

'Well Dad, if we don't get him to hospital quickly, he's going to die.'

I knew Dad was like myself, and that our human instinct would make us act with one accord. And this young man, enemy though he was, we just couldn't allow him to die.

The only solution we could come to was take him to the Royal United Hospital, in Dad's bus. So Dad and I carried the young man down the lane, Dad with his arms underneath his armpits, while I supported his legs. He wasn't heavy really, but by the time we reached Dad's bus we knew we weren't carrying feathers.

This young man was in dire need of medical attention, and we had to show a little mercy, and transport him to hospital as quick as possible, so we put him carefully down in the gangway of the bus. I thought how pathetic he looked, just lying there. I suppose for him, unconsciousness was a blessing in disguise, for he knew not what was going on.

Truly I felt sympathetic towards this young airman. Was it possible I was becoming soft, actually feeling sorry for the enemy? But perhaps we should always remember that the Germans saw us as their enemy too. And in God's eyes, were we not all members of the same family, fighting against each other? It sometimes seemed as if both sides were prepared to sacrifice everything, simply to destroy one another.

'I'll stay with him Dad,' I said, 'for fear he may roll underneath the seats.'

'OK, Paul. But holler, should he come around.' But I knew this to be very unnecessary, for the young man was too far gone. Anyway, Dad started up his bus, and we were on our way.

In normal times, seeing a local transport bus in the hospital grounds would be out of the ordinary, but at this particular moment no one took any notice of us as we drove quickly up to Casualty.

Nurses, some wearing cloaks, were darting about everywhere, and not one even acknowledged us. Why should they? Little did they know we had a casualty on the bus, and certainly a special one too. For this was war, where the unnatural was happening all the time.

Anyway, when Dad stopped his bus, I jumped out first, and made my way to Casualty, whereupon I met a Staff Nurse.

'I have an emergency case for you,' I exclaimed.

Suddenly two porters came to my assistance, pushing a bed trolley, and when they got outside they were surprised not to see an ambulance. A bus belonging to the Bath Tramways was distinctly unexpected. Dad opened up the door of the bus.

'A young man,' I said, 'is inside, and badly hurt.'

'Best get a stretcher,' one porter shouted to the other. And when on the bus, one of the porters shouted out, 'Gawd blimey! A bleeding Jerry!' A remark which was quite appropriate to their findings. Then one of the porters looked at Dad. 'Where in hell did you find this one?'

Dad and I remained silent; it was if we wanted to safeguard anything personal belonging to the young man. And so he was wheeled inside, while I followed as far as a cubicle, where he was taken in for examination by a doctor.

I approached the Staff Nurse again. 'Not much good in my staying, is there?'

'Not really,' she answered.

'Anyway,' I said, 'should you require any further information, I'm attached to the Civil Defence, now operating from number eight office at Bath main police station.'

'I'll make a note of that,' said Staff. 'And best I have your name.' After she had taken my particulars, I thanked her, and then left the hospital to rejoin Dad, who was now sitting at the wheel of his bus.

'Everything all right, Paul?'

'Everything is OK, Dad. He stands a fifty-fifty chance of recovery.'

'But he'll automatically become a prisoner of war,' said Dad.

I was now sitting beside Dad as he drove the bus home, and it indeed was a beautiful morning, following one hell of a night. I then said to Dad, 'Won't it be lovely when it's all over?'

Dad gave me a quick glance. 'Not out of the woods yet.'

I knew exactly what he meant, for from now until the termination of war the uncertainty of surviving would always be with us.

Dad parked his bus in the usual place, and then we almost strolled along the top road into the lane.

Turning the corner, we were surprised to see so many people, all of whom appeared in deep conversation. I then noticed Mum, together with Alfie and Iris, and when she saw me tears filled her eyes. I hoped they were tears of joy at seeing me, and not tears of grief at the outcome of our home, but I guess it was a mixture of emotions.

Amongst the assembly of people stood a man with a brief-case tucked underneath his arm, and who looked very official. I then heard him speak to Dad. 'It's Mr Quintin, isn't it? Must introduce myself. I'm Mr Munro, from the local district housing department.' He stretched out his hand for a handshake from Dad. 'So sorry about all this,' he said, 'but the situation as it is will mean you'll all have to be evacuated. Unfortunately we cannot put you all together. This problem has worsened, of course, owing to so many being blitzed, and needing suitable accommodation. However,' went on Mr Munro, 'I can assure you that the best of accommodation will be made available for your wife and family.'

Then Dad spoke, looking at Mr Munro. And with all sincerity he said, 'I very much appreciate your kindness for the offer you have made me. But, Mr Munro, I've decided to stay put.'

'But Mr Quintin,' gasped Mr Munro, 'it'll take ages to clear up all this mess. Besides, it could be unsafe. And who knows,' he went on, 'it may not be fit for habitation.' I could now sense that the little man was getting agitated, for he continued to speak in an excitable manner. 'You understand, Mr Quintin, I have a job to do, and responsible I am for the welfare of the people. So won't you take my advice and evacuate?'

Dad, now standing with his arms folded, was looking almost complacent when he said, 'Her walls are thick and strong, and what we do require now is a large tarpaulin.'

'Oh, this is ridiculous,' stormed Mr Munro.

'Well,' said Dad, 'if you can supply me with a large tarpaulin that will cover the roof, I'll be most grateful to you.'

Mr Munro was now looking at Dad as if he had lost an argument. 'You mean to stay then.'

Dad then looked at Mum. 'All right with you, Nell?'

Mum's smile was enough for Dad.

'Well, I suppose,' said Mr Munro, 'if you insist on staying, I can do no other but to help you all I can.' Now he was grinning at Dad. Then he said, 'OK, I'll arrange to have a tarpaulin sent up. But I can't promise you any labour to help out in all this salvage clearance.'

'Thank you, Mr Munro, but I think we'll manage.'

'You realise, Mr Quintin, you are in one hell of a mess. Still, I admire your spirit, so I'll do what I can for you.' With his final words spoken, he walked off down the lane.

I myself was left feeling proud of my Dad, and happy to think we wouldn't have to be parted. All of us, with hearts of lions, had decided that we would not and could not forsake the old homestead; we were determined that we would rebuild, even if it meant doing it with our bare hands.

Unfortunately Rob was already at work, and I would be following him at 2 p.m., but I had many hours spare in which to help Dad, and luckily too Dad was on a late start.

We had, of course, plenty of room to put things in the garden. We were aware of the disadvantage of treading all over Dad's flowers, yet we had one great thing in our favour: it was the weather, for the sunshine was already bringing in its warmth.

I immediately noticed the wire mesh on the chicken-run: although it was twisted up a bit, there was nothing abnormal about the chickens strutting about as usual, and waiting for something to eat.

'We must get them fed,' said Mum. 'But oh dear,' she exclaimed, we've got no water to mix up their bran mash.' So instead we resorted to throwing handfuls of maize into the run; they soon gobbled it up.

What a predicament we were in. No water, no gas, no electric. But somehow the good Lord provides, for suddenly Dad remembered that the copper was full of fresh water, and safeguarded by a heavy lid. Now we knew we were OK for the time being, at any rate.

I could see that Dad was studying up what to do first. He then called out to the children, and told them to go down the garden and collect all the firewood they could see.

'Grandad,' said Iris, 'are we going to make fires like the Red Indians?'

'Don't be daft,' replied Alfie. 'Indians only make smoky fires for signals.'

They scampered off down the garden, highly delighted at having such a task put upon them. What was more, they were off school — unofficially, of course, but I knew that this day they would have fun with their freedom. Mum, Dad, and myself had one objective in mind, to start and clear up and retrieve what we could from the debris.

I looked at our old ottoman: it was sticking its nose out of the dust and rubble. Its usual place was at the bottom of Mum and Dad's bed, and its only contents were blankets. This was, however, a good start, for we opened up the back door, which was hanging on its hinges, and dragged the ottoman out on to the lawn; on opening it up we found it was dust-free. We then spread out two of the largest blankets, and Mum suggested we should put our clothes and bedding on them. This unfortunately was not easy, for everything was covered with gritty creamy dust, from the stonework.

Bit by bit we salvaged what we could, yet really we were making no impression, for it was the remains of heavy furniture that was blocking us everywhere, and I knew it needed more than one pair of Dad's hands to shift it.

With the sun rising higher in the sky, the atmosphere was getting much warmer. This indeed was a blessing, for we were still in the month of April, and there was inevitably the possibility of showers. However, so far, so good.

The children by now had collected quite a lot of twigs, and Dad suggested that I should get a fire going; with a bit of luck, I might even make some tea. So, sending Alfie down to the farm for fresh milk, I set to. First I made a square of four big stones. Then, with the aid of some paper, I set the twigs alight, with all intentions of making a good fire. But alas, something went wrong, for all I got was whirling smoke.

Iris was looking on, as if she had an inkling that it was a Red-Indian fire after all. I was pleased when Dad came to the rescue; he removed one of the stones, which immediately gave an air vent, and soon bright flames shot up. 'Hooray!' shouts Iris. And again we were lucky: we kept coal in an outer shed, so by placing knobs on one at a time I soon had a super fire going. After finding a saucepan and cups, I managed to make everyone tea, so we all sat around the fire in the garden.

It was a most unusual picnic, and one I would forever remember, for we were more like raggle-taggle gypsies. Still, what odds, we were happy enough. I saw Dad was enjoying his home-made cigarette of the best St Julien tobacco, and even Mum was now enjoying the relaxation by herself having a smoke.

It was strange, but here we were in the middle of turmoil, yet peace and calm surrounded us. And, war or no war, the birds were still singing in the trees. Even our hens were still clucking around, not forgetting the occasional crow from the cock birds. To me it was a true example of the fact that Nature is indeed undefeatable, and dominant over all else.

The laughter from Rob made me look up quickly.

'What's brought you home, lad?' said Dad.

'Mr Griffin has closed the garage for the day to give us a chance to sort ourselves out,' said Rob. 'Mind you, even the garage is in a bit of a mess.'

What could escape last night, I thought. However, the satisfaction at having a day off from work gave me much relief. I was now free to help out all day.

I handed Rob a cup of tea. 'Sorry no sugar, Rob.' However, he gladly accepted it.

Now he was smiling. 'You know, Quinner, I couldn't help but see the funny side when I walked into the garden, and saw you all squatting around the fire like you were. You reminded me of refugees.'

'I suppose we are refugees of a sort, Rob.' Now, I thought, with Rob's help we might make some progress in moving some of the big stuff.

Our home contained good old strong furniture, which stood up to the knocking about it got, so piece by piece we retrieved it out from the debris. All of it was damaged, but, thankful to say, repairable. Soon, lined up in regimental style, there stood chests of drawers, dressing-tables with broken mirrors, and sideboards very scratched and marked; piled on top of them were pictures with broken frames and glass.

It all stood alongside the chicken-run, and looked like an open-air auction. We could not salvage many ornaments, because the majority of them were either chipped or smashed, and I know the little knick-knacks which Mum treasured were nearly all destroyed. But work we did, to retrieve what we could.

*   *   *

It must have been almost midday when Bill Harding called over the hedge. 'How you doing?'

'Getting through,' I answered.

'Well, I've to tell you, Paul, they're putting a soup kitchen on, or to that effect.'

'Oh!' I exclaimed. 'Where?'

'The Firs. First big house across the field. And we are all going down in a half-hour's time. Might as well join us.'

'Righto, Bill. Oh, and thanks for letting us know.'

'See you later then.'

And so it was that all of us from Primrose Hill assembled to walk across the fields to the big house called The Firs that lay off the roadway. A slow-moving procession of neighbours we were, as we walked down the lane and then down the slope that led across to the fields. We were all in deep conversation with each other, for there was so much to talk about — the previous night's happenings, plus the fact that Dad and I were said to have captured a German.

'Oh, but it wasn't like that at all,' I exclaimed.

All being together like this, it reminded me of the tribe of Israel, and how they must have felt. None of us were clean, and our clothes were all dirty and soiled. Yet I was full of admiration for the unity that existed among our group of neighbours; we were all in it together. Old Sam, the landlord of The Retreat, had his terrier at his heels, barking and enjoying the run in the grass. The children raced on ahead, and Ma Billett's son was trying to get a tune out of his mouth organ.

When we finally arrived in the driveway of the big house, I noticed two WVS vans parked alongside each other. So our ladies in green had once more come to the rescue. I already knew what a splendid organisation they were, and now we had come to depend on them also.

We must have all been hungry — I myself was ravenous — and as we entered the large front door the aroma of food hit my nostrils. In an orderly fashion we were ushered into the servants' quarters, where we were seated at long kitchen tables, and within minutes we were given bowls of hot vegetable soup. Everyone remarked how good it was. Then our next course consisted of corned beef, with plenty of mashed potato. All was quiet while we ate and enjoyed our meal. To finish off we each had a cup of tea, and sugar if so desired, and what better could we have asked for? So all credit must certainly go to the ladies of the WVS.

We left the big house, some of us in groups, while some were content just to sit on the grass a while. It was quite pleasant in the warm sunshine, and for many of us it was very tempting, for we were all in need of a rest of some sort. But I knew that we Quintins had so much to do and that it was vital not to waste any time, so our family made our way home. In spite of all, I heard the occasional laugh; our morale was not to quaver.

When we reached the lane we came across several workmen and two of them were carrying this very long tarpaulin. Immediately I saw Dad with a smile on his face. 'By Jove, they've been quick to get this up,' said Dad.

One of the workmen spoke. 'Any of you be Mr Quintin?'

'I'm Mr Quintin,' replied Dad.

'Tarpaulin for 'ee.'

'Good,' remarked Dad. 'Up here please.' He then led the way up to our cottage.

'What's it for?' said one of the workmen.

'It's for the roof,' answered Dad.

'Bloody hell,' remarked another workman. 'Have we to put it on then?'

Dad intervened. 'I'm sorry about this, but I don't rightly know who is responsible for putting it on the roof. I only know, the sooner it's on, the better.'

Then one workman spoke to the other. 'Can we put it on for them, Ben?'

Now it would be Ben's decision, but he was quick to the point. 'Ah, I suppose so. Better fetch up two long ladders.'

I sensed that Dad was pleased, for had not the tarpaulin arrived sooner than he had expected? And what's more, it was going to be erected immediately.

I think we all watched the men doing their job. It was tricky, and no one but experts could have completed the task, and so when it was finished, Dad tipped them handsomely for their trouble, for indeed he was very grateful. So the workmen went away, taking their ladders with them, and pleased I dare say with the few extra shillings in their pockets.

With the tarpaulin covering the roof, the interior of the cottage was obviously much darker, yet there was sufficient light to see what we were doing. One consolation was, we had a roof over our heads, even if it was only a black tarpaulin.

I now could see Dad and Rob working extremely hard. I dare say Dad wanted to get done as much as he possibly could before going off to work.

I got the children on with pieces of rag, wiping off the surplus dust that still settled itself on the furniture, while Mum and I were kept busy stacking stones and slates. I know my hands were beginning to feel sore, and I guess Mum's were too, but she did not complain and we all went about our tasks regardless.

Now it was almost mid-afternoon. Dad had to pack in and get ready for work, but we got an unexpected surprise visit from Tim, and I'm sure he almost wept at seeing us all safe, especially his own children.

I remember his words to Mum: 'I've been almost out of my mind worrying. Such a lot of rumours I heard. I went straight to the commanding officer, who immediately granted me forty-eight hours' compassionate leave.' Then he looked around in bewilderment. 'Oh Mum, what a mess everything is in.'

'I know,' replied Mum. 'But thank God we are all safe. Although I'm still anxious about Dolly and little Jimmy.' (Dolly was my brother Tom's wife.)

'Like me to pop over to Twerton and see if they are OK?'

'Oh, would you mind, Tim?'

'Might as well before I change.' And so, after a few words with Dad, Tim was off; and knowing Tim, he would practically run all the way.

Now it was time for Dad to go. 'You will enquire about Vi and little Patricia then?' said Mum.

'Don't worry, Nell. I'll pass the house on my way to work.'

'Anyone like a cup of tea?' I called out.

Rob replied, 'Wouldn't mind at all. Shift some of this dust that's in my throat.'

We stopped to drink our tea, while Mum enjoyed another rolled cigarette, and after that we seemed to be working that much harder. Anyway, in due course Tim returned with the good news that Dolly and her son were OK. 'Thank God,' whispered Mum.

The next thing, Tim changed into some old trousers and a shirt belonging to Dad; and across the top of the wire mesh on the chicken-run he hung up his uniform. Tim took up where Dad had finished, himself and Rob working with extreme determination, and at long last they had the kitchen clear. Then it was just a matter of sweeping out, and lighting a fire in the kitchen grate.

It was astonishing, but we were now ready to move back in. In first came the kitchen table, followed by the sideboard, and I was amazed at our old wireless: it was powered by an accumulator, and it still worked, for when I switched on, out came the music of Henry Hall's dance band. And when Mum's mats, after a good beating, were placed on the floor, it sure showed a resemblance to our former humble home.

Then Tim and Rob carried in the bedsteads; very heavy they were, made of iron and brass, so they had withstood the bashing they got. They were assembled in the sitting-room, alongside the shelter, which already had its mattress in.

I looked around me now, and thought of the old saying, 'Where's there's a will, there's a way'. For had not that very morning everything looked impossible? Yet it was Dad's determination that gave us all the encouragement to uphold him and to support him, by staying put. I knew now that our toiling had not been in vain, for certainly we had achieved our goal, and in spite of the remaining dirt and dust we were all satisfied with our achievement.

With another fire on in the sitting room, and the modern dance music playing on the wireless, we were all truly uplifted in spirit. If only we had had plenty of water, we would have scrubbed out, but alas, all we had was our precious water in the copper boiler, which was for drinking purposes only. So, with a pan of water on the hearth, we made tea, and thanks to Tim, who had brought some provisions, it was possible to make a spread of some selection; and although sardines and beans don't go well together, we were certainly thankful for food.

Being in our little cottage again gave us all joy, and when I stop to think about it, it was one of the most remarkable feats our family ever accomplished. We won through, and without water, gas, or electricity, we survived.

I now felt myself nodding in front of the fire. I guess the heat was too much for me, and sleep was what we all needed badly. However, I went into the garden, for there was still much to do, and the best way, I thought, was to soldier on. I started sorting out what was left of the picture frames and ornaments, and being back in the fresh air gave me a wonderful boost. In a way I was happy. My mind was full of hope, and as a matter of fact, I started humming to myself, when suddenly I heard a whistle. It came up from the garden. It couldn't be! But it was, it was Jim's whistle.

With excitement I almost dropped the little statue I was holding in my hands, for I flew down the garden, which sloped to the bottom, and running with such speed, I nearly knocked Jim over. We were now in each other's arms, and he whispered, 'Thank heavens you are all right.' I felt my cheeks pressing against his khaki uniform, and then my feelings somehow mingled with the tiredness which I could not hide, for the tears I could not stop, they just flowed down my face.

Don't cry, pet,' said Jim. 'We've got each other.' Then Jim pulled his khaki handkerchief out, and I used it to wipe my eyes. 'Feel better now?' said Jim. I braved a little smile.

He now had his arm around my shoulder as we walked up the garden path. Then he stopped, and looked at me, and laughed. 'Now how could I take you to a ball? Your eyes are red, and your clothes are all tattered.'

'Oh Jim, I must apologise for my appearance.'

'Had it rough, pet, I can see you have.'

I wanted to say more, but could not speak, for my lips were sealed with Jim's kisses.

Then Jim, holding my hands, looked me squarely in the face, and with his big blue eyes almost penetrating through me, he said, 'Paul, there's something I want you to know. When I heard the news about Bath being blitzed badly, I was suddenly seized with the fear that I may never see you again. It made me think, and realise how very much you really mean to me. I know I've told you many times how much I love you, but that's not enough. Will you marry me soon, Paul? You do love me, don't you?'

Flinging my arms around his neck, I whispered, 'Of course I do.'

Still strolling up the garden, Jim now had his arm around my waist. 'I know I should say something wildly romantic,' he said. 'But I think you understand me, Paul.'

I was indeed very happy at this moment, especially with Jim beside me. When we reached the back door, Jim squeezed my hand. I then called out, 'Jim's home!'

'Well, this is a pleasant surprise,' said Mum. 'Come, meet Tim. He'll be pleased to see you.'

After the introduction was over, Mum said, 'I'll put a pan of water on the fire, and we'll have some tea.'

Jim was now looking around him. 'I can see you all have had a rough time.'

Then Tim said, 'How did you manage to get leave?'

'Well, I tried phoning through, but all communications to Bath were down, so I made up my mind I would get here somehow.'

'You've been lucky,' said Tim, 'for I had one hell of a job to get away. I was told that only next of kin was allowed to go into Bath.'

'Mind you,' said Jim, 'I didn't get away so easily. Our commanding officer, when I told him of my circumstances, he was very abrupt, and said, "Damn it man, you are only engaged to the girl." However, I was granted a forty-eight hour leave, on the understanding that I would have to forfeit forty-eight hours from my next leave. I just had to come, Tim.'

'I know,' replied Tim. 'I know just how you felt, for the suspense about killed me. Still, all's well, thank God.' Tim then chuckled. 'We're all in a bit of a mess, and what we all need now is a spruce up. But the water situation is critical.'

'Is there anywhere I can get some?' said Jim.

'We could try the farm,' said Tim. 'Sure they could oblige us.'

Hearing their conversation, I intervened and said, 'I'll pop down to the farm, and see Mrs Chubb.' So, hurrying down the garden with two buckets, I jumped over the wall and was soon on the farm. Milking time was well over, so my guess was I would find

Mrs Chubb in the dairy.

I peeped round the half-door, and there was Mrs Chubb swilling down the floor with a hose-pipe. When she got her eye on me, she stopped. 'Good gracious me! It be Pauline Quintin. And what a mess you be in.'

'I know,' I replied.

'How are you all, up there on the hill?'

'We are all OK, thank you, but Mrs Chubb, our cottage caught it last night, and we are without gas, electric, and water.'

'As bad as that, me dear? Well, we've been fortunate, just a couple of sheds blowed over. Being in a hollow somehow protected us a bit. Anyway, me dear, we must help 'ee all we can. First, you must have a bath here, and anyone else come to that. Come, let's see if the water is hot enough.'

'It's very kind of you, Mrs Chubb, but if you don't mind I'll fill my two buckets first, take them up home, and then come back.'

'All right, me dear, but come straight back.'

'I will, Mrs Chubb, in about five minutes' time.'

'See you later then,' she said. 'And anyone else wanting a bath are welcome.'

I returned the buckets of water to the lads, saying, 'I'm off to have a bath. Mrs Chubb has kindly offered her hospitality, and anyone else wanting one would be more than welcomed.'

'A very kind woman, is Mrs Chubb,' said Mum. 'Anyway, off you go now. And enjoy it.'

I raced back down the garden, and was soon at the door that led into the farmhouse. I gently tapped twice, the door opened, and Mrs Chubb greeted me. 'Come along in, me dear.'

I followed her in, and then upstairs to the bathroom. A real luxury indeed, for at home, even at the best of times, we had only the tin bath in front of the fire. So imagine the pleasure I got when I stepped into a bath, a real one, for the very first time in my life. (I had never actually used the bath at Mrs White's.) The large old bath was almost two-thirds full of delightful warm water, lathered by carbolic soap. I dipped and washed my hair at the same time, and was now feeling absolutely marvellous. I stepped out, and with a towel borrowed from Mrs Chubb I gave myself a good rub down. Mrs Chubb kindly lent me one of her clean dresses, scented highly of moth-balls. Truly it did not do me credit, for the dress was above my knees, as I was much taller than Mrs Chubb. Never mind, it served its purpose, for now I felt like a new pin, and was very grateful to her.

I went down to the farmhouse kitchen, and I could smell the newly baked oven bread.

'All right, me dear?'

'Oh yes, thank you, Mrs Chubb.'

'Well now, me dear,' she said, wrapping two small loaves up in tissue paper, 'take these up to your Ma.'

'Oh, thank you,' I replied. 'We'll never be out of your debt.'

'Go along now, and don't forget, anyone wanting a bath, tell 'em just to come down and see me.'

I almost ran back up the garden path. I was wearing my strong heavy black shoes without stockings, so I was far from being elegantly dressed, and I was not surprised at being laughed at; and really I was amused myself, but what odds, I felt as sweet as a nut.

'Had a beautiful bath!' I exclaimed. 'And Mum, you go down, and take the children with you. Oh, and Mrs Chubb has given me these two loaves for you.'

I could see Mum was delighted. 'I think I will go down,' she said. 'Then I can thank her personally.'

The menfolk were content in talking, and then decided to go into The Retreat for a drink. It wasn't quite opening time, but then Old Sam's place was always open.

Now that I was alone I decided to dress into something different. I slipped into one of Mum's dresses. In fact it was the only one I could find, and anyway I knew Mum wouldn't mind. I felt nice in it, for it was still perfumed from the lavender bags.

It wasn't long before Mum returned with the children, exclaiming, 'We've all had a bath!'

'Oh, I am glad. And Mum, is it OK my wearing your dress?'

'Of course — it suits you.'

So, putting more coal on the fire in the garden, we sat around it. And how tired we all were, with the children yawning their heads off.

'Time you children were in bed,' said Mum. So off they went into the sitting-room. I followed them.

'We have no pyjamas to wear, Auntie Paul.'

'Better sleep in your vests then.'

I tucked them in, and then waited until they said their prayers. Then Alfie spoke. 'Auntie Paul, are we going to the Pitmans tonight?'

'Only if the siren goes,' I replied, and in my thoughts I sincerely hoped it wouldn't, for we all needed a good night's sleep.

Kissing the children goodnight, I returned to Mum in the kitchen. She was now making a cup of tea, and this I thought was a grand opportunity to talk to her about Jim and me wanting to get married soon.

'Have you definitely decided then?' said Mum. 'Or should you think about it? Decide it may be better to wait, until the war is over.'

I could see Mum's point of view. But knowing Jim was much older than I, I had acquired a strong feeling of security — although not financially, that I knew. I also had this added feeling of happiness. And truly I loved him. And was he not my first love?

The menfolk returned. They had now been joined by Dad, and lo and behold, they were in high spirits. I guess the intoxicating liquor had given them all increased joviality.

I could see Dad was amazed to see our little cottage a bit shipshape, for when he had left us to go to work, we had still had much to do.

Then Dad turned on a switch. No lights, so we had to depend on candles. But the unexpected did happen, when Dad turned on the water-tap, for out flowed the beautiful water.

'Bravo!' shouted Dad. He then called to Mum to fill up the boiler, while he himself prepared a good fire underneath.

'We'll need plenty of hot water for the lads,' he said, 'and for myself. We are all in dire need of a good sponge down.' So when the time came for the menfolk to start their ablutions, Jim and I decided to go for a stroll and let them get on with it.

It indeed was a beautiful night, with the same old moon shining high in the sky, and as we walked hand in hand, Jim told me that he had talked to Dad about our getting married soon. 'And Paul,' said Jim, 'he gives his consent and blessing. But,' he went on, 'the thing is, while I'm in the army we won't be able to set up home together. It'll mean you will have to remain at home for the duration. And God knows how long that will be.'

It was indeed the proposition I fully expected, and indeed accepted, and really I was happy with the idea, knowing that I could go on living at home until the end of the war. I wanted to get married, but I was also concerned about my parents; they were not as young as they had been.

'Darling,' said Jim, 'there's something else. You don't mind getting married in a Catholic Church, do you?'

'I don't mind at all,' I answered.

'Well, my pet,' said Jim, 'if that's OK, it'll be up to you to name the day.'

Then, on the spur of the moment, Jim suddenly burst out laughing. He grabbed at my waist, then hoisted me up into the air, at the same time whirling me around into a spin. I myself was almost in hysterics, shrieked with laughter and struggled to free myself; consequently we both landed on the gravel stones.

'You all right?' gasped Jim.

'Just about!' I said.

When Jim got me up on my feet, he suggested we return to The Retreat for a drink, so slowly we strolled back along the top road. As we did so we heard a woman's footsteps walking briskly behind us. The footsteps were closer now, almost on top of us, so I couldn't help but glance over my shoulder, and to my surprise it was Rene, Tim's wife, and the mother of Alfie and Iris.

'Hello there!' I called out.

'Why, it's Pauline.'

I guess she was also surprised to see me, especially in the company of a soldier, and almost immediately I said, 'Meet Jim, my fiancé.'

Jim held his hand out for a handshake from her, and while still holding on to Jim's hand, she gasped out, 'The children, are they all right?'

'Tucked nicely in bed, and fast asleep,' I replied.

'Thank God,' she said. And in the moonlight, I could just detect tears glistening on her cheeks. Tears no doubt of both joy and relief, knowing her children were safe.

Then Jim proposed we should all have a drink together. I linked Rene's arm in mine, quietly saying, 'Come on.'

Rene and I then entered Sam's lounge. It was not very big, but big enough for an old piano to stand in the corner of the room, along with an antique stool; the instrument was still in great demand for the occasional sing-song, especially on Saturday nights.

During Jim's absence while collecting the drinks from the bar, I had the idea that Rene would take the opportunity of talking to me in confidence, and she did.

'Oh, Pauline,' she said, 'I was in total misery last night during the raid, being constantly reminded of the children. I feared my guilt was slowly creeping up on me, and I felt I was being strangled with regret and misery. I feel ashamed,' she went on. 'I was so selfish, and I behaved so badly towards Tim and the children.'

Again her eyes became misty. What could I say at this moment, for the admission of her wrongdoing was something to be admired in her. It was almost like a confession. It made sense that she was truly sorry. How could anyone judge her? I could only offer her instead sympathy and all understanding.

Jim returned with our drinks, so we talked, and even laughed. I could see already the change in Rene, knowing that what she needed now was the best tonic in the world, and that was company, especially when the pangs of depression lurk around; and depression did lurk around for Rene, for undoubtedly she put a lot of blame on herself.

For myself, I could only blame the damn war.

Jim then got up and went over to the piano. Lifting the lid, he strummed a note or two, and then, sitting down on the stool, he started to play. He next placed a sheet of music on the stand, and behold, it was from Ivor Novello's *Perchance to Dream*, the song being 'We'll gather lilacs in the spring again.' How sweet was the music that echoed round the room, especially coming from such an old piano.

A silent hush was now everywhere as people listened to Jim's playing. Such was the attraction that it brought people in from the next room, until the little lounge was full to capacity.

I had finished my grapefruit juice, and I thought it a good opportunity to pop into home for a minute; as a matter of fact, I wanted to see Tim, to tell him about Rene being in The Retreat with us. So, excusing myself, I hurried out of the pub and up the stone steps into the lane.

I opened our front door quietly, and on entering the kitchen I saw that Dad, Tim, and Rob were having a game of cards in the candle-light. When they saw me, they were very much surprised, for it must have been nearly 10 p.m.

'Where's Jim then?' said Dad.

'He's playing the piano, entertaining some of Sam's customers. But I've come in specially.' And with my eyes fixed on Tim, I said, 'Rene is in The Retreat with us. She was anxious about the children. Jim and I met her, so we took her in for a drink. And it would be nice if you would join us for a half-hour.'

Even in that very dim candle-light, I detected resentment in Tim, and knew that bitterness was still within him.

'Pop in and see her, Tim,' said Dad. 'Bring her in for some supper.'

Tim did not speak, and it was only very reluctantly that he put his tunic on. However, at least he was coming back in with me to Rene. As we walked back down the lane, he said, 'Got a feeling I'm not doing the right thing.' I did not speak. I felt his comment was best unanswered, and I led the way back into the lounge.

I think Rene was surprised at seeing Tim; however, he did sit beside her, and started talking to her, and so I walked over to Jim and placed my hand on his shoulder while he continued playing, knowing that any reconciliation of any sort between Rene and Tim would perhaps benefit the children.

It was almost closing time when Jim and I returned to the table where Tim and Rene were sitting. I immediately sensed a glimmer of hope, especially when I saw them talking quite freely with each other. I looked at Rene, and winked, and in return she gave me a smile. Was it just a woman's intuition that all was well between them?

'Shall we all go in home now?' I said.

'Better,' replied Jim, 'or Old Sam will be throwing us out.'

So, in the candle-light, in our little kitchen, it was definitely a contrivance of a reunion, for now everybody was talking, and I realised that Rene and Tim had once again been reconciled.

Consequently, after a snack, it was not surprising that Tim suggested taking his wife home.

'All right if we come up for the children tomorrow?' he said.

'Why of course,' replied Mum. 'I'll have them all ready.'

Dare I say a happy ending? It might be, for the time being at any rate. Before going off, they took a peep at the children, and then, bidding us all goodnight, they went on their way.

It was now decided that we would all retire for bed. Rob was off first, knowing that his bed was in the shelter, followed by Mum and Dad, leaving Jim and me alone in the kitchen.

'Will you be all right on the couch, Jim?'

'Of course, I'll sleep like a log. So don't worry about me. Off to bed yourself, for you must have lost a lot of sleep.'

I kissed Jim goodnight, tiptoed into the sitting-room, and then crawled into a bunk-bed which Mum had made up for me. My tiredness had gained control, and I was soon off to sleep.

I knew no more until I was awakened by the early morning chatter of the children.

'Shush,' I whispered. 'Grandma and Grandad are still sleeping.'

'Can we get up, Auntie Paul?'

'All right then, but don't make a noise.'

They scampered off into the kitchen; meanwhile I made the attempt to dress myself in the dark.

When I entered the kitchen, I was astonished to see Jim up, and the fire on too, with a saucepan of hot water simmering on the hob, almost ready for making the early morning tea.

'Hello, pet,' said Jim. 'Had a good sleep?'

'*I've* had a good sleep, Jim, but it's my guess you haven't.'

'I didn't do so bad,' replied Jim. He was now sitting beside the children, who at this moment were enjoying the warmth from the fire, being only in their vests. While mashing the tea, I overheard bits of conversation between Jim and the children.

'Is it true, Uncle Jim, you drive real steam trains?' This question came from Alfie, and before Jim could answer, Iris popped yet another question. 'What makes the trains smoky? And Uncle Jim, if you are a soldier, why do you have to drive a train?'

The curiosity and inquisitiveness from the children was really overwhelming, especially at that time in the morning. However, I soon quietened them down with drinks of milky tea, and then I sent them into the sitting-room for their clothes. By this time Jim was getting some peace to drink his own tea. And talking of peace, how thankful I was that Jerry had decided to leave us alone last night, and that Bath itself had had a reprieve, at least for the time being.

Now Mum and Dad were up, and so was Rob, all feeling refreshed and ready for some breakfast no doubt. Well, Dad started toasting the bread in front of the fire, while Mum slowly cooked scrambled eggs in a large frying-pan. Nothing tasted nicer, for we were all hungry.

Then it was time for Rob and Dad to go off to work. I heard Dad say to Rob, 'I'll give you lift down.'

After clearing away, we got the children ready to meet their parents, putting on their very best clothes. 'It's not Sunday,' said Alfie. 'So why are we having our newest clothes on? And where's Daddy?'

The time had come for me to break the ice. 'Darlings,' I said, 'I've got a special surprise for you both. Mummy and Daddy are coming to fetch you, to take you back home.'

Both children were without enthusiasm, and I was beginning to think I had not made myself clear.

'But Auntie Paul,' said Alfie, 'have we really got to go back home?'

'I placed my arms around the both of them, saying, 'You see, you both belong to Mummy and Daddy, and they need you, as much as you need them. And so you must go home, and be together.'

'We weren't together before,' said Iris.

In my heart, I felt sorry for the children. I suppose that, from a child's point of view, their consternation was not surprising.

Jim was beside me, fully aware of the children's feelings. I glanced at him, hoping he would say or do something to alleviate the situation and to ease the predicament which had suddenly arisen. One thing I was sure of, Jim's good humour alone would comfort and reassure the children.

'Well,' said Jim, now looking at Alfie, 'I do declare, I'm looking at a little toff.' Then, deliberately glancing at Iris, he said, 'You too look very nice in that pretty dress. How about coming for a little walk with me?' Believe me, they both jumped with joy.

This practical suggestion of Jim's was just the very thing, so off they went together, as happy as sandboys. In the meantime, Mum and I packed up their belongings in one large suitcase.

'I'm going to miss them very much,' said Mum.

'Me too,' I replied. 'Still they'll be coming up to see us, and who knows, we might even get round to visiting them.' Mum was now smiling, for I had reassured her that she was not going to lose them entirely.

It must have been an hour later when Jim and the children returned, and I noticed at once that the children were full of elation.

'Oh, Auntie Paul, do you know where we have been?'

'I can't imagine,' I replied.

'We've been in a field where they buried Roman soldiers!'

I knew then exactly where they had been. Before the start of Sion Hill, on the left-hand side, one observed a small field, cordoned off by railings; it was here that a recent excavation had unearthed a stone coffin of Roman origin, and it's my guess, knowing Jim, that he had exaggerated, making an exciting episode of the Roman past.

'It was a big stone coffin, Auntie Paul,' said Alfie. 'With funny printed letters on it.'

'It was Roman writing,' exclaimed Iris.

'Goodness me,' I said, giving Jim a wink as I spoke.

It was mid-morning when Tim and Rene came to fetch the children. As was natural, Alfie and Iris were pleased to see their Mummy, and so I was thankful that it turned out to be a happy reunion.

After saying our farewells, Mum, Jim, and I watched them all going down the lane, the children waving frantically; then they disappeared around the corner. For myself, I somehow gained a contented feeling that all was well. But not Mum; there were tears in her eyes. She was a devoted grandmother, and I knew she had given her best for her grandchildren. I placed my arm in hers, and almost guided her back into the kitchen, where I was sure she would shed a few more tears.

Jim had gone off into the kitchenette, for I heard cups rattling. He must have guessed that we all needed a cup of tea. I joined him.

'Is your Mum all right?'

'A little weepy,' I replied.

'Reckon she'll miss the kids, but sure she'll get over it. You know, your Mum needs a break sometime, for she's always on the go.'

'I know,' I replied. 'But Mum's always been the same.'

I took Mum in a cup of tea, leaving her alone with her thoughts. Meanwhile I went back to Jim.

'What are your plans today, Paul?'

'Not much choice really, for I've to be at work at two p.m.'

Immediately I noticed the disappointment on Jim's face. 'Oh darling, you're not going to work today? My time with you is short, and very precious. Perhaps if you saw your boss he would understand, and give you the day off. And there's your Mum — you can't leave her all day on her own.'

Jim was right of course, and his amiable suggestion was perhaps necessary. 'Point taken,' I said. 'We'll go to town, and I'll pop into the garage and see Mr Griffin.'

'Well, it would be worth the try, pet,' said Jim. After all, Jim was only with me for a few hours, and our time together, as Jim said, was very precious indeed.

We decided we would walk into town, and we asked Mum to join us. She accepted gladly, for she had a little shopping to do.

Jim and Mum waited outside the garage, while I popped in to see Mr Griffin, who I found most understanding and considerate. 'I should imagine,' he said, 'there'll be very little doing today, Miss, so you might as well take the opportunity of enjoying a day off. Anyway it'll give my nephew (meaning Hoppy) something to do. Of course, I'll see you tomorrow, won't I?'

'Oh yes,' I replied. I then thanked Mr Griffin, and almost skipped out of the garage, happy as the flowers in May. I'm sure Mum and Jim knew I had been given the day off, for they were both smiling.

'OK?' said Jim.

'Yes, I've a free day.'

'I'm glad,' he replied.

Mum then suggested she would do her shopping, and said, 'Perhaps I could meet you in an hour's time outside Marks and Spencer's.'

'That'll be fine, Mum. OK with you, Jim?'

'OK by me,' answered Jim.

And so Jim and I wandered around the town. Everywhere unfortunately appeared desolate, and very few shops were open, which made it all look so dismal and dreary. Many of the streets were deserted, and there was absolutely no traffic at at all. In retrospect this was not in the least surprising, because 400 people had been killed in the previous two nights, and an immense amount of damage caused. However, when the hour was up we made tracks to meet Mum, and when we did arrive she was already waiting.

'Couldn't do much shopping,' she exclaimed. 'Very few shops are open.'

I think the only real activity we saw was amongst workmen, who were busy loading up waggons of debris and rubble. We were astonished to see so much damage done, and I know Jim could hardly believe it. 'Jerry certainly made a mess of things,' he exclaimed.

I knew only too well that everything was disorganised, and I realised it would take ages to get everything back to normal.

What to do next to fill the time? First we went into a little pub for a drink; then we wandered back to Evans's fish-and-chip shop, where I went in and bought three twopenny pieces of fish, and one pennyworth of chips each. We sat on a nearby wall, eating our outdoor meal with our fingers.

Then I hit on an idea. 'How about going up to see Grandma?'
Immediately Mum's face beamed. 'That'll be lovely,' she said.
'All right with you, Jim?'

To which Jim replied, 'Yep.'

So we took the bus up to St Martin's Hospital and then made
our way to Grandma's ward. She was delighted at seeing us, and
looking at Mum she said, 'I've been worried about you, gal.'

I then introduced Jim to her, and I could see her dark-brown
eyes glistening in approval at seeing him. After talking a while,
Gran said, 'You have my blessing. And I'm sure you'll both be very
happy.'

I kissed Gran on the cheek, and whispered, 'So glad you
approve.'

Shortly afterwards, to our surprise, the ward Sister herself
brought us in a tray of tea and biscuits; Mum thanked her kindly.

We sat and chatted to Gran for quite a while, and were just
about to say our farewells when who should walk in the ward but
brother Pat, in his naval uniform.

'Gran,' I chuckled, 'you've got the Army *and* the Navy come to
see you today!'

An introduction between Jim and Pat was easy. Pat, of course,
was always the teaser. He would pull Gran's leg, but the affection
that was between them both was very noticeable. However, the
time came when we had to leave Gran, so saying our final
farewells, we left the hospital to catch a bus that would take us
back into the town. It was apparent by now that Jim and Pat were
making good friends, so much so that when we got as far as The
Retreat they decided on a drink together. They wanted Mum and
me to join them, but we said we would go on in home, Mum
suggesting that she would prepare some kind of a meal.

'Enjoy your drink in your own leisure time,' I said.

'We will,' replied Pat. 'And Jim's all right with me.'

When Mum and I reached home, however, we were rather
surprised to see quite a number of workmen in the lane. It was
obvious that they were a house-repair gang.

'Didn't expect to see you so soon,' said Mum.

'We are just up to check, Missis,' said one of the men. 'Can't
have you living in an unsafe house, can we?'

They were all over our cottage, giving it a full inspection and
making notes as they did so. After they had finished, the head man
approached Mum. 'It be only just safe,' he said. 'We'll have to prop
up the outside walls, and it'll have to be done immediately.'

'Whatever you say,' answered Mum.

'Right, that's OK then,' said the man. 'We'll try and do it later
on in the day — if not, first thing in the morning.' Then they left
us.

Curious to know if the gas was on, I turned on the tap, and was delighted to hear the gas hiss out. 'Mum!' I shouted out. 'The gas is back!' I could see Mum was pleased, for now she could cook on the gas stove, so between us we started preparing a meal.

It was strange without the children around. I kept expecting them to come bouncing in with their noise and laughter, and I guess Mum was feeling their absence too. But we did not speak of it; instead we concentrated on what we were doing.

When Jim and Pat came in, they were full of humour, and joked accordingly.

'See, our Paul, I've brought your Jim home. So now I must hurry home to Vi.' So, kissing Mum and me, Pat dashed off.

Dad arrived home soon after Pat's departure, so the four of us sat down to a meal.

'Did the children go off all right?' asked Dad.

'They were happy enough when they left us,' replied Mum. Then Mum spoke of our visit to Gran.

'How is she?' asked Dad.

'About the same, Pat. Anyway she was so happy at seeing us all.'

Then Mum mentioned about the workmen, telling Dad that it was necessary to have the outer walls propped up. 'And you know, Pat, our little home is only just safe.'

'Well,' said Dad, 'it would take a lot to knock down our little homestead, and I'm so glad we decided to stay. But the work will enhance our safety.' I knew that Dad, like us all, loved our home, and we would not forsake it. Then Dad asked Jim what time he was leaving for Southampton.

'Catching the eight-thirty train out of Bath,' said Jim. So before long he and I made ready to walk down to town. Mum and Dad saw us off at the front door, and we almost ran down the lane and waved back as we turned the corner. We had much to talk about, so it was not surprising that we arrived at the GWR station very quickly, and lo and behold, who should be standing next to the ticket collector but our Pat.

'Well, this is a surprise!' I said.

'Come to see Jim off, and then I can take you home, young lady.'

Now I just wondered if these arrangements had been made previously. I smiled, to myself, not mentioning the fact.

The three of us climbed the wooden stairs that led up to the platform, and surprisingly enough many were waiting for the train already, including the familiar sight of men and women in uniform.

I suppose in a way, Pat's presence was good: it would ease the parting of Jim and I. I stood very close to Jim; almost motionless

I was, clasping my hand in his. Then a big steam engine came roaring in, covering us all in smoke; the carriages passed by one by one, until the train finally stopped.

So the time had come for Jim to leave us. Shaking Pat's hand, he wished him well. Then, turning around, he looked at me with those big blue eyes of his, and said, 'It's time to go, Paul.'

I knew his feelings. I sensed them through his eyes, for the eyes, they say, can never lie. Embracing me, and giving me a kiss, he whispered, 'Take care of yourself.'

Only moments elapsed before the guard was closing the carriage doors; he then blew his whistle. Meanwhile Jim had managed to drop a window down to give his last farewell. Then the train gave a couple of jerks, and very slowly started to move out. I held on to Jim's hand as long as I could, finally having to let go.

'I'll write as soon as I get back,' called out Jim.

I could now only blow a kiss, and wave continually until the train finally disappeared out of sight.

I then felt Pat's arm link mine. 'Come on, old girl.'

Through misty eyes, I smiled. Dear brother Pat, he was there to console me, so I thought how lucky I was. We walked out of the station and then up to the Parade Gardens, where we caught a Lansdown bus straightaway.

On reaching home, we found that Mum and Dad had a visitor, a lady whom I recognised immediately, and whom I had wondered about often, for had she not come out of the cottage where dear little Jean had died, during the raid?

I smiled at her and said, 'Hello.' Then she hastened to go, whereupon we exchanged farewells. It was not until she had gone that Mum told me that little Jean had been adopted by the couple living next door to this lady, who were her friends.

'The poor woman,' said Mum. 'She was heart-broken when she talked of little Jean. Almost as if she was blaming herself for what happened.'

In a war such as this, how could any of us know if, or when, our end would come, for we were all living a life of uncertainty.

Dad suggested we all four go into The Retreat for a drink, and we were all in favour; I knew it would cheer us up. So before long we found ourselves in Old Sam's lounge, beside the window, where beautiful scented geranium plants stood. Old Sam liked his plants, and took much pride in his flower-gardens.

After a while Reg Elley, a neighbour, put his head in the doorway. 'What a pity we ain't got Jim to play the piano for us,' he said. 'Still, we'll have a singsong later on.'

Personally I didn't relish a singsong without a pianist. However, when we were joined by others the singing was in harmony, and 'The white cliffs of Dover' went down very well.

The singing was a grand vent to us all, an opportunity to let one's hair down. A drink for many I knew would drown any sorrow, and many like myself suddenly forgot what we had been through, those recent nights of hell. Really we were all enjoying ourselves so much that we didn't realise it was almost closing time. However, we were reminded by Old Sam's voice calling out, 'Time, ladies and gentlemen please.'

I'm sure the majority were in high spirits; this, of course, was the result of the intoxicating liquor consumed by Sam's customers. Anyway, I was glad to notice that our morale was high, and the bombing we had endured had not got the better hand of us.

Back in our cottage, Pat said goodnight and then made tracks to his own home. We retired to our beds, contented and happy, and hoping yet again that Jerry would give us a peaceful night.

The following morning, I was up early, and decided I would visit Pat, Vi, and little Patrica around midday, before starting work at 2 p.m.

When I arrived at Pat's place I was made very welcome, as always, and we had so much to talk about that I just had to keep watch on the time. I sat and enjoyed a snack Vi had prepared, while little Patricia played at our feet.

'I like Jim,' said Pat. 'I think he's a nice fellow. Do you remember the day you met him, Paul? St Andrew's Day, wasn't it? And how I kidded you up into writing to him?'

'You did.'

'And aren't you pleased?'

Yes, I said, I certainly was. Our conversation was so pleasant that I had to remind myself that the time was passing all too quickly. 'I'll have to get a move on,' I said, 'or I'll be late for work.' So, saying my farewells, I left Walcot Street and walked briskly towards the Pierrepont Garage, only to find everything quiet when I arrived.

After changing into my boiler suit, I went below to see Rob, who was busy greasing a back axle.

'Hi, Quinner,' he called out. 'Is it two o'clock already?'

'On the dot,' I answered.

'Have you heard if Jim got back all right?'

'Not heard anything yet,' I replied. 'Must dash upstairs, our Rob. See you.'

Already I had a customer waiting on the forecourt. I rushed out, apologising for my delay, and smiled when I recognised who it was: it was Mr Smith of the Civil Defence.

'Hello, Miss Quintin. Busy?'

'I've only just come on,' I exclaimed.

'Put four gallon in for me please.' After I had taken his coupon and money, he said, 'Oh, by the way, we've got new permanent headquarters for the Civil Defence, along Combe Park.'

This did surprise me indeed. 'You mean,' I said, 'alongside the Royal United Hospital?'

'That's right, Miss. You can't mistake it. Got a flag-pole sticking out from the front lawns.'

'I'm glad to know that, Mr Smith, because I'm on duty Monday and Tuesday of next week.'

'Right then, Miss, best be on my way.' He then jumped into his car and drove off, leaving me wondering what our new headquarters would be like. One thing was certain, it was nearer to home.

Coming back into the garage, I met Mr Griffin. 'Good afternoon, Miss. Guess you'll be wondering where young Freddie is. I've sent him on an errand, he shouldn't be long. Incidentally did you have a good day off yesterday?'

'Excellent, Sir,' I replied.

'Anyway, if you need me, I'll just be in the house.'

'All right, Sir.'

'In general, the afternoon went over pretty quiet, so I occupied myself cleaning out the oil containers; it was always surprising how quickly the measuring cans became sticky with the oil.

When Freddie finally did turn up, he had quite a mischievous grin on his face. 'Hello, Miss,' he said. 'You'll never guess where I've been.'

'Can't imagine. Where have you been, Freddie?'

'To Miss Shaw's house, and, with a bunch of flowers!'

'Well, that's all right, Freddie. We all know Miss Shaw is a friend of Mr Griffin's.'

'You know, Miss, I reckon there's something going on between them two.'

'Freddie!' I was almost dumbfounded at Freddie's remark. 'You know, Freddie, I'm surprised at you saying things like that. For you are not sure, are you?'

'Well,' said Freddie, 'he does attend to her red sports car personally.'

'Oh, Freddie. Disperse the idea from your mind, and come and help me put all these cans back.'

Later, when I was sitting in our little office in the garage, thinking about Jim, I was startled by the phone ringing.

'Pierrepont Garage,' I answered.

'Paul, is that you?'

Immediately I knew it was Jim. What a coincidence. 'Hello, Jim, good to hear you!'

'Ringing you up to let you know I had a good journey back. And, of course, I wanted to know how you were.'

'Lonely and miserable,' I chuckled.

Then Jim answered with a long drawn out sigh. 'Never mind pet,' he said. 'My next leave will soon come around.'

Our conversation was interrupted by an impatient motorist, hooting and tooting on the forecourt. 'Must go Jim, someone is waiting for petrol.'

'Well, cheerio for now,' said Jim. 'I'll write soon.'

'So long, darling,' I replied. Putting the receiver down, I almost ran out to the forecourt, and at the same time thinking, where the devil is Freddie?

'Can't wait here all day, you know.' This was a greeting I got from a taxi-driver.

'I'm sorry,' I said. 'I was answering the phone.' While I served this man with petrol, I couldn't help thinking how he lacked patience; yet to my surprise he gave me a two-shilling tip, muttered something underneath his breath, and then drove off. I looked at the florin in my hand: it was a good tip. Maybe I could overlook his sarcasm; after all, I suppose he was in a hurry to get somewhere.

It was 10 p.m., and I was ready to go home. Having sent Freddie off earlier, I had to close the big doors myself, which I had to admit wasn't easy. Well, I had closed the first door, and was on with the next, when an American voice called out, 'Hi there — like some help?' And before I could answer, square shoulders were pushing the heavy door along on its rails.

'Thank you,' I said. 'Thank you very much.'

'A pleasure.' Well, the American did what I'd hoped he do, walk away without further conversation, so I deliberately took my time in locking the doors. Once all was secure, I popped the keys through the letter-box of Mr Griffin's house, and started walking home.

A slight drizzle came on, but it was good to feel the gentle rain splashing on my face; it made my skin feel fresh and alive. I was almost home, and turned into the lane, when through the dim light I saw huge battens, propping up the outer walls of our cottage. I realised then that the workmen had returned to complete their job.

On opening the front door, I discovered that the electricity was on, and then I heard Mum's voice call from the top of the stairs, 'Up here, duck.'

I went upstairs to find Mum and Dad battling with the rain that somehow had leaked through the tarpaulin. Vessels of all shapes and sizes were placed on the floor to catch the dripping water; even the chamber-pots took their role.

'Goodness gracious!' I exclaimed. 'I thought the tarpaulin was waterproof, and nothing could get through.'

'I was under that impression too,' remarked Dad. 'Must be leaking through at the sides.'

'And this is only fine rain,' said Mum. 'Behopes we don't get a deluge.'

'Come on,' said Dad. 'We'll go downstairs. Can't do any more up here.' Dad was right, of course, we could only catch the dripping water, which made different plops as it entered different vessels.

'Jim phoned me tonight,' I eagerly announced. 'Got back all right.'

'Good,' said Mum, while Dad remarked, 'He's thoughtful, you know.' And after a light snack we were soon into our beds.

The following Sunday, we were all off work together. The usual chores had to be done, of course, but when dinner was over we all looked forward to that little bit of leisure time. It was not quite warm enough to sit outside, so I nestled in an armchair beside the fire, reminiscing maybe, as I had much to think about, especially if Jim and I were to be married soon.

I could only be dreaming if I was thinking of a white wedding, for I knew that in wartime circumstances that would not be possible. My dress would have to be something more conservative, for the majority of servicemen who were getting married were wearing their uniform; so if Jim married me in his khaki, I would just have to settle for wearing something appropriate, like perhaps brown and pink.

Mum and Dad were still having their siesta, so I decided to prepare tea. I felt the absence of the children very much, because it was all so quiet now. I supposed we would have to adjust, and get used to the idea that we no longer had the children around us.

With tea soon over, out came the newspapers. Then the usual thing was to listen in to the church service on the wireless; often enough it came from St Martin-in-the-Fields.

After the service, the news came on, and the announcer began reading a recent extract from King George VI's diary. We all listened intently to what the King had to say, and one can imagine the surprise we got when it actually concerned us, for it went as follows:

'It is outrageous that the Germans should come and bomb our cathedral cities and towns like Bath, which they know are undefended and contain no war industries, as 'Reprisals' raids for what we are doing to their war industries.'

'Well, said Dad, 'that's as near to the truth as any.'

'But fancy,' said Mum, 'being mentioned on the news.'

And I knew only too well that other towns, like Exeter, York, Norwich, and even Canterbury, would surely suffer in the same way.

Monday morning came around only too soon, for I was on the 6 a.m to 2 p.m. shift, and I was thankful for the lift into town in Dad's bus, which ensured that I was to arrive at the garage in all good time.

It's remarkable how Monday mornings at the garage were almost always busy, and this very morning was no exception. There were always the usual businessmen to take to the railway station, repairs coming in and out, and petrol sales high, so before I knew where I was, I was being relieved at 2 p.m.

I took the bus home that afternoon, and as the bus took us up Lansdown Road I couldn't help but notice the front gardens, many of which were cluttered up with rubble; yet spring flowers, like the daffodils, were shooting through, as if in defiance of their unnatural surroundings,.

I reached home to find a letter from Jim. As a rule, his news was nearly all consistent, but in this letter he had something special to write about. He suggested that on his next leave he would like to take me up to Gateshead to meet his people. It was only natural that Jim wanted me to see his folk, and the proposition sounded excellent, providing, of course, I was able to get time off work.

There was no one at home, but Mum had left me a little note, like she always did, saying that she would be home no later than 4.30 p.m. I made myself a cup of tea and a sandwich, and then I looked around to see what wanted doing, for we still had much to do before we were really shipshape. So I worked happily away, engrossed maybe with my own thoughts, and with the prospect of my future visit to the north-east.

When Mum did arrive home, I anxiously told her of Jim's suggestion.

'Quite right too,' said Mum.

Monday evenings came around, and I was to go on duty at our new Civil Defence headquarters, along Combe Park. Giving myself plenty of time, I was nearing the Royal United Hospital when it suddenly occurred to me that I should have made enquiries long before now about the young German airman that we took into Casualty.

Glancing at my watch, I found I had plenty of time to spare, so I thought it a grand opportunity to make some enquiries. I soon found myself in Casualty, talking to a Senior Nurse, who kindly looked up records for me.

'What did you say his name was?' she said.

'I'm sorry,' I replied, 'but I did not know is name. All the information I can give you, Nurse, is that he was a young German airman who was in real bad shape.'

I stood watching the Nurse, as she turned page after page over in a large report book. Then she paused. 'Ah, here it is. Transferred to Ward Two, after an emergency operation.' Then she looked up at me, saying, 'Sorry, that's all the information I can give you. But I dare say if you went along to Ward Two, and saw Sister, she perhaps could give you more detail.'

I was curious if not concerned over the young German pilot, and so in my eagerness to know I advanced my steps along the corridor towards Ward Two.

The door of Sister's office was slightly opened, enough for me to see her busy writing at her desk. I gave two gentle taps on the door, and then a quiet voice called out, 'Come in.' Sister gave one look at me and then smiled. 'Please sit down,' she said. This I did. 'Now, what can I do for you?'

'I'm just making enquiries, please.'

'About whom?'

'About a young German airman.'

Sister was now looking at me in rather an odd manner, I thought. I had an idea what she was thinking. After all, why on earth should a young lady in Civil Defence uniform make enquiries about a wounded German airman? Now I was sure Sister was herself curious to find out what connection there could possibly be. And indeed she had every right to know, so quietly I explained how Dad and I had brought the patient to the hospital.

Sister then place her hand on mine, and giving me a re-assuring smile she said, 'I'm pleased to tell you he came through all right, and then was transferred to a military hospital. Actually, he was a quiet boy, spoke a little English. That reminds me,' she said, getting up from her chair and opening up a cabinet door behind her. 'I have something for you.' And she produced what appeared to be a small book wrapped up in brown paper. Written on the paper was a message: To friends, that made it possible I should not die.'

'But Sister,' I exclaimed, 'surely this belongs to the hospital staff, whatever it is."

'No,' said Sister, smiling. 'It belongs to you. You brought him to us. Remember, you were the deciding factor, making it possible for him to live. You know, some would have left him to die.'

I thanked the Sister and then departed from her office, clutching on to my little parcel.

It was tempting to open it up immediately, but on second thoughts I decided to wait until I got to our new depot, which I came across quite easily, for it was identified by a white flag-pole that stood many feet up.

I walked up the driveway of our new headquarters, which indeed was narrow, but I imagined there was sufficient width for ambulances to drive up to the large old house. I opened the heavy old door, and was now standing in a large hall, with exuberant black and white marble flooring, evidence of a stately home at some time or other. From the hall there were many doors leading off, and from one of the doors that stood ajar I heard a familiar voice: it was Flo's.

I rushed in, gasping, 'Flo!' and her reactions to me were of sheer delight.

'Oh, Miss!'

'How nice to see you, Flo, how are you?'

'I'm fine now,' she replied. But somehow there remained a sadness in her very expression; it was understandable, knowing that she had lost her first baby. I knew Flo's contribution was essential to Civil Defence, and being kept busy I would hope she had no time to grieve or ponder over her loss.

After talking to Flo I quickly adapted myself to observing the layout of our new depot. Our sleeping quarters consisted of six bunk-beds to each room, so glancing around I chose a vacant bed in a ladies room. I placed my helmet and respirator on a small table, and then decided at long last to open up my little treasure.

Undoing the well-worn string that kept it together, I unwrapped the brown paper. What mystery was held in its contents?

Some sort of a little book it was: its cover was of black leather binding. I slowly opened it, as if afraid to do so, and immediately I recognised that it was a small German Bible.

I scanned the pages carefully, expecting to find something I perhaps could read, and then a slip of paper dropped into my lap.

It was important to me, for it was written in English. Some lettering was in the wrong place, and it was written in pencil, but nevertheless it was readable, and so the message was clearly to be understood.

'I don't suppose, my friends, I will ever know you, but whoever you are, I would like to give you one of my dearest treasures. It was special to me, because it was given to me by my Mother. I feel you are a Christian or Christians like myself, so I give you my Bible willingly, that I will share with you a strong Christian unity, and pray like you must do, for the end of the war to come quickly, so we shall all once again be reunited with our families and loved ones.

My gratitude,
Hoch — Auf Wiedersehen.'

I read it over and over again, and strange I thought it that he gave no name of himself. It didn't matter really, but I couldn't get over the fact that this young German had made remuneration with his very own Bible.While wrapping it up again, I began to think highly of this young airman, and it was indeed a favourable opinion I had of him, enemy though he was. To start with, he appeared to be a devout Christian, who I'm sure loved his Bible for the reason he had explained. Yet he had given it away. I must admit that the young German's action made me more knowledgeable; for it is so easy to give away something you don't want, but to give away something that is desired for one's self is something to be honoured.

Perhaps this gift, and the way in which this young man gave it, made me feel a little different towards the enemy. They were human like ourselves. So what gave us the right to hate them, and show emotions of extreme dislike? That surely would be showing hatred towards ourselves, which definitely was no way for rectification, was it? After all, the Bible teaches us to love our enemies.

My meditation was interrupted by someone calling my name. I looked up to find Mr Booth, our Assistant Superintendent, standing in the doorway. 'On duty all night, aren't you, Miss?'

'Until five-thirty in the morning,' I replied. 'For I have to be at work at six o'clock.'

'Well, if it's all right with you, me dear, perhaps you could help me out with some clerical work. Only we are in a devil of a mess with it, for a lot of our records were destroyed, as you know. And to get reorganised will take some doing.'

I was happy to oblige and help out, and so the hours through the night went over quickly, although I did feel kind of sleepy around 4 a.m. However, we had enjoyed yet another peaceful night, without any air activity.

The time came when I had to leave the depot and make my way to the Pierrepont Garage. It was daylight and the air was warm, which made my walk very delightful. I experienced a somewhat vigorous feeling, for my tiredness had suddenly gone.

That morning was quite busy in the garage, and I did well for tips, so I bought cream slices for everyone to have with their cocoa. Before I knew where I was, it was 2 p.m., and feeling a little tired by now I took the Lansdown bus home. When I reached home, I found several workmen doing repairs to our cottage, but still the large props remained in position.

I showed Mum the small German Bible. Then Mum looked at me saying, 'He's been a good-living boy. Keep it, duck. Put it amongst your souvenirs.'

After a meal, and with Mum's persuasion, I went to bed to get some sleep. 'You must be tired, duck,' she said. 'And you are on duty again tonight, aren't you?'

'It's my last night for the week, Mum,' I answered.

'Well, off you go now, and behopes the workmen don't make too much noise to disturb you.'

At first I did hear knocking and hammering, but somehow I must have dropped off, and when I awoke, all was quiet. Feeling as though I had had a good sleep, I got up, and was surprised to see Dad and Rob home. The clock on the mantelpiece showed 7 o'clock, and Mum, who was darning socks, looked up when I entered the kitchen.

'Had a good sleep, duck?'

'I went sound, Mum.' I then looked at Dad, saying, 'Did Mum show you the German Bible?'

'She did,' answered Dad. 'And I also read the note.'

'Well, what did you think of it, Dad?'

'Umm — well now. Reckon that young boy came from a decent family. And judging by the yapp that binds the Bible, a well-to-do family, I should say. One outstanding feature, he was appreciative of what we did for him. And even if we can't read German, it's a very thoughtful gift.'

'Shall I put the news on?' said Rob.

'Do,' replied Dad.

The announcer talked of the raid which British bombers had made on Lübeck, only about a month previous, saying that we had destroyed half the town. Consequently, said the announcer, the Germans responded with their so called Baedeker raids on cities of historic interest.

'That's us,' remarked Rob.

'And mark my words,' said Dad, 'there'll be other towns yet to suffer in the same way.'

I knew Dad was not a pessimist, but what he said was the obvious of what would happen.

After the news we had much to talk about, Dad being extremely pleased that the workmen had started renovating already.

'You on duty tonight, Quinner?' said Rob.

'It's my last night for the week,' I replied.

'I'll walk you down to Combe Park — when you're ready, of course.'

I accepted with pleasure, so we left home around about 9.30 p.m. I always enjoyed Rob's company. We laughed and joked as we went along, so we arrived at the depot in no time at all. I insisted on Rob coming into the depot. At first he was reluctant, but with my powers of persuasion he finally gave in. Inside, I felt several eyes were upon us: they would wonder who the tall, fair and blue-eyed young man was. Meanwhile, Mr Penny joined us, and I introduced Rob to him.

'Have we a new recruit then?' said Mr Penny.

'Afraid not,' replied Rob. 'I'm in the Territorial Army, doing two nights a week at the drill hall, plus all the roof spotting.'

'Well, I guess, lad, you're doing your bit. Essential, this roof spotting.'

I knew this system was of great importance. Having men looking out for aircraft which were actually in the vicinity helped to localise the air-raid warnings, and so prevent disruption. At the start of the war, factories in a wide area had stopped work for long periods when there was no real danger.

Mr Penny then excused himself and walked away.

'I'd better be off home too,' said Rob.

'OK Rob, and thanks for bringing me down.'

'Well, Quinner,' said Rob, now with a grin on his face, 'I'll enjoy a nice walk home, and if I'm not too late I might even get a shandy in Sam's.' Giving me a wink, he whispered, 'Try and get some rest tonight, for you look awfully tired.'

I suppose lack of sleep did make me look heavy-eyed.

When Rob left the depot, I went over to the switchboard and had a chat with Flo. Then I went back to my bunk, took my shoes off, and lay outstretched. Immediately I felt my muscles relax, but although I was tired my mind remained very active. I was thinking of Jim now, and my future visit to Gateshead. Just lying there, I came to the conclusion that I had experienced so much over the past two or three years. So much had happened in so short a time, and I was still only twenty years old. One thing was for sure: although I was inexperienced in some ways, I felt that I had seen a great deal of life and death for someone of my age. Maybe the war was responsible, I really don't know.

My thoughts became cloudy and I dropped off to sleep. Then I was suddenly startled by the alert bell ringing. Gosh it was noisy. Like a fire-engine bell ringing.

I jumped up quickly, feeling around for my shoes, which I slipped on. I think the majority of us ladies had been sleeping, for we were in a bit of a commotion, flashing our torches all around.

I shone my torch on my watch. It was 3.15 am., and I realised then that I had been to sleep for at least four hours. I made a grab for my bag and helmet, and with the others hurried into the big hall. So there we were ready, waiting in anticipation, come what may.

Being near the Gas Works, we heard the siren blow, and sat and waited for what seemed like ages. Then we heard aircraft approaching. Now we could only wait in suspense. Then the hum of the planes faded; they were the enemy, and they had passed over.

'Some poor blighters are going to get it,' remarked one driver.

'It's the Huns' damn so-called Baedeker raids,' said another.

'One thing's certain,' said Mr Penny. 'They're going south-west.'

'Poor old Plymouth or Exeter then,' said someone.

'Wouldn't be surprised,' answered another.

Then to all of our surprise, we heard more aircraft: there sounded to be many more than in the first wave.

We then recognised the sound of our own fighter-planes, probably Spitfires, for we distinctly heard machine-gun fire.

'Our boys trying to intercept,' said a female attendant.

Oh, the pity of it all, I thought.

Now we were all curious: who was being the target for this early morning raid? Somewhere south, without a doubt. Maybe they were using the south-west as a detour — who knows? However the 'all clear' went an hour afterwards, so back in our rooms we went, with hot cups of tea.

Well, the remainder of the night went over quickly. Good job really — for us I mean, not forgetting, of course, the people who may have suffered through their unwelcome visitors.

So, once again I left the depot to make my way to the garage. I didn't feel quite so tired this particular morning, so walking briskly in the early morning air gave me that added feeling of freshness, appreciative of the sleep I had had at the depot.

Before reaching the garage, however, fine drizzling rain came down, and it made me think of the roof on our cottage. I sincerely hoped the workmen had made a good repair job of it.

Opening up one of the big doors, I next changed into my boiler suit. I hung up my uniform to dry, and I started at once with the usual routine, checking corresponding figures on the petrol pumps and unlocking the oil cabinets which stood on the forecourt. Last but not least, I put the air-line through.

Freddie should have been on at 7 o'clock, but as yet there were no signs of him. However, at 8 a.m. Rob arrived.

'OK, our Paul? Did you manage to get some bo-peep?'

'I did Rob, a nice four hours.'

'According to the early news,' said Rob, 'the RAF fighter bases in Kent got it. Also parts of London.'

But what about the south-west, I thought. Every time I heard of raids, I shuddered to think of all the misery they caused. I always had the sickening feeling of despair for the poor innocent people who were the constant victims of bombing.

I managed my morning's work without difficulty — after Freddie turned up at 8.30 am., apologising for sleeping in. When I was relieved at 2 p.m. I hurried out of the garage in time to catch a Lansdown bus home.

When opening the front door, I called out, 'Cooee!'

It was then I heard Mum's voice from the top of the stairs. 'We're up here, duck,' meaning, of course, that Dad was with her.

I hurried up the stairs to find them both busy trying to make the bedrooms a bit shipshape. Some of the walls were bulging outwards, showing daylight through, and there were no windows left, with the result that dirt and cement were still everywhere.

'Hang on,' I said, 'I'll give you a hand.'

We were still a long way behind from being normal, but, thank God, we were recovering. It was Dad's perseverance and determination which had made it all possible, by refusing evacuation, and staying put; and I felt instinctively that, from now on, things would improve.

PART FIVE

IN THE weeks to follow, life appeared to fall back into a routine. We had occasional air-raid warnings, which were really of no consequence, and therefore we were experiencing a lull of some sort; indeed we rather enjoyed the relaxation it gave us.

My time of course was much occupied with my own personal life, for now it was only a week away from the time when Jim would come home on leave, and together we would travel north. But a letter from Jim somehow altered plans a little, so an arrangement was made that I would travel up to York on my own, and meet Jim there; then we both could continue our journey to Newcastle.

I somehow felt doubtful about travelling on my own, perhaps because I had never done it before; yet on the other hand, I realised that I had to stand on my own two feet sometime or other, so perhaps this time was as good as any. I was always used to having protection from my parents, who forever sheltered me in more ways than one.

So it was that the morning arrived for my departure. After contemplating my attire, I was ready to leave. Mum and Dad were coming down to the LMS railway station, to see me off. It was only natural that Mum wanted to fuss over me, being concerned to see that I had everything I required, but as it happened it was Dad's intervention that eased the situation.

'Now, Nell, don't you be worrying over our Paul. She's quite capable of looking after herself. I'm certain she'll enjoy the journey to York. And once she's reached there, she'll have Jim to look after her.'

Mum, now smiling at me, had been reassured by Dad.

A small engine puffed into the station, pulling two small coaches behind it, and the destination boards were clearly marked 'Mangotsfield and the North.'

Then Dad spoke. 'You know what to do, Paul. When you get out at Mangotsfield, just wait for your connection that will take you to York. And it's bound to be an express train.'

Mum and Dad both hugged and kissed me, and I then stepped up into one of the small carriages. It was not very clean, mark you, but I placed my suitcase on the seat and then went over to the window to give my last farewells.

'Remember me to Jim,' said Dad.

'Oh, do that for me,' said Mum. 'And don't forget to let us know when you are coming home.'

'I won't forget,' I called out. Steam was escaping from everywhere. Then I felt a jolt inside the carriage as the little train started moving. Amidst the steam and jostling on the platform, I noticed Mum's eyes were misty. All I could call out now was, 'Bye bye!'

The train started to gather speed, and while still waving, I suddenly developed a horrible lump in my thoat, for there they stood, my dear Mum and Dad waving back at me. Tears rolled down my cheeks, and I let them roll freely, for the distance I was away, my tears would not be seen.

This sudden parting from my parents had not been easy, and to be honest, I was impassioned by it all; and so when I could no longer see the platform, I sat down next to my suitcase, wiped my eyes, and then gave my nose a good blow. I was glad I was alone at that moment.

The distance to Mangotsfield was approximately eight miles. Actually it was a substation, with no amenities whatsoever; thus it was nick-named the phantom station, for its only existence really was as a pick-up point for expresses going through.

On arriving at Mangotsfield, however, I was surprised to see so many people, the majority of whom were servicemen and women, many of them fully equipped; they were waiting for their connections to take them to their various destinations.

Being alone, and perhaps a little shy still, I stood and just listened to the laughter and chatter that surrounded me. I was conscious of glances made at me. I would have preferred civilian dress, but I didn't have enough clothing coupons for a new outfit, so I was wearing my Civil Defence uniform. I was wearing trousers, a jacket, white blouse, black tie, and a peaked cap, and written in gold braiding across my shoulder armlets was 'Ambulance Driver'.

Music came to my ears, and it was to the left of me, so giving a quick glance I noticed two airmen with a portable gramophone. The record being played was of a mezzo-soprano, and I couldn't understand the words that were being sung. Somehow it didn't seem appropriate at that particular time.

I continued to feel a bit bashful, until, to my great relief, a big steam engine pulling lots of coaches drew up alongside the platform.

The hustle and bustle were everywhere, with carriage doors opening, and porters shouting, 'All aboard for Birmingham, Sheffield and York.' So this was my train.

Everyone was now scrambling on to the train, and I followed suit, but awkward I appeared, and almost fell up the steps of the carriage. When I reached the corridor, I could go no further, for each side of me was jam-packed with soldiers, some of whom had full kit with them.

I experienced embarrassment to the full, and felt my cheeks getting hotter, for what a predicament I found myself in. Here was I, a young lady surrounded by fellows. I could only stand where I was. Maybe I should have tried another carriage before aimlessly getting aboard, but alas, it was too late now.

A couple of soldiers brushed passed me, one of them giving me a little whistle, while the other remarked, 'How about that?' And when the express pulled out of Mangotsfield, I held on to the brass rail for support.

I must say there was much joviality around me, with a group of lads dealing a pack of cards for a game. The train was travelling much faster now, with myself clutching tighter on to the rail.

We must have travelled quite a distance when I noticed a ticket-collector struggling to push through. This gave me ample time to get my own ticket ready, and when he finally reached me he was puffing and blowing, trying hard to mop his brow with his handkerchief, for the atmosphere in the train was hot and stuffy. I couln't help but feel sorry for the man. However, he gave me a smile, and punched my ticket. Then he said, 'Follow me, young lady, I might be able to find you a seat.'

I followed the man, pushing my way through as he was, and it took us a ridiculously long time before we even reached the next carriage. Twice I nearly tripped over kitbags lying on the floor. We had to squeeze and push past so many, apologising and excusing myself the whole time, so that when we finally reached the Guard's van, I suddenly felt free.

'Hi, Tom,' said the ticket-collector to the Guard. 'I've been trying to find this young girl a seat.'

'I should imagine it be impossible,' replied Tom, who was now looking at me over the top of his spectacles. 'How far are you going, Miss?'

'York,' I replied.

'Well now,' said Tom, 'if you care to stop here until the train empties a bit, you're welcome.'

Knowing I had no other choice, I replied, 'I'll be much obliged,' with which I sat down on a stool which was bolted to the floor. So now I was alone with Tom, the Guard, who continued on writing at his table.

At least I thought I was alone with Tom, until I heard a whimper from one of the two baskets lying in the corner. I wanted to get up off my seat, go across to the baskets and investigate, but thought it best to withdraw my curiosity.

It could have been telepathy where the Guard was concerned, for immediately he spoke. 'Couple of alsatians, security dogs, going up to York. Surprising at times, what's carried in these vans.' And before I had time to comment, he spoke again. 'Care for a drop of tea, Miss?'

'Oh, yes please,' I replied gratefully, so out came his billycan. Although it was a strong brew, I relished it with delight, and in return I offered Tom one of Mum's ham sandwiches. Between us we enjoyed the refreshment, although when biting into the ham sandwiches I was reminded of home, and knew I would miss Mum, Dad, and Rob. Still, I thought, the parting would not be for long.

'All right if I throw some bits in for the dogs?' I asked.

'It'll be OK,' answered Tom. 'But don't get too near 'em. They could be vicious to strangers.'

Feeding dogs in the Guard's van was the last thing I had expected to be doing. Yet the mere company of these animals helped to while away the time, for the train had many hold-ups, standing at the red signals for long periods at a time; hence we were well past schedule.

I thought of Jim having to wait a long time on York station; most probably we would miss our connections to Newcastle. And so it happened. The train emptied itself at Sheffield, and thanking the Guard for his kindness, I looked around for a comfortable seat, where I settled down for the rest of the journey. Just before we reached York, I was able to tidy myself up, so I was all ready to leave the train as soon as it pulled into York station.

I stepped out on to the platform, holding tightly on to my suitcase, and was bewildered at seeing so many people around; in fact they consisted in crowds. Then the outlet valve from the engine roared, sending the steam full blast to the roof of the station, and the banging of shutting doors made a considerable noise. Confusion was all around me. I'm afraid I became panic-stricken, wondering how on earth Jim and I would find each other amongst all the crowds of people.

I glanced at my watch, which told me I was an hour late already. I must try and move along the platform, I thought, so I pushed and almost shoved my way past people. Suddenly I felt I was lost, and strange as it was I felt so alone in the crowd. Looking for Jim was like looking for a needle in a haystack. A sudden and infectious fear was creeping up on me. Suppose Jim was not here at all for some unknown reason, what should I do? Looking at so many soldiers made me bamboozled.

Then, out of somewhere came Jim's whistle, and I think at that moment I could have wept for joy.

Before he even spoke, he grasped my hand in his. With his other hand he took my suitcase. 'Quick, pet,' he said, 'we've only got a couple of minutes to catch the Newcastle train on platform two.'

Our steps were hurried, and we only just made it in time, for a porter was already closing the carriage doors. We both flopped down in the first seat we could find.

'Glad we made it, Paul,' said Jim. Now I was content at Jim being beside me, and so happy I was, I just flung my arms around his neck. We were together, that's all that mattered.

And so we settled down to the two-hour journey which would take us up to Newcastle. Once there, we took the tramcar to Gateshead, and on arriving at Colville Street Jim's folks were there to greet us.

Jim's mother put her arms around me and kissed me. She was a buxom woman with lily-white hair and a very pale complexion, but with the loveliest blue eyes.

Next to shake my hand was Jim's Dad. He was small in stature and wearing glasses. I could see he loved his clay pipes, for they were lying on a small table. Later I discovered that although he was in his late seventies, he had a job of work, making sausages for a butcher in the High Street; he also served mass on the altar of St Joseph's church.

After introductions we all sat down for a meal. I was relieved that they seemed to have accepted me, for after all I was a southerner, a good deal younger than Jim, and not a Catholic. So I particularly appreciated their hospitality; but I must admit that I was taken aback at the family's poverty. Jim had a sister and two brothers; both the brothers were now in the services, and I could not imagine how they managed when they were all at home, for they lived in a very small flat. The furniture in the living-room consisted of a table and four chairs, with one armchair and a smaller table in front of a narrow window. Only a coal fire and a gleam of a polished brass fender brightened the room. The toilet was reached by going down a long flight of wooden stairs to the small backyard; there, pieces of newspaper were hanging on a string. There was nowhere to wash but in the sink in the scullery; for a bath you had to go to the Mulberry public baths and pay twopence, which Jim and I did the next morning.

The days that followed passed quickly. We went by train to visit Durham, where I was enchanted by the beauty of the cathedral; this contrasted sharply with the run-down state of Gateshead at that time. We were also lucky in that Jim's Aunt Peggy offered to put us up for a few days at her boarding-house at Tynemouth, on the coast.

On one of these days, while we were out for a walk, we sat down to rest, and as Jim was smoking his pipe I noticed a serious expression on his face. Then he spoke. 'I don't know, Paul, I can't offer you much, can I?' I was puzzled at what he had just said, and he continued, 'I regret having lost my job on the railway through my own stupidity.'

Now I wanted to cheer him up, and I think I gave him the right answer. 'Jim,' I said, 'if you had still been on the railway you would never have been in the army, so we would never have met.'

He must have realised that I had talked sense, for then he smiled, put his arms around me and hugged me tight.

Our stay in the north consisted of seven days, which were very enjoyable, but like all good things it had to come to an end. So once again we were travelling back to York, where we had to separate, each going in different directions. Our separations were getting harder, but we comforted each other with the knowledge that we would soon be joined together in wedlock.

My train was to leave before Jim's, so he was able to see me off, and as my train moved out of the platform I knew I was leaving behind someone very dear to me. However, I put on a brave smile, and I waved to Jim until he was out of sight; then, sitting in my seat, my mind was full of thoughts.

The journey home was quite pleasant, and I had Mum to think about. The main thing was, could I ever settle down in such a place as Gateshead? Poverty could be seen everywhere, in the houses and the cobbled back lanes with the washing-lines strewn across them; the depression of the 1930s must have hit Gateshead hard. These thoughts filled my mind on the way home, but fortunately I had the disposition to look on the bright side. In the future, everything could change for the better.

To my delight Mum was there to meet me on the LMS station. We had so much to talk about and I was full of eulogies for Jim's family. Mum knew I was very happy, and she was happy for me.

In the summer months to follow, Baedeker raids continued, and cities like Canterbury suffered as we did. Nevertheless, the beautiful long summer days were a tonic to us all. For me there was an added excitement too, for now I was making preparations for my wedding, which would be on the 17th of October of this year, 1942.

Still very much occupied at the Pierrepont Garage, I maintained my two nights a week service with the Civil Defence. Somehow things had quietened down considerably. We had very few alerts, and we began to take things for granted, so much so that we eased up a little on routine. Men and women of the Civil Defence often did only one night on duty, instead of two, and to those who were on duty it meant a rest.

I suppose this lull we were now experiencing gave us an opportunity to attune our nervous stability, and so we felt the benefit from it; it was only looking at a newspaper, or hearing the news on the wireless, that reminded us we were still at war.

On Primrose Hill our little cottage just had to look nice for my wedding, but alas, it sadly needed decorating. Wallpaper and paint were difficult to get hold of, so we had to be content just to distemper the walls; of course it was not what we wanted, but it was the next best thing, this so-called coloured whitewash.

We did the bedroom walls in pastel shades, such as silver grey, lilac, and pale green, while downstairs we used the ever-popular cream. When it was finished, one could say it was remarkably clean.

After completing our decorating, and with the aid of clean floral-design curtains, our cottage was once again attractive, although we still retained the large battens that supported the outside walls.

My selection of a trousseau was easy because clothes were of course rationed. My sister-in-law Dolly came with me to Bristol, and I bought a plain brown dress, knowing I could make it look attractive by adding a strip of orange velvet six inches from the hem. Accessories consisted of a brown hat and shoes, gloves, and a handbag, not forgetting my short fur-fabric coat, which put the final touch to my outfit.

During the next two weeks, I was kept extremely busy, making periodical visits to the Convent in Bath. It was suggested by Jim that I should see the Nuns there. He said they would help me, and enlighten me about the wedding ceremony which was to be held at St. Alphege's in Oldfield Park.

The Nuns were very kind and helpful, and surprisingly I felt at ease in their presence. I listened carefully while they spoke of matters concerning the Church, and as I was not committed to any particular religious denomination it was easy for me to accept the teachings of the Catholic Church. I believed always that there can only be one God, who rules all mankind that believes in Him. Christian unity is still not fully established as yet, but I was sure I was an idealist of its future, and I believed all religions to be equal. So really all that mattered to me was having faith in God, for God we can trust; it is mankind that still needs to be checked out. No matter what Church I prayed in, all was unvarying. Hence my strong belief in this new great thing called Christian unity.

It was the 16th of October, 1942, and Jim was due in Bath. When I met him at the station, he was full of exhilaration, like myself. We had so much to talk about, even over tea, and our conversations were of so much interest that we did not realise time was passing quickly. However, Jim went into The Retreat and made a phone call to the YMCA in Broad Street, to confirm a booking he had previously made for bed and breakfast that night. Everyone was agreed that on our wedding-day we should only meet in church, and that's why Jim was having to stay in town.

Around 10 p.m. Jim left the cottage, giving me a hug and a kiss, and saying, 'See you in church tomorrow, darling.'

After Jim had gone, I still had much to do. Apart from having a bath and washing my hair, I had packing to do, and so it must have been around midnight when I went to bed.

And so my great day had arrived. Through the night it had rained heavily, yet at 6.30 a.m. this Saturday morning, when I jumped out of bed, the sun came streaming into my bedroom. I felt so very happy.

I made the early morning tea, and when awakening Rob I reminded him of his role as best man. I reminded him also that the arrangements were that he meet Jim outside the YMCA at 10 a.m.

'Only gives us an hour, our Paul, to get up to Oldfield Park. That's if the wedding ceremony starts at 11 a.m.'

'Eleven prompt,' I replied. 'So don't forget to get your skates on when you leave the YMCA. We can't keep the Reverend Canon Hackett himself waiting.'

'Don't worry, our Paul. We'll make it.'

It was before breakfast when Dad and I collected the flowers from the local nursery. My bouquet consisted of white and red miniature roses, which had the most delicate fragrance, and a large cardboard box contained white carnations for the men, along with sprays for the ladies.

As we walked back, I remarked to Dad what a beautiful morning it was, for everything appeared so fresh and alive after the rain. We were already in autumn, and the beautiful colouring of the leaves dampened by the rain was almost twinkling in the early morning sunshine.

After that walk, Dad and I were ready for our breakfast. But with breakfast over and everything cleared away, time was our own. Rob was the first to be ready, and I must say I looked upon him with admiration. I felt so proud of him, and happy with the thought that he was going to be our best man.

It was a shame that my other brothers would be absent from my wedding, but I knew they would be with us in thoughts. Jim too had no one to support him: his family were too far away to join us. This was a common situation in wartime weddings.

Previous arrangements had been made that Mrs Harding would be coming into our home to make preparations for the reception, which would be held at around 12.30, and before I had actually started dressing she was already in, making a start with the sandwiches. She was a little lady in stature, nimble, and with an amazing adaptability that would just fit in anywhere. I had much confidence in this little lady, and I knew the setting out of the reception table would be of her best.

After taking great pains over my cosmetics, I dressed and then went to Mum's long mirror on her dressing-table to view what I hoped would be pleasing to the eye. But something was not quite right. My hat — that's what it was, it wasn't sitting properly on my head. However, after a slight adjustment I had completed my outfit perfectly.

Then I remembered my little gold cross that Jim had given me; it would be the only jewellery I would be wearing, apart from my engagement ring, on which there were three small diamonds. I carefully placed the pendant around my neck, and felt satisfied that I was looking my best.

Then came a knocking on the front door, and as I hurried downstairs I heard laughter. On opening the door, there to my delight stood my sister Nellie, alongside my Aunt May and Uncle Jack, who also had come down from Sheffield.

Nellie just flung her arms around my neck, and whispered, 'You do look lovely, our Paul!'

Then it was Aunt May's turn to give me a kiss, followed by Uncle Jack giving me a kiss on the cheek. They had travelled all night, but showed no signs of fatigue.

Soon the cars arrived to take everyone to church, and I must say the ladies looked adorable in their short dresses and little perky hats. Mum was the last to leave with them, and giving me a hug she quietly said, 'All my love and blessings be with you, darling.'

Despite all the excitement going on, Mrs Harding was not perturbed and carried on at a steady pace; already she had set the large oak table beautifully, with an enormous bowl of white chrysanthemums right in the middle.

I don't know exactly what it was, but I started trembling, and Dad was quick to notice. 'You all right, Paul?'

I smiled at Dad, knowing I was looking upon a fine handsome man still, one whom I still relied on very much. 'Guess I am a little shaky,' I said.

'It's understandable,' replied Dad. 'Never mind. I've got just the remedy.' Then, taking a bottle of best Scotch whisky from the sideboard, he filled three small glasses, giving me a wink as he did so. 'This will be our little secret.' He then gave Mrs Harding a glass, who in return said, 'Your health, Mr Quintin, and to you, Paul, all happiness, health and good luck.' All three glasses clinked.

Holding the small tot of whisky in my hand, I somehow felt a little guilty. After all, I shouldn't indulge in any intoxicating liquor, especially before going to church. Dad must have read my thoughts, for he said, 'Drink up, Paul, it's purely medication. It will do you good.' Believing always that Dad did everything for the best, I swallowed the toddy in one gulp, shuddering at its bitterness. However, in minutes it did the trick; my trembling had stopped.

The next thing was that the taxi-driver arrived at the door, telling us he was ready to take us to church. Well, Mrs Harding came to the door to see us off, and out in the lane our few remaining neighbours had assembled, making sure I guess that the blushing bride had a good send-off. And how true, for I really felt myself blushing — or was it the little tot of Dutch courage? Anyway, I was so happy, the morning was so beautiful, and the war was far away to me now; to be honest I felt it didn't exist.

Getting into the taxi, I noticed two broad white bands of ribbon arraying the bonnet, which made me very conscious of the fact that I was on my way to church to be wed. But when we arrived outside St Alphege's, there was no one about.

'Must be all inside,' said Dad, who then opened the large door that led to the portico.

Inside, we met a layman, who whispered, 'Good morning.' Then, apologetically, he said, 'there has been some delay with Canon Hackett. If you just wait a moment, I will try and find out what is happening.'

So meanwhile Dad and I just stood, myself admiring my bouquet of roses, and thinking what delicate gentle flowers they were. Once more the layman appeared, again full of apology.

'I'm sorry', he said 'but it is with regret that Canon Hackett will not be able to attend and officiate. But instead there's a Father Dolan who will take his place, so if you please wait a little longer, he shouldn't be long.'

I don't know if I was disappointed or not that Canon Hackett was unable to marry us. Anyway, the three of us waited, and then we heard a car door close.

'That'll be Father Dolan now,' said the layman.

Another five minutes must have gone by, and then the layman quietly opened the interior door and whispered, 'You may go in now.'

I held Dad's arm as we walked down the aisle. Unfortunately we had no organ music, another consquence of the war, so all we could hear was our own footsteps walking on the tiled floor.

Looking straight ahead of me I could see Jim and Rob standing almost in the centre of the altar, and in front of them was a very young Priest, whose face was beaming with goodness and all sincerity. As I approached he gently nodded, and beckoned me over beside Jim; at this stage, I let go of Dad's arm.

The wedding ceremony had begun, and for all that the service was nearly all spoken in Latin, it was most beautiful and was solemnised in the perfect surroundings of the church.

After Father Dolan had shaken hands with us, we followed him into the presbytery, where we both signed the register.

Coming out of the presbytery, Jim and I started walking arm in arm back up the aisle, and looking around I could see more people than I had anticipated. To my surprise, amongst them were some of my old colleagues from Civil Defence. Only one thing saddened me: there was no one belonging to Jim here. But then I told myself that from now on my friends were his friends.

Up in the porch now there was much laughter going on, and in the midst I overheard a voice say, 'Can't call you Miss Quintin any longer!' Why, if it wasn't Mr Penny himself, and indeed I was pleased to see him. I introduced Jim to him, and then he handed me a parcel. 'Congratulations,' he said, 'from all your friends at the depot.' I was so overwhelmed, and I thanked Mr Penny kindly.

Outside the church we all posed to have our photographs taken by the photographer from the local paper, and in the meantime we were being showered with confetti. It was not real confetti of course, because you couldn't get it, but a good imitation, made up of small pieces of paper with numbers on, a tail-end of some sort of a waste product; however, it was all good fun. Jim and I then left for home, with tin cans and all sorts tied on to the bumper of our taxi; so now the whole wide world knew that we had just been married. And on arriving in the lane there were more to greet us, not only neighbours but strangers that had come out of The Retreat. I saw a man I had never seen before. He just raised his pint glass and called out, 'Best of luck to you both.'

Up went many cheers. I felt honoured, and I'm sure Jim must have felt the same way, and when we finally reached home, Mrs Harding was standing at the front door. She hugged and kissed us both, and at the same time giving us her blessings; and bless her too, for she had everthing ready and under control.

It was while we waited for everyone returning that I decided to open up the parcel which Mr Penny had given me. Unwrapping the brown paper, I had yet to open up a cardboard box, curious as to what it contained. Then to our delight, I lifted out two beautiful silver candlesticks.

'Oh Jim, aren't they lovely?'

'A very nice present,' answered Jim.

I went across to the table, and placed a candlestick on either side of the flowers. 'Meant for the occasion,' I said.

'By golly, Paul,' said Jim. 'Aren't they lovely? Fitting for a Queen, to be sure.'

And so, when we were all together, there was great merriment. We had plenty to eat and drink, and for a wartime reception I can only say it was fabulous. When Mum played the piano we all joined in at singing and dancing. A most happy occasion indeed and long to be remembered. Meanwhile, time was passing quickly and soon Jim and I would be leaving on our honeymoon.

Surrounded by relatives and friends, we all walked down into town to the LMS station. There was so much laughter going on, especially when we were at the station. I noticed Mum and Dad: they were laughing too, and this made me happy. I realised that this parting would not be a sad one, for now I had Jim, my husband, beside me.

We travelled up to Nottingham, where we stayed overnight in a pleasant little house, and not until Jim placed my suitcase on a chair did I realise why so many people had stared at us, and all with smiling faces — for out of the corner of the case dangled a blue baby's bootie.

'Jim, look!' I said, and we both burst out laughing together.

The following morning there was still quite a lot of sunshine, so we decided to stroll around Nottingham. And how enjoyable it all was, seeing new places and people. I realised that I was overcoming a great deal of shyness, for I could converse with people more freely.

After a good lunch, we made our way to the railway station. Our intention, of course, was to catch the first train to Newcastle, for we were going up to spend a few days with Jim's people. We sat on Nottingham station, waiting for our train to come in, and when it did it was packed with troops. I would be quite justified in saying that the troops were packed so tightly on the train they were like sardines in a tin.

'We must try and get on,' said Jim. So Jim opened the first door at hand, and we both managed to squeeze on. Then Jim said, 'Wait here, Paul.' I saw him struggling up the corridor, and he was gone some time, but eventually I saw him making his way back; he was smiling. 'Come on, Paul. To the next carriage.'

We both squeezed past everyone and finally reached the next carriage, where to my surprise Jim stopped outside a compartment that had the blinds down. He gave three taps on the door and one of the blinds immediately went up, and next I was looking upon an American in uniform. He was alone, I could see, and to my astonishment he was untying a rope which had been securely tied round both inside handles of the door. Quickly he let us in, once again securing the handles of the doors with strong-looking rope.

I was bewildered by it all.

'This is my wife,' said Jim.

'Pleased to meet you, Ma'am.' We shook hands.

The American's stature, I could see, was of the small wiry type; around his waist he wore a holster, and from it protruded a pistol. There was no mistaking it, he was a security man, and responsible for the two brief-cases that were very close beside him.

All I did was to sit and listen to the American and Jim, and while watching the stranger I noticed that his right hand never left his side. Without a doubt he was ready for anything, his fingers so close to the trigger.

If the blinds had not been down I would have been able to look out of the window at the passing scenery, but as it was I could only sit still and watch the American. The three of us sat in artificial light, passing the time away with the odd conversation.

I dare say Jim and I were grateful for a comfortable seat, so providence had its way with us, and we were privileged to be in this American's company. It somehow amused me to see what he did with his right hand, for he produced a tobacco tin out of his pouch pocket, and still with only one hand he made a home-made rolled cigarette, lit it, and then spoke: 'You don't mind, Ma'am?'

'Not at all,' I replied. Soon Jim was filling his pipe.

The American spoke of his home in Texas, and I was honoured to think I had met a real live cowboy, for that's what he was; and of course my imagination was so great that I could actually see him on a horse and driving many hundreds of cattle, not forgetting his ability to manipulate a gun.

And so as the journey went over it was made pleasant with the interest of the American's presence. Naturally we were grateful to him for allowing us into his compartment.

As the train pulled into Newcastle, we once again shook hands with the American guard, and thanked him. It never dawned on me until afterwards — would he ever know we were only newly-weds, and on our honeymoon?

Out of the station, we took the tram over to Gateshead. We arrived at Jim's home just in time for supper, and his family welcomed us both with all their love.

So began our married life. We did not have a honeymoon in Paris, as a modern couple might, and we knew that we would not be able to set up a home together for some time; but our stay in the north-east was nevertheless a happy one.

Inevitably, the time came when we had to leave the north-east and return to Bath. When we did arrive back home, Jim could only stay a few hours with me before he had to go back to his army duties, but those few hours were precious.

In the weeks to follow I missed him desperately. However, our letters and telephone calls kept us in constant touch. I continued with my Civil Defence duties, and life in general appeared on an even keel. I could almost say it was routine, for there was very little air activity; and so the lull in the war continued, for the time being at any rate.

Sir Stafford Cripps was determined to put an end to private motoring. Official posters were being displayed everywhere; for example, one asked, 'Is your journey really necessary?' People were encouraged to beg lifts from lorry drivers, and this I might say included girls. Shocking, some would say. Our own Civil Defence gave us instructions that we could give lifts if we wished, on condition we did not go out of our way. This was happening everywhere, and girls not only hitch-hiked, but plucked up courage to go into pubs.

November of 1942, with General Montgomery's victory at El Alamein, marked the turning-point of the war. Winston Churchill was cautiously optimistic when he said, 'Now this is not the end. It is not even the beginning of the end. But it is, perhaps, the end of the beginning.'

The autumn of 1942 also saw the publication of the Beveridge Report, which laid the foundations for the welfare state. Beveridge argued that family allowances should be given for all children, that a National Health Service should be provided, and that mass unemployment could be avoided. Nearly everyone welcomed these ideas and believed that they should be adopted. In the meantime, free milk was provided under the National Milk Scheme, and the number of subsidised meals to schools was increased.

November the 15th 1942 was a special day for me. I had become twenty-one. I spent the day quietly with Mum, Dad and Rob. I received presents, and a special one from Jim, who incidentally rang me up, saying how he wished he could have been with me.

In the weeks to follow, and just before Jim's next leave, I had the occasion to visit Doctor Scott-White, who after giving me an examination revealed that I was pregnant. We were all delighted, and I couldn't wait to tell Jim, so I wrote to him immediately. His return letter to me was most wonderful, and it was only natural that it gave me added joy.

Feeling fit and well, I decided to continue on working, and to carry out my duties with the Civil Defence. Meanwhile, Jim came home on leave, and for all that it was so very cold, with snow on the ground, it was a heavenly time we shared together; most of the days were spent before the fire, making plans for our future.

Christmas came and went, and January brought heavy falls of snow and drifting. By this time I was beginning to find I couldn't cope with some of the manual work at the garage, so I realised the time had come when I must give it up. When I explained to Mr Griffin, he was so nice and understanding about it.

'We'll all miss you, you know,' he said. And I knew only too well that I would miss the life at the garage, for each day I came in contact with so many nice people. I was aware also that I would have to say goodbye to all my dear friends at the Civil Defence. However, I had some compensation; I was to have a little holiday.

It was Jim's suggestion, weeks previous, that I should go to Wem, and spend a few weeks with him. So my little vacation began in February of 1943. The weather of course was still very cold, and Mum and Dad were rather concerned about me, especially when the time came for me to go, making sure I was well clad in warm clothing.

I travelled to Shrewsbury by train, and Jim was there to meet me; we then caught a bus to Wem, where the military had their own railway base. After alighting from the bus, we stood on a country road, and looking around I was aware that we were right in the heart of the country.

Jim then pointed to the right saying, 'That's the depot over there.' We continued on, walking up the road. It was afternoon, yet the air was still crisp with frost. I hung on to Jim's arm, while our steps were brisk.

We passed a field of sheep enjoying their feed of mangel-wurzel. Still walking on, we came to a tiny row of cottages, picturesque I'm sure in summer-time. Jim stopped outside one of them, and opened a small gate that led up a pathway. Then, placing his arm around my shoulder, Jim walked me up the pathway, saying, 'Our little home, Paul, for two weeks.'

Following Jim inside, I was surprised to see the cottage so well furnished, and I knew that once we had a fire on we would be nice and cosy.

I glanced around me, observing the small kitchen with glee, for there stood a gas stove, and alongside it all the amenities required for cooking. There was also a clean white enamel sink, on the small side perhaps, but ideally suitable. I then explored the bedrooms, two in all, again well furnished with plenty of bed-linen on the beds.

So this was to be our home for two whole weeks. It was the first time we had been really alone together, living as man and wife, and was to be almost the only such occasion until the war was over.

Jim smiled at me. 'Like it, Paul?'

I nodded happily.

Jim set about putting a fire on, while I made myself busy in the kitchen. First I made a cup of tea, for that's what we wanted, and then I remembered I still had sandwiches in my bag, so while we watched the fire burn brightly we tucked in.

'I've made arrangements,' said Jim, 'for you and I to call in at the army cook-house, round about seven o'clock. The chef there has offered to make us some supper.'

'That's very kind of him,' I said. 'But will it be all right, Jim? I mean, my going into a military camp. Don't want to get anybody into any trouble.'

'Strictly under the hat, of course,' said Jim. 'But it's a quiet time, and we have the chef's approbation. Nice chap, you'll like him.'

Around seven o'clock, we were ready to make our way to the camp. I felt a little apprehensive, especially when Jim and I walked through the two big barbed-wire gates that led into the depot.

'Mess-room over here,' said Jim, as he pointed to the right of us. Then he caught hold of my hand as he led me to a large tin hut that comprised both cookhouse and canteen. Jim opened a small iron door, and we both entered into what looked like a dining-hall, with its long tables and forms. 'Sit down, Paul, I'll see if Jock's around.'

Jim then went over to another little door and opened it, whereupon I heard a Scotsman's voice call out, 'Hello, Mac!'

A tall man was Jock, who came striding across to me, wearing his chef's attire. And when Jim introduced me to him, I felt a handshake of warmth and friendliness. In no time at all we both sat down to a good supper, which consisted of a fry-up, but was nevertheless enjoyable. After we had finished, we thanked Jock, left the canteen, and so back through the barbed-wire gates and on to the roadway.

The dimmed lights of the local bus were coming up the road towards us. 'Just the job,' said Jim. 'We'll catch the bus to The Pig and Whistle.'

The bus then took us a good mile up the road, and when we got off we were right outside the small local pub, the appearance of which was similar to The Retreat back home. When we entered we were greeted by the landlord himself, who spoke with a Welsh accent. The atmosphere appeared very friendly, and amongst the locals were many servicemen from Jim's depot, who exchanged greetings.

I noticed that many of the soldiers were coloured, but they mixed freely amongst the locals, so I realised that there was no race discrimination here, only a mixture of well-being and esteem. I watched with interest, as so many were enjoying a game of dominoes, and I observed much laughter amongst the conversation.

Two coloured men came across to Jim and I, so Jim introduced me to them. 'Couple of my pals,' said Jim. Immediately their faces beamed with amused expressions, showing off their beautiful pearly white teeth. Again the handshakes of friendliness. 'I spoil them you know, Paul,' said Jim, who by now was grinning at the both of them.

'We sure wouldn't know what to do without you, Mac.'

'Ain't that just so,' remarked one to the other.

I couldn't help but admire these black men, for here they were doing their bit for their country.

During our stay at The Pig and Whistle, I was introduced to many more of Jim's friends who had settled in for the evening. After all, it was their only recreation, for Shrewsbury was almost six miles away, much too far to go for a drink. I suppose it made sense anchoring at a local pub; they were close to the camp, which was especially useful if they should have one too many.

The time came for us to leave The Pig and Whistle, so saying goodnight to everyone we made our way back along the country road towards our little cottage. The night air being so very cold, we hurried our steps to keep warm, and were pleased to see the fire still burning when we got in.

After Jim had given the fire a poke, he placed another knob of coal on, making the little room so warm and cosy. We didn't hurry up to bed; we were content just to sit and chat. We talked of the lads at the depot, and then our conversation drifted into things in general. But sleep was catching up on the both of us, for we started yawning, so I made a hot drink for Jim and I before retiring.

The bed was very comfortable and so we were soon off to sleep, and the next morning we were both up bright and early, for Jim had to be at the depot at 8 a.m.

'I'll be back at two,' he said. 'We'll go into Shrewsbury, have a look around.' He then kissed me, and was off. His army boots clattered as he walked down the pathway of uneven stones, then we waved to each other until he was out of sight.

The early morning sunshine was struggling to break through, and I myself was just in my element as I pottered around in the cottage. I must say the environment in which I now found myself made me extremely happy, and so when all was spick and span I sat down to write home.

I had almost finished my letter when I heard a little tap on the front door. Wondering who it could be, I hastened to open the door, and to my surprise there stood a frail little old lady, with snowy white hair.

Her smile looked sincere. 'Good morning,' she said. 'I live next door. I've come to see if you are all right.'

I smiled back at her, and held my hand out, and she eagerly clasped mine tightly. 'I'm Mrs McCann,' I said, 'and I'm pleased to meet you. Won't you come in a minute?' This she did.

She wore a black shawl around her shoulders, and loosened it off as she sat beside the fire. 'I called,' she said, 'because I thought I might be of some help to you. Knowing, I guess, you being a stranger to these parts.'

I assumed the old lady wanted to conciliate me, and as a matter of fact, I think I was of the same mind, so I offered her a cup of cocoa, which she gladly accepted. Then suddenly her face beamed, for she said, 'What I really wanted to know was who my new neighbour was.' So at least she was honest about it. After all, we all possess inquisitiveness, and the dear old lady was no exception.

'Now I am happy,' she remarked, so I must have come up to her approval. Anyway, I listened with interest as she talked of the small village of Wem, its people and its traditions. Then the little old lady departed, thanking me for her cup of cocoa and the hospitality I had shown her. When she had gone, I realised that I still didn't know her name. Anyway, finishing off my letter, I popped it in my handbag ready for posting.

Jim arrived punctually, and myself being all ready we soon caught the bus into Shrewsbury. On the bus I told Jim of my early visitor.

'I guess the old dear was curious as to who you were,' he said.

And so we arrived in Shrewsbury, noted for its Shrewsbury biscuits, and it was fascinating just walking around the old market town. I was only reminded of the war by the piled-up sandbags around the big buildings, such as the Town Hall. I observed also the people, just going about in an undisturbed manner, and shopkeepers maintaining their politeness and respecting the old saying, 'The customer is always right.'

I very much enjoyed my afternoon, just strolling around with Jim, and although the weather was very cold it was dry, and we were both well wrapped up. We then had a high tea in a most select restaurant, and then finally stood in a queue to see a movie.

It was while we were standing there that it happened: I felt a hand go into the side-pocket of my little short fur coat.

I turned around quickly. I wanted to know who could have done this despicable thing. Only a coloured boy in the khaki uniform of the US Army was standing right behind me.

On the spur of the moment I wanted to shout out. I could easily have accused the soldier of pickpocketing. But somehow I couldn't. I knew that what was in my pocket was not worth taking: only my handkerchief, and a couple of hair-grips. Anyway, I thought it wiser not to mention this incident to Jim, knowing that it would surely have resulted in a scene.

The queue moved up a little, and it was no good, curiosity overcame me — I just had to glance behind me, to see if the man was still there.

He was.

His defiance angered me. I thought him brazen to remain standing in the queue, for he must have known what he had done. My fury must have made me blush, for Jim had noticed. 'You all right, Paul?' I nodded, but imagine how thankful I was when we sat down in our seats and settled down to enjoy the film. For the time being I soon forgot about the little incident, and it was not until we returned home on the bus that I mentioned what had happened.

'You should have told me,' said Jim. 'He wouldn't have been standing long, if I had known. It's no wonder you blushed up, for I had that feeling something was wrong.'

And so another evening had come to a close.

How the days flew over. One evening of the second week, Jim took me to a local dance. The servicemen outnumbered the females, but what odds — we were all out to enjoy ourselves.

Jim and I could not dance, and knowing Jim I realised that he would be content just to sit and smoke his pipe and enjoy the accordion music. However, I did make the effort of getting up on the floor, and tried dancing a few steps, and really I was doing all right until suddenly up went my legs and I landed on my bottom. I fully expected Jim to rush over and pick me up. But he didn't. He only saw the funny side of it, and laughed, and continued puffing his pipe. I was now a damsel in distress, and I thought no one would come to my rescue. But how wrong I was, for a handsome sergeant lifted me up on my feet, and asked me if I was all right.

'Yes, thank you,' I said. I then went over and sat beside Jim, who said, 'You did look funny!' Whereupon I had to laugh with him.

Jim and I were extremely happy, and on my last evening I decided to give a party — you might say a farewell party. The following day I would be travelling back home, and knew that any sort of a party would lessen the heartaches of our separation the following morning.

So, on my last day, and when Jim had gone to the depot, I caught the early bus into Shrewsbury to do a bit of shopping. With only my own ration book I knew I could purchase very little. However, there were still things off the ration, and amongst the latter I bought 2 lb. of shrimps; and then, with my bag full of odds and ends, I caught the bus back to Wem.

Preparing a buffet supper was easy. Mind you, the shrimps didn't look very elegant sitting alongside the Shrewsbury biscuits, but I managed to make the table look attractive. I then put on my very best dress and waited for Jim and the lads.

I heard laughter: my guests had arrived, each bringing a couple of bottles with them. At first we sat around the fire talking. Then one of the lads, who had brought along his portable gramophone, put on one of the latest records, 'Jealousy.' We were all so merry it somehow reminded me of Christmas, with everyone enjoying the eatables from the table.

At the end of the evening our friends left us with a formal praise of having enjoyed the little party, and Jim and I were alone.

'I'm going to miss you Paul,' he said.

And I knew only too well of my own feelings.

We were up very early the next morning, and with the weather turning a little milder it started to rain very heavy.

I was all packed and ready to leave with Jim, for he was coming to Wem station to see me off, which was a good mile away. I felt sad at leaving the little cottage, where Jim and I had spent two glorious weeks which now abruptly had come to an end; all that was left was sweet memories, never to be forgotten.

We started walking down the country lane, with Jim carrying my suitcase and myself tightly hanging on to his arm. It was dark, and the rain was lashing down into our faces, so by the time we reached Wem station we were drenched. My wet hair draggled around my neck, and where I stood I made a pool of water from my dripping mackintosh. I looked at Jim: his khaki overcoat was soaking, and the rain was still running down his face.

'Oh, Paul,' he said. 'Wish you hadn't to go. If I had known it was going to be like this, I would surely have made arrangements to have had time off to come up to Shrewsbury with you. Anyway, when you get on Shrewsbury station, don't forget to get yourself a hot drink.'

I could tell that Jim was already worrying about me. 'Don't worry, darling,' I said. 'I'll be all right.'

The little train came puffing in, and it was almost empty, and so Jim selected me a clean compartment all to myself. We said our goodbyes there and then, with Jim giving me his last hug.

'Look after yourself, Paul.'

I felt like crying, and looking into Jim's eyes I saw I was not mistaken: they were misty too.

I got up to the window and waved. Jim stood there, pathetic and so alone, on almost a deserted station with the clouds sending down more heavy rain. Then the train gave a jerk and started moving. I myself put on a display of bravado with the biggest smile I could possibly give.

I then lowered the window, and Jim called out, 'Write as soon as you get back home.'

'I will,' I replied. 'And God bless you, darling.'

Now it was only a matter of waving as Jim's figure got smaller and smaller, until at last he was completely out of sight.

Our partings were getting harder each time.

I then moved into a compartment, got myself in the corner seat and cried. Now I felt so utterly miserable, and being damp with the soaking of the rain did not improve matters. However, the little train soon got to Shrewsbury, and my connection was already waiting in the station. On impulse I immediately stepped on to it, ignoring the fact that I should have got myself a hot drink as Jim had suggested. But the way I felt, I just wanted to be alone and settle down on the Bristol train, only to curl up in my own little world of dreams.

I found a comfortable seat, and placed my suitcase on the rack above. When I sat down I knew I looked a mess; indeed I felt very uncomfortable and was glad to get my wet shoes off.

Then the compartment door opened, and a soldier entered, putting his valise on the seat opposite me. He did not speak, but I was fully aware of the side glance he gave me. Then he went out of the compartment and disappeared.

By now I was beginning to shiver, and I longed for the train to start moving, so that the heating would come through. I looked out of the window. There was much activity on the platform, with lots of people going here and there. But I was not interested; I could now only think of Jim, and the lovely time we had spent together.

Then the door of the compartment opened again. I looked up, and saw that the soldier had returned. In each hand he carried a jam-jar of steaming hot tea, and holding one of the jam-jars out to me, he half smiled and said, 'I got this for you. I kind of thought you needed it.'

'Oh, thank you!' I answered, eagerly reaching out to take the jam-jar. I sipped the tea, occasionally looking up at the soldier who was doing likewise.

Then he spoke again. 'Not a very nice morning, it it?'

'It isn't,' I timidly answered. I felt the hot tea now warming me through, and certainly I was beginning to feel much better.

Then the soldier spoke in a hesitant manner. 'None of my business, but it bain't wise you sitting in those damp things.' I immediately detected the dialect; he was a west-countryman to be sure.

'Yes,' I said, 'I best change into something dry.' Having finished my tea, I was about to get my suitcase down when the soldier leapt to his feet, and lifted the case down for me.

Feeling around the suitcase, which was now half opened, I pulled out a woolly dress, a cardigan, and a pair of stockings, which I quickly bundled up and placed underneath my arm; and it was in the toilet I changed, being thankful at having something dry to put on.

I returned to the compartment with a wet bundle under my arm. I slipped the clothes into my suitcase, and immediately I had done so the soldier got up on his feet and lifted my case back up on the rack.

'Feel better now?' he said.

'Yes, thank you. And do please let me pay for the tea.'

'Oh, that's all right,' he said. And now almost chuckling he added, 'Only be one penny a jam-jar.' The soldier was now looking upon me with a friendly smile. 'Must look after you young mums,' he said. 'My wife is the same. Expecting our first in June.'

Now I understood why the soldier was so sympathetic towards me.

During my journey to Bristol, many other people kept coming and going in our compartment. This interested me, for just listening in to different conversations kept my thoughts occupied. A petty officer offered me a sandwich, and its relish flavour of mustard cured my pangs of hunger. At other times there was silence in the compartment. I didn't mind, I was just content to sit quietly and think my own thoughts as the train was speeding along, getting me that much nearer home.

Not far from Bristol, I pulled out my shoes from underneath the seat, and to my dismay I could see that they had shrunk: the toes of my shoes were literally curling up. I knew at once that I would never get them on my feet. However, I remembered that I had my slippers in my case; I would have to get them out. Oh dear, I thought, I'll have to trouble the soldier again. Now I felt myself being a nuisance. I looked at the soldier, who was now reading, and I was hesitant about interrupting him.

'Excuse me,' I said. 'And I'm sorry to have to bother you. Only it's my shoes,' I exclaimed, now clutching them in my hand and holding them out on display.

'Goodness me,' said the soldier. 'They ain't half shrunk. Got another pair?'

'Yes,' I replied, 'and they would have to be in my suitcase, wouldn't they?'

'Hang on, I'll get your case down.'

'Sorry to give you all this bother.'

'It bain't no bother,' he replied. 'And you must have something on your feet.'

How could I ever forget this soldier's kindness, for he had looked after me as an older brother would. I fumbled around for my slippers, knowing that they would perhaps look idiotic with my fur coat, but there it was — I had no other choice.

Eventually the train pulled into Temple Meads station, and after saying cheerio to the soldier, I alighted. Now to make enquiries about a train up to Bath. I was just about to speak to a porter when I heard our Rob's voice shout out, 'Paul!'

I spun around. 'Why hello, Rob! How good to see you.'

We embraced each other, and then Rob took my case. 'Come down to fetch you home.'

'You're a pal,' I answered.

'Wait till you see her,' said Rob. 'She's a little smasher.'

'Oh?' I was now wondering if Rob had got himself a girl. My curiosity was aroused, and when Rob suggested we go out of the station, I was full of inquisitiveness, anxious to know the outcome. So you can imagine my surprise when Rob shouts out, 'There she is!' At the same time pointing to a green Riley.

I couldn't help but burst out laughing. 'Why Rob, it's a car! I fully expected seeing a girl.'

Rob was now smiling. 'Just couldn't afford two,' he said. 'Although I bought it cheap, almost for a song. A bloke was hard up. Got it for a fiver.'

We chatted happily while Rob skilfully drove me home. I was longing to see Mum and Dad, and how pleased they in turn were to see me; their happiness and mine combined and made it quite a reunion. There was so much to talk about. I constantly talked of Jim and I, and I was sorry Rob had to go back to work. However, I reminded him to thank Mr Griffin once again for letting him off to meet me at Bristol.

'Doesn't our Paul look well, Pat?' Mum's eyes were now fixed on Dad, who was staring at my feet.

'Golly,' said Dad. 'You're wearing slippers! Where are your shoes?'

It was Rob who spoke, now almost ready to go off to work. 'Paul had a bit of a catastrophe with her shoes — they got shrunk in the train.'

'You got them that wet?' said Mum. 'It's a wonder you didn't catch your death of cold. You'll have to take more care, duck, with baby coming along.'

I helped Mum to wash up, and afterwards we sat around the fire, right up until the 6 o'clock news. Then we heard the front door open, and a voice which we recognised at once as that of Old Sam.

'Be you there, Pauline?' I jumped up, opened the kitchen door, and saw the outline of Sam in the doorway. 'It's Jim, he be on the phone.'

I was possessed with wild excitement, shouting, 'Thank you!' to Old Sam as I flew past him. I ran down the steps into The Retreat and picked up the phone, saying, 'Hello?'

Jim's voice echoed in my ears. 'Hello, darling. You all right? Just had to ring you up.'

Quickly I gave him all the news, and was so full of my own happenings that I almost forgot to ask him how he was.

'I'm fine, Paul, but missing you terribly. Anyway,' said Jim, 'I'm happy to know you are OK. So I think I'll go down to the pub for a pint, and a chat with the lads.'

After we had said cheerio to each other, I replaced the receiver. Then, turning to Sam, I thanked him.

'Well, how be Jim then? He's gonna miss you.' And I could have sworn Old Sam had a twinkle in his eye when he spoke. Anyway, we bade each other goodnight. Hurrying back in home, I settled down with happiness and contentment, knowing that all was well with my husband.

A couple of weeks later, I was beginning to feel restless. Maybe it was because I wasn't working. I felt that I should at least be doing a part-time job; I was feeling quite fit, and capable of doing any kind of light work. I talked it over with Mum and Dad, but they were both unhappy about my wanting to do a job of work.

'You must think of the baby,' said Mum.

I knew Mum was right, of course, and it was really a selfish attitude on my part, but I still had this desire to help the war effort. In any case, a few days later the opportunity arose. It was while I was doing some shopping in Bath that I saw this poster which told me about civil servants being required for the Admiralty, and that part-time staff would be considered; the latter interested me. I did not hesitate but made enquiries at once, whereupon I signed a form of acceptance to undergo an entrance examination. I'm afraid impromptu came over me; I acted upon impulse rather than thinking about the consequences.

Going home on the bus that day, I felt a little uneasy, for I knew Mum and Dad would not be pleased with what I had done. Yet I knew that if I was accepted it would only be on a temporary basis.

Mum and Dad were in when I arrived home, and over tea I discreetly announced that I had intentions of becoming a civil servant for the Admiralty.

'But, duck,' said Mum. 'You cannot type or do shorthand.'

'I know, Mum, but maybe I'll fit in where longhand is required, and I'm sure there'll be lots of writing to do.'

Dad was now surveilling me thoughtfully. What could be his opinion in the matter? I think I was ready to expect discouragement from him, but instead he was quite the opposite, more to my surprise.

'Well, our Paul, you're attempting to keep the old flag flying, and why not.' Then Dad looked at Mum. 'She'll be all right, Nell. It'll keep her occupied, anyway.'

I couldn't help it, but just had to kiss Dad on the cheek, for now I was happy at his approval. And Mum, she was smiling, so I guessed that in the end I had talked them round.

As I expected, an official letter arrived two days later, giving me the date and time on which to undergo an entrance examination. This I successfully passed, and I was given an assignment to start with DNA (the Director of Naval Accounts), their base being at Combe Down, which was situated on the outskirts of the city. It meant I would have to take two buses to get there, but this I didn't mind, for I knew the nice weather was ahead, and travelling in buses would be somewhat of a novelty.

In almost a week I had settled down to be a civil servant, and the work I was engaged upon was pleasant and most interesting, having dealings with Naval allowances. I must say I had difficulty with the filing system; however, I aimed at getting it off to perfection and eventually I won. I was indeed very happy at my work, for most of it was straightforward, and I got along fine with everyone, regardless of my condition.

Writing as I do now, I can let secrets out, for amused I was at many a sailor who turned out to have more than one wife, and who all sent in their claims for allowances. Well, part of my job was to write to all the ladies, asking for their marriage certificates; this was the only means by which I could obtain identification. I'm afraid I had to disappoint quite a few of them.

I was classed as grade III, doing all of my work in longhand, and being sedentary I had no bother at all. Content I was. I was still contributing to the war effort, and feeling very well; I had no cause for enervation. However, someone must have thought different, for one day I was told that I was going to be transferred to Kingswood School, on the Lansdown Road; my destination was CE in C (Civil Engineering in Chief). No explanatory reason for my transfer was given, but I had the idea that someone was being very kind to me; for after all I was pregnant, and Kingswood School being only ten minutes' walk from home would certainly alleviate my travelling.

And so came my first encounter with Kingswood School. It was to be at 9 a.m. this lovely morning in April of 1943, and as I made my way up to the School I noticed all the lovely flowers coming out in the gardens; an April shower, followed by the sunshine, had given the scene that added freshness.

Kingswood School was incredibly Victorian. The buildings were made of Bath stone, so old, yet so dignified by long standing and their history of teaching fine young English gentlemen.

Myself, I thought it a shame they had to be occupied by the Admiralty, but under the circumstances of war I suppose it just had to be.

So here I was, wearing a loose blue silk coat, standing right outside the big iron gates. The next thing, I was confronted by a patrolman, who, after seeing my pass, smiled and let me through.

I walked up the driveway and then paused at the entrance, with its huge panelled wooden door; above it was nobly displayed the coat of arms. I went through the entrance, only to be met by another official in uniform.

'Good morning,' he said.

'Good morning,' I replied.

'New, aren't you, Miss?' Then the man was suddenly aware of his error, for he spoke again: 'It's Mrs er. . . .'

'Mrs McCann,' I blurted out.

'Right, Mrs McCann. Would you kindly take a seat. I'll get someone to attend to you.'

He was on the phone directly, and then said, 'Someone will be coming down to look after you.'

'Thank you,' I answered.

By this time I had taken off my fine cotton gloves, and was clasping my handbag, fingering Jim's regimental badge of the Royal Engineers, which I had neatly sewn on it for ornament. This was a very popular thing to do with badges at the time; it reminded women of their menfolk, and anyway I was proud to display Jim's badge of the REs.

The next thing, a young lady approached me. 'It's Mrs McCann, isn't it?'

I smiled, and then got to my feet, at which point I felt the young woman's eyes upon me. I think she was rather surprised at seeing me in my condition, but in fact it was nothing out of the ordinary to see expectant mothers continuing to work as long as they were able.

'Do follow me, please.'

I followed her through what seemed endless corridors, with attaching small rooms, and it was outside one of these rooms that she stopped abruptly. Then she gave two knocks on the door, and I heard a man's voice call out, 'Come in.'

We both entered. 'Mrs McCann, Sir,' said the young lady, who then turned around and departed.

I was standing almost motionless, facing a man seated at his desk. At once he got up and shook hands with me.

'So pleased to meet you, Mrs McCann. I'm Mr Gordon.'

'Pleased to meet you, Sir.'

He then looked at me in an amiable fashion. Maybe he admired me for accepting a challenge, knowing that I was not deterred through pregnancy. I quickly guessed he was a man of middle age, pleasant, and most understanding, for he put me at ease straightaway.

'Come,' he said. I'll show you to your little office,' and he led me into an adjoining room. It's a bit pokey,' he said, 'but I dare say you'll manage.'

Taking my coat off, I hung it up on the stand. Then my new boss looked at me and smiled.

'I guess you are anxious to know exactly what we do here. Well, you and I will be responsible for handling a large Naval benevolent fund. This of course is only one of my many jobs. But you, Mrs McCann, will be devoted entirely to the work of the fund. So you'll have a free hand, to work completely on your own. You'll find you'll deal with lots of correspondence, but it's pretty straightforward, and I feel sure you will be able to cope. For myself, I'll be away most days. But today, as it happens, I'll be here all day. So it will give me the opportunity of showing you what to do.'

Mr Gordon then went through the work with me, and was most helpful, explaining carefully every little detail. The work involved receiving and forwarding cheques, and keeping control of the financial side of the fund. Lunchtime came around before I knew where I was, so at 12 o'clock I went home, until I resumed again at 1.30 p.m.

The days that followed lengthened into weeks, and Mr Gordon was very pleased with my work, so much so that I was raised in salary. The job was interesting, and involved corresponding with all the Naval bases; Rosyth was my biggest, the strength of membership being very high there.

The time was approaching when I would have to leave the Admiralty, to have my baby, when an incident occurred which gave me much concern at the time. It all happened one day in the powder-room.

The powder-room in itself consisted of six toilets, each toilet partition having a six-inch gap from the floor. Well, one day I was in one of these toilets when I distinctly heard two clicks; actually I didn't take much heed until a sheet of paper slid underneath the gap, as if someone had dropped it. It was only natural that I should pick up the piece of paper and examine it, and clearly stated in bold red ink was the word 'Confidential.' It appeared that someone had dropped this mysterious piece of paper accidentally, but before I had time to think about returning it to its rightful owner, I heard the door of the next toilet open and shut, followed by the outer door. I was too late. Whoever had dropped it had gone, and the only clue to the identity was the strong fragrance of perfume which entered my nostrils; and there was no difficulty in identifying the pleasant aroma of Yardley's Lavender, for it happened to be my favourite brand of perfume.

Perplexed and puzzled, I went back into my office, wondering what to do with this confidential paper, and curious as to why it should have been taken into a toilet of all places. I slipped the sheet of paper into the top drawer of my desk, deciding that I would hand it over to Mr Gordon as soon as possible. But the thing was, when would Mr Gordon be back in his office? This sheet of paper aroused my suspicions, and I was wishing I had never found it, or better still left it lying on the floor.

I tried to dismiss it from my mind, but I couldn't, and even while walking home I started to question myself. Had I done the right thing, locking it away in my desk? For my desk was no place to file a confidential document. But what could I have done with it? If only Mr Gordon had been in his office, I could have handed it over to him and had done with it. Now I was going to have to wait until the following day.

Arriving home that late afternoon, I did not speak of the incident to anyone, not even Mum or Dad. Being in the Civil Service, I was honoured to secrecy about what went on.

The very next morning I arrived at the School, feeling perhaps a little apprehensive. Nevertheless I showed my pass to the official on the gate, who smiled and jokingly remarked, 'Reckon you'll be needing two passes shortly.' I too saw the funny side, and chuckled.

Settled in my office, I unlocked my desk and pulled out the drawer. There was the secret paper staring me in the face. I quickly closed the drawer again, making up my mind that I would think of it no more until I saw Mr Gordon.

That morning the mail was heavy, so I had a lot of correspondence to do, and that kept me occupied. I had very little time to think of anything else, but I had at least one thought in mind — the hope that Mr Gordon would be in the office sometime today.

I looked at my watch: 10 a.m., and no sign of my boss as yet. Then the girl came around with the cocoa, which was still free of rationing. I stopped writing to sip my cocoa, and then at last I heard Mr Gordon come in. Popping his head in the doorway he said, 'Good morning, Mrs McCann — everything all right?'

'Yes, thank you,' I replied. I gave him time to settle at his desk, and then went in to see him, holding the confidential paper in my hand. 'Sorry to bother you, Sir, but I came across this paper quite by accident.' I held it out, and he gently took it from me.

Glancing at the paper, he simultaneously showed facial signs of concern. Now looking at me, he said, 'Where on earth did you find this, Mrs McCann?'

'In the ladies powder-room, Sir.'

'You mean it was just lying around in the powder room?'

'Yes, Sir,' I answered. I wanted really to explain exactly how I had found it, but instead I just said, 'I picked it up off the floor,' which was true, up to a point.

'Have you any idea who may have dropped it?'

Being so unsure I answered, 'Don't rightly know, Sir.'

'This, you'll gather, is rather serious, Mrs McCann. Some negligence of secrecy has been exposed, and someone will be responsible for this carelessness. I'll have to make further enquiries. Meanwhile you mustn't worry about it. It remains with me now.'

I excused myself and then went back into my office. Oddly enough, while Mr Gordon was thinking that someone had carelessly lost a valuable paper, I was thinking quite differently. But then, Mr Gordon didn't know the full facts of the matter, did he? Maybe I should have told him about the perfume, but then I realised it was insufficient evidence to go on.

It was two days later, while I was washing my hands in the powder-room, that the outside door opened and in walked a smartly dressed blonde. I didn't take much notice of her actually, until she passed me, and then I got a whiff of the peculiar charm of Yardley's Lavender. Suddenly there sprang up an association in my mind. This must be her! And again my suspicions were aroused.

Oh, this is ridiculous, I said to myself. It was nothing to do with me. Hadn't Mr Gordon got the matter in hand? But fate had it that I just had to be in the powder-room at that particular time, for once again I heard two distinctive clicks.

Curiosity overcame me. I just had to know what was going on. So, deliberately positioning myself right outside of the door of the cubicle which the blonde lady had entered, I just stood and waited.

Many girls came in and out, and some of them looked at me in an odd manner. I guess I looked a bit strange, just standing where I was, but now I was determined to know the truth, and to find an explanation for these mysterious clicks.

Suddenly the door opened, and I was face to face with the blonde. 'Oh!' she exclaimed. I must have startled her, for now she stood staring at me. Embarrassment was felt on both sides, that was for sure. I just wondered if she knew what I knew about her. Or was I jumping to conclusions only too quickly? I simply didn't know.

Anyway, the blonde lady went over to the wash-basin to wash her hands, placing her large handbag beside her. I too went across to wash my hands, for the second time. I suspected that the blonde lady was using some kind of camera, and if she was doing that sort of thing, it was espionage.

What should I do now?

To apprise my superiors was the only solution. I would have to tell Mr Gordon what I knew.

The blonde lady left the powder-room, with myself almost on her heels. I decided to tell Mr Gordon straightaway, knowing that he was a sensible man and quite capable of dealing with a situation such as this.

I gave a gentle tap on his door, and he looked surprised to see me as I entered. 'May I have a word with you, Sir?'

Mr Gordon, placing his pen down, said, 'Certainly, Mrs McCann. Please sit down.'

'I have further information, Sir, about the confidential paper I found in the toilet.' I told Mr Gordon all I knew, including the perfume and the clicks I had heard.

'And do you know who is responsible for this?'

'Yes, Sir, I do'.

'I'm afraid, Mrs McCann, I'll have to ask you the name of the person concerned.'

'Well, I don't know her personally, Sir. I'm not aware of her name. But I do know her face.'

'Splendid detection!' said Mr Gordon. 'Maybe you could help me further. I think tomorrow I'll send you up to Archives. Incidentally, it's located in the strong-room, where government records are kept. It's possible,' said Mr Gordon, 'that you may come across our mystery lady, and even find out her name.'

I felt I was under an allegiance to do exactly as Mr Gordon wanted me to do, so the following morning I was up at Archives. 'Don't forget,' said Mr Gordon, 'look around. You have my authority to do so.'

The strong-room was situated at the far side of the School, and, as I imagined there would be, there was an official on the door who glanced at my special pass authorised by Mr Gordon.

I entered, and was really amazed at what I saw. The room was filled with long tables on which there must have been literally thousands of files. Several people were in the room, glancing at different documents of importance. I did not want to make myself too conspicuous, so I contented myself with browsing through the files of seamen in the Royal Navy. And after finding out how the system worked, I came across my own brother's file. I read it, then re-read it, and was just about to replace it when who should walk through the door but the blonde lady herself. She was beautifully attired in a mauve dress, and as she passed me she almost stopped, as if wanting to speak to me. And in my way of thinking at that moment, her hesitation could have been a sign of guilt. But I now told myself that guilt or innocence was no concern of mine.

All that was required of me was to find out her name and what department she belonged to.

I slowly walked over to the official on the door, and politely asked the blonde lady's name.

'Oh,' said the man, 'cannot help you much. See, I be new on the job. But I do know she's a secretary to one of the nobs.'

I left the strong-room, and although my mission had not been accomplished, I hastened along the corridors that led to our section. When I arrived, Mr Gordon was absent from his office, so I was glad to flop down on my own seat; for all that I had not completed my assignment, I could rest assured that I could do no more.

When Mr Gordon did arrive back in his office, I went in to see him, and he gave me a smile as I entered.

'I'm sorry, Sir, but I cannot give you much information. All I know is that the lady we spoke of is a secretary to one of the higher officials.'

'Oh,' exclaimed Mr Gordon. 'Anyway, Mrs McCann, thanks for all your help. And I would like you to know that, should any unpleasantness arise, you will not be held responsible, for you acted with discretion and without defamation.'

I excused myself and then went back into my own office. I certainly did not expect any sanction for reporting my observation and I was content to know that I had done my duty. Finally settling down to my work, I dismissed the idea of espionage as something that had been generated by my own introspection.

So, another day at the School was over, and when I arrived home there to greet me was a letter from Jim. Dear Jim, I could tell that his anxiety for me was increasing, for he constantly reminded me in his letter that he would be home as soon as the baby was born.

The following week I gave in my notice to leave the Admiralty — much of course to my regret, for I had made many new friends, and loved my work as a civil servant.

Mr Gordon was very understanding, as always, and remarked, 'You know, young lady, you have done extremely well, and should you ever require, in the future, a post with the Admiralty, you can always depend on my recommendation.'

What Mr Gordon had said to me was in fact rewarding. Always I endeavoured to do of my best, and my work had given me the satisfaction of having done something worthwhile. It was, however, two days before I left, that something happened which gave me added peace of mind.

Mr Gordon called me into his office. 'Sit down, Mrs McCann. I have something to tell you.' Then, smiling, he said, 'The mystery of the confidential paper has been solved. Evidently our blonde lady was doing an experimental test.'

Now I was full of perplexity, and ready to listen further to what Mr Gordon had to say.

'It appears no one knew of this experiment, including myself. You might call it a wager, between two top brasses, to test the security here. For other incidents occurred, besides the one we had knowledge of. I'm only sorry, Mrs McCann, that you became involved. But your observation was fully appreciated. And so you deserve all the dignity of a civil servant.'

Imagine how delighted I was that my blonde lady was not a spy after all. And so I left the Admiralty with a lighter heart, after an experience which had a happy ending.

During the month of May, 1943, the morale of the British people was high, for at this time Tunis was captured by Montgomery. Yet many lost their lives in this campaign, and also many men were taken prisoner by the Italians, including Jim's youngest brother Frank, who eventually escaped into Switzerland, where he remained for the duration of the war.

What else was happening at about this time? Well, our gallant leader Churchill met up with President Roosevelt at Casablanca. And our allies the Russians were building up men and *matériel* on a massive scale, resulting in their victory at Stalingrad. My own theory was that they intended to go in for the kill. For already we had been at war for three and a half years, and a sudden ending would be appreciated by all.

Did we still feel animosity for the enemy? For myself, I wanted the war to end quickly, knowing that everybody longed for peace in the world, and indeed prayed for it.

With my confinement getting near at hand, I contented myself with being at home, making preparations for my baby coming. Mum gave up her job at the hospital, so that she could be on hand to help me, and Mum and Dad insisted that I take their bedroom, which had the open door that led on to the veranda. Wasn't it just the most pleasant room in our cottage? For facing west, one had a clear view of the open fields, plus the exquisite scenery of the most beautiful sunsets.

Dad, bless him, made the necessary alterations in the room, making it appealing as well as meeting Nurse Thomas's requirements. Everything was ready, even the wash-basin stand was all intact, with Dettol, and Johnson's baby powder, and all the other requirements needed for a new arrival, the whole being covered with a muslin cloth to protect and keep clean.

260

I think, in this little adorable room, the main feature was its bed, with its brass rods and knobs, both top and bottom, all shining like gold in adoration of Mum's best white counterpane, which itself looked whiter than snow. And so the little bedroom was ready when I was.

About the 12th of June, we had a visit from Bill, who was my sister-in-law Dolly's brother-in-law. He was a dark-haired young man, with wit as keen as mustard, and ideally suited at his job, for he was a test pilot at Filton aerodrome in Bristol. He used to say, 'When a plane skims the roof-tops, it'll be me!' He spoke of Jerry planes falling to bits, so it was no surprise to him to hear of our encounter with the young German airman we had found in the garden. 'I tell you,' he said, 'the stuff's not going into the making of Jerry planes. Fly a distance in 'em, and zoom, they drop to bits. That's probably what happened to your young German.'

'I think he must have bailed out,' said Dad. 'Could have been his parachute that was at fault.'

'He could have been killed,' said Bill.

'He very nearly was,' replied Dad.

Anyway, what mattered was, he was still alive, prisoner though he might be.

I recall the 14th of June. The weather was so beautiful, so very warm and sunny, that I spent most of my time in the garden, just resting. Tea-time came around, and it was after tea, after clearing away, that Rob suggested I go with him and his pal Horace to Weston village, for an outdoor fête was being held in a field adjoining Church Road. 'It'll do you good, our Paul,' said Rob.

But Mum showed signs of dissent, 'I don't think you should go, duck. It's so near your time, and it's quite a walk across those fields.'

'I'll look after her,' said Rob. 'Make sure she doesn't go on any roundabouts.'

'Heaven forbid!' exclaimed Mum.

Now the decision was left entirely up to me, so I decided to go with the boys; like Rob said, it would do me good. So the three of us, Rob, Horace and I, went off to Weston village. With it being so hot we strolled across the fields, passing contented cows just grazing and swishing their tails to avoid the annoyance from the flies.

When we came to the stile of the last field, Rob suggested we call in at The Crown for a quick one, before going on to the fair. We found the little pub quieter than expected, but then it was early in the evening; however, I sat down to a long cool drink of orange, while the boys enjoyed their pints of mild and bitter. Then Rob, giving me a wink, said, 'Don't tell our Mum I brought you into a pub.'

I chuckled and said, 'I'll not let the cat out of the bag, Rob.'

After our refreshing drinks, we proceeded on to the fair. Our first encounter of the fair was music coming from an organ, and as we got nearer to the large field we came into contact with lots of people, including many children who were all dressed prettily in their colourful summer clothes. I was surprised to see so many stalls of every description, and observed that the ice-cream sales were doing very well in their takings. There was such joviality and laughter everywhere, what a wonderful boost it must have given us all. In defiance to war, people were out to enjoy themselves.

Well, the three of us just mingled with the crowds. It was such fun, and I was really enjoying it. I almost lost Rob and Horace, who I noticed several times eyeing up the girls, and smiling to myself I pretended I hadn't noticed.

We came across a coconut stall, much to my surprise, for I hadn't seen a coconut in years. Well, Rob was determined to get one, for the money he spent in trying to knock one down must have amounted to shillings, even at a penny a go; it would have been cheaper to have bought one. Meanwhile Horace and I looked on with hopeful expectations.

Then it really happened. Rob knocked one off, and it fell into the sawdust, Now Rob was full of excitement for he shouted out, 'I did it! I did it!'

'Three cheers!' said Horace, and I joined in the cheering.

Rob then proudly presented me with his win. 'There you are, Quinner, won gallantly by your little brother.'

I treasured the coconut, hugging it close to me, and so we continued on, walking around, cracking jokes, and laughing at anything that amused us. I realised it had done my egoism good, just coming out with the boys, and so I was pleased I had made the attempt.

The fair had to close at 9.30 p.m. on account of the no-lighting rule, so at about 9.15 p.m. we decided to make our way home. And we were good — we passed by The Crown. 'We'll have a drink in The Retreat,' said Horace.

Well, I just had to take my time waddling up the slipway. 'You lads better go on,' I said, 'or you'll be too late for a pint.'

Horace then shook hands with me, and wished me all the best. Then he said, 'I dunno, all the best girls are married.'

I smiled back at him and remarked, 'You good fellows have plenty of time yet.' The two of them ran up the slipway, waving back at me before they disappeared through the gateway of The Retreat.

Mum, I could see, was more than pleased to see me home. 'You all right, duck?'

'I'm fine, Mum, just fine.'

'Did you have a nice time with the boys?'

'Rather,' I answered. 'And look, Mum, what our Rob has won.'

'A coconut! It's a long time since I've seen one.' I then gave Mum the coconut, not mentioning the amount of tries Rob did have to acquire it.

The same evening I helped Mum to prepare supper, for Dad was due home any time now, and with Dad still bringing his bus home, I knew Mum was missing her walks to meet him. I knew her strolls across the common had always been enjoyable to her. However, when Dad did arrive home, and heard of my outing with the boys, he was more than surprised.

'You mean you walked all across those fields? Didn't you feel exhausted?'

'Not a bit,' I replied. 'But it was a bit of a struggle coming up the slipway.'

'I bet,' said Dad. 'Anyway, it'll have done you good, no doubt.'

The following day, Nurse Thomas came to see me. She was a robust lady, in her late fifties I would say, but nevertheless full of vitality. She held the record for bringing the most babies into the world in the Bath area, and without a doubt she was known for her dedication to duty in the highest degree. Knowing I was to have her services made me feel honoured indeed. Although strict, she had a fine sense of humour, which hid her irritability a little. After all, her only means of transport was on a bicycle, and her figure didn't help matters. Having a patient such as I, living on top of a hill, was no easy matter. She had to push her bicycle up the slipway, especially in hot weather.

'Now Mrs McCann,' she said. 'Tonight, I want you to have a hot bath, and drink a full glassful of castor oil. We'll just have to help this baby along, you know.' Nurse Thomas then looked at Mum. 'Make sure, Mrs Quintin, she takes it. It's important.' Then Nurse Thomas bade us goodbye, saying, 'You know where to find me, should you need me.'

We watched her pushing her bicycle down the lane. 'Castor oil!' exclaimed Mum. 'I haven't any. I must go down to the little shop, they're sure to have some.'

The little shop was situated at the top of Sion Road. It was quite a walk for Mum to go, and I was sorry she had to go out on such a special errand. However, when Mum did return with the castor oil, six small bottles in all, she also had purchased some fruity pastilles, remarking, 'After the castor oil goes down, duck, you can enjoy yourself with these.' Dear Mum — thoughtful at all times.

It was Mum's decision that I should have my bath at around 8.30 p.m., and then an early night in bed. This time was convenient, for Rob was going out, and it was more than likely Dad would be going into The Retreat for his usual game of crib with Old Sam and a few of the locals.

At 8.30 prompt, Mum placed the tin bath before the fire, and the water she added was really hot. 'What's it to be first, duck, castor oil, or your bath?'

I decided to get the worst over first, so Mum emptied the six little bottles into a glass. The thick white liquid looked far from appetising. 'Have I to drink it all, Mum?'

'I'm afraid so. It's what Nurse Thomas wants.'

This to me was quite an ordeal, which I knew it would be. Holding the glass in my hand, the smell alone gave me a feeling of nausea. But I knew I had to take it, so with one big gulp I started swallowing. However, I had to stop, for as soon as it touched my epiglottis I had the feeling of wanting to return it as quick as it went down. I started to vomit, so quickly I popped a fruit pastille in my mouth, reassuring myself that the castor oil would stay down. I took many more gulps, and many more pastilles did I suck. Meanwhile the bath water was cooling, but after the struggle of getting into and out of the tin bath, I was ready for bed.

It being mid-June, the sun was still shining brilliantly and I didn't feel tired in the least, but while lying in bed I would have the advantage of resting. First I opened the veranda doors wide, and standing on the veranda I gazed down in adoration of Dad's flowers. The roses alone made it all so picturesque, and the perfume from the wallflowers was overpowering. That song about an English country garden, that's what it all reminded me of; it seemed appropriate in such surroundings.

There was hardly a breath of air, and perhaps the atmosphere did make me a little fatigued now, so I made up my mind to get into bed, and was content with just a sheet over me.

While resting I must have dozed off, for the next thing I heard was laughter coming up from the garden. One of the voices I recognised as Dad's. I guessed he had a friend with him, and was most probably cutting flowers, which he often did for friends who came down to see his garden. However, all went quiet again, and I must have gone off into a sound sleep, for I knew nothing more until I heard familiar noises that told me it was around 6 a.m.

It was milking time down on the farm, with the usual clatter going on, and amidst all this was the whistling and singing of the birds, blackbirds in particular with their shrill of high-pitched notes, not forgetting the skylarks, who were singing high in the sky. Our own hens too were making quite a din, with the cockerels crowing their heads off. But this was nature — it just had to go on in spite of everything.

I was about to get up and make the early morning tea when there came a little tap on the door, and imagine the surprise I got to see Rob, for in his hand was a cup of tea for me.

'Hi Paul, you OK?'

'How come, our Rob, you're up so soon?'

'Mistake, Paul. Thought it be much later.' Then Rob sat on the edge of my bed. I couldn't recall him doing this before, so now I knew he had something to tell me.

'Didn't see you last night to tell you, our Paul. But I have to go for a medical tomorrow, and if I'm OK, I'll be in the Army.'

The emotion aroused by this unexpected news made me sit right up in bed. 'You mean you've got your calling-up papers to go in the Army?'

Rob smiled. 'Cheer up, and stop your worrying.'

I couldn't help it, but always expressed the truth in my face. Suddenly I felt miserable. It was bad enough being parted from Jim, and I knew that without Rob around as well life could become awfully lonesome. 'Are you going in to work today?' I asked.

'Not today, Paul. Mr Griffin said I could take today and tomorrow off.'

'Understanding man,' I remarked.

Rob was now yawning. 'Why don't you go back to bed, Rob?'

'That's not a bad idea,' he replied. So off he went.

Still sitting up in bed, and sipping my tea, my thoughts were wandering everywhere with a resulting mixture of emotions. Relevant to the up-to-date happenings, I realised that I was now going to be the only young one left at home. Dear Mum and Dad, I had feelings of responsibility towards them both, for they were getting on in years. I was thankful for the knowledge that I would remain with them for the duration. Indeed I appreciated Mum and Dad's loving care for me, so I had every intention, after my baby was born, of devoting my time solely to my baby and my parents. The war made it impossible for Jim and me to set up home together, but I would at least be able to return kindness, where so much love and kindness had been shown to me.

The next thing I heard was Mum getting up. Then she popped her head in the door. 'All right, duck?'

'Fine,' I answered. 'Be down in a minute.'

Soon I was helping Mum with the breakfast, and at the same time discussing Rob's medical.

'He's so very young to leave home,' said Mum. (Rob was in fact nineteen at the time.)

'I know,' I replied. 'But our Rob knows how to look after himself.' Unfortunately, whatever I said made no difference; I knew our Mum was concerned. 'Mum, you mustn't worry. He'll be all right, I feel sure of that.'

It was discussed further at breakfast. 'What regiment will our Rob go in then?' I said.

'Can only be the REME (Royal Electrical and Mechanical Engineers),' said Dad. 'Anyway, it'll give him the opportunity of finishing off his trade as a motor fitter. And it's more than we had in my day.'

Mum, I could now see, was taking everything in a more logical manner.

After breakfast, as on many recent mornings, my first task was preparing my bedroom in readiness for an event which could take place at any time. It was strange how that particular morning I acquired a sudden surplus of energy, wanting to do more than usual, so it was no bother at all to polish up the brass rods and knobs on the bed with Brasso; using a little elbow grease, I made the brass reflect all the light in a brilliance of gold.

I helped Mum with some odd jobs, and it was Mum's suggestion that we should have an early lunch, for Dad was on a late turn. At midday I set the table, and when all was ready I called Dad and Rob up from the garden.

We all sat down, myself feeling very hungry, and it was right in the middle of lunch that I experienced a sharp pain. I couldn't tell whether it came from the back or front of me; however, it didn't stop me from eating and enjoying my food as I always did.

We were all through with lunch then, but before I got off my chair another pain did I take, this time noticed by all. Immediately it was action stations.

'Rob, get your bicycle out quickly, it's time to fetch Nurse Thomas.' Mum gave all the information to Rob on a piece of paper. 'Should she not be in, Rob, go straight to the obstetrics and midwifery clinic in Rivers Street. And if that should fail, and Nurse Thomas is not available anywhere, ask for any other midwife at the clinic.'

So, without any hesitation, Rob was off. Mum in the meantime was heating up three large saucepans of water, so, happy to say, we were all organised.

The next question to be asked was, would Nurse Thomas be in time? But, knowing Rob, we were certain he would have sped down Weston hill in an attempt to reach Nurse Thomas in the shortest possible time.

Now I was up in the bedroom with Mum, and taking more frequent pains I found much relief in clasping Mum's hands. 'Hold my hands tighter, Mum.' It was all I could say.

And Mum's reply was, 'I know, my darling. I know.'

266

At the next stage, I sat on the new white enamel bucket, and was still sitting on it when Nurse Thomas arrived, puffing and blowing. It was the slipway that did it: pushing her bicycle up it on such a hot day as this was very hard work, for it must have been 80 in the shade.

Taking off her wide-brimmed navy-blue hat, she came across to me, examined me, and almost shrieked out, 'On the bed quickly, baby's head is visible.'

I was getting more pain, so to ease myself I pressed hard with my feet against the brass rods on the bed, and almost laughed when one of the knobs flew off and bounced on the floor.

'You just save your strength, young lady,' said Nurse. She was smiling at me now, and remarked, 'You are doing fine, it'll all be over soon.'

And so a new baby had arrived, and with all confidence and efficiency Nurse Thomas attended to baby first. The sudden cries of my baby overwhelmed me with joy.

'A fine baby boy,' declared Nurse Thomas, who by now had wrapped the babe in a blanket, and placed him in the wooden cradle that Dad had made. Then Nurse Thomas attended to me, observing that I needed further medical attention.

The appearance of Mum was greatly welcomed. 'Everything all right?' she said.

'Everything is satisfactory, Mrs Quintin. You have a fine grandson. A whopper to be preponderate. A good ten pounds, I shouldn't wonder.' I could tell Mum was much relieved and eager now to do anything to help. 'It'll be necessary, Mrs Quintin, to have the Doctor up for your daughter. Always sutures are necessary, when big babies arrive. How about that nice young man that came for me — would he mind going for the Doctor?'

Dear Rob, once again he came to the rescue, this time in pursuit of Doctor Scott-White, who lived in Green Park in town.

Nurse Thomas again attended to baby, and the first glimpse I got of my son was when he was swinging in a net bag, obviously being weighed by a hanging scale.

'Ah! Correct,' said Nurse Thomas. 'A good ten pounds.'

Then Nurse bathed him, putting on a new little vest and nappy, with a binder to support his back, and last but not least a white flannel robe, tied with a bow behind him. And so, at long last, Nurse Thomas handed me my precious gem. I just held him in my arms, noticing he had little tuffs of blonde hair; and although his eyes were still closed, I imagined them to be blue. And so with all sincerity I looked up into Nurse Thomas's face and said, Thank you.'

Her reassuring smile was pleasing. Then she said, 'You know your baby was born with a caul over his face.' Now I knew why

Nurse had been quick to attend to the baby first, for the caul had to be removed immediately. 'A lucky omen indeed,' she said. 'Superstition has it that a baby born with it will never drown. And should a captain of a ship have such a man in his crew, he also has the belief he will never drown. So my dear, there's faith in its value.' This in fact I knew already, because my brother Pat had been born in the same way.

Mum came back into the bedroom, this time carrying a tray with tea and biscuits for Nurse Thomas, who by now had flopped into the bedside chair. Her stiff white apron was soiled, and her hair with a plaited bun at the back of her neck was all disarranged. But give credit where it was due, she had brought my baby into the world with a safe confinement, and there were no complications; all that was needed now was for me to have further medical treatment by a Doctor, and once again Rob had delivered the necessary message.

But imagine the surprise I got when a slip of a girl arrived, announcing herself as Doctor Tinsdale. After attending to me, she departed, and so did Nurse Thomas, who said she would be returning in the evening.

After feeding my baby and settling him down, and within the quietness of the bedroom, I must have gone off into an exhausted sleep. I awoke only to hear the whispers of voices which I recognised as Mum's and Rob's.

'Isn't he a lovely babby?'

'A little blond,' said Rob.

Mum, seeing me awake, said, 'You all right, duck?'

'I'm OK, Mum. Could do with a cup of tea though.' Mum vanished, leaving Rob standing at the bottom of the bed, looking upon baby and I with wonder and pleasure. Dear Rob, I was so grateful to him, for he had had all the running around to do. 'Thanks, Rob, for all your help.'

He chuckled, then kidded me up by saying, 'This was supposed to be my day off. And I bet the next thing, our Paul, you'll be wanting me to send off a telegram to Jim.'

'Oh Rob, would you?'

'Of course, Quinner. For you, anything. But this time, I'll be taking the bus to town. Had quite enough cycling for the day. Anyway,' said Rob, 'I'm meeting Horace, and we'll most probably land in a boozer. Cause for celebrating, you know. Don't have a brand-new nephew every day. Anyway, Quinner, putting jokes aside, I'm pleased everything went off all right with you.'

Mum had now returned with a cup of tea for me, which was most refreshing, and really I felt marvellous. I could almost have jumped out of bed, but I had to adhere to Nurse Thomas's instructions that I should remain in bed for fourteen days, this being the completion of my accouchement. The best way then was to resign myself to the fact, knowing that the best medical technique was to remain in bed for two whole weeks.

It must have been around 7 p.m. when Nurse Thomas gave me yet another visit that day, strutting into the bedroom like a proud peacock. 'And how's Mother and baby?' she asked.

'We're just fine, thank you,' I answered.

Taking off her coat, she hung it up behind the bedroom door and then attired herself in a clean white apron. Proceeding with her duties to make baby and I comfortable, she explained to me the correct way of putting on binders etc., and when she had finished she gladly accepted a cup of tea and digestive biscuits from Mum.

Again she spoke of the caul on baby's face. 'I had to get it off quickly, for fear of suffocation,' she said. Then Nurse showed me the caul that she had placed on a piece of brown paper. All it was, was a thin layer of skin, and on touching it, it felt like velvet. I myself was most impressed.

The bedroom was now smelling of Johnson's baby powder, adding that smell of delicacy, and so it was time for Nurse to go. 'See you in the morning,' were her words as she left the room.

Mum went to the door to see her off, and then joined me up in the bedroom. I noticed at once how tired she looked. 'Do sit down a minute, Mum.' She did, and I was glad.

'I must go to town tomorrow. Baby will have to be registered, and there'll be little odds and ends I must buy.' Dear Mum, she had so much on her mind, and she was already thinking of the next day.

About 10.30, I heard the front door open. Dad was home, and within minutes, he peeped his dear face in the door.

'You all right, Paul? I saw Rob, and he gave me all the news.' Then he almost tiptoed around the bottom of the bed, and gazed upon his new little grandson. 'The little angel,' were his words. Then, looking at me, he said, 'And you, Paul, are you feeling all right?'

'I'm OK Dad. We've had a busy day.'

Mum then called Dad down for his supper. Dad kissed me, saying, 'See you later, Paul. And glad it's over.'

Before I settled down for the night, I was pleased to have the company of Mum, Dad and Rob. We talked over many things. One consolation was we were all happy and content, for the 16th of June 1943 had certainly brought its blessings.

*   *   *

That night I went into a sound sleep, and before the cocks crowed the next morning I was awakened by a tapping on the front door. Suddenly I was filled with excitement. It could only be Jim, I thought. And it was! The mingled voices were both Rob's and Jim's.

Then footsteps came almost running up the stairs, and without speaking Jim flung his arms around my neck and kissed me.

'Oh, darling,' he said. He sat on the edge of the bed, and his eyes were misty, for he contained every essence of joy that a proud father would. With his eyes steadily fixed on me, he said, 'It wasn't too bad, was it, Paul?'

I smiled. 'All was worthwhile,' I said. 'Now go on, take a peep at your little son.'

With all caution, as if afraid, he moved towards the cradle, and then stood he did, and gazed down in adoration. 'Oh, Paul, isn't he just a little beauty? A blond too.'

The next thing, Mum appeared with cups of tea on a tray, so as the dawn broke we were in deep conversation. 'I'm only on a forty-eight hour compassionate leave. I was on the engine when I got your telegram, and how happy it made me. I went straightaway to our commanding officer, who sanctioned my immediate leave, and it was then I made a dash up to Shrewsbury to catch the 9 p.m. train to Bristol.' Then Jim laughed. 'Funny, but I had to hitch-hike up to Bath in a container carrying sheep, so having walked the rest of the way, here I am. I'm tired, but very happy. I'm only sorry,' said Jim, 'that I've disturbed you all from your rest, coming home so very early in the morning.' He then placed his hand on Mum's shoulder, saying, 'Mam, thank you for everything.' Then looking at me, he said, 'Sorry, Paul, I haven't brought you any flowers or anything.'

'You've brought yourself, that's all that matters,' I replied.

Mum then suggested we all have an early breakfast. 'It'll be a good start for the day,' she said. 'And Jim, I'll call you down when it's ready.'

'OK, Mam,' replied Jim.

Mum had just left us, when a cry from our little son echoed round the room. 'It's his feeding time,' I said. 'Would you like to hand him over to me, Jim?' So very carefully he placed baby into my arms. Mum then called out to Jim to go down for breakfast; meanwhile I fed and attended to baby, leaving him lying on the bed. Then Jim brought my breakfast up on a tray, so baby went back to his cradle.

After I had finished my breakfast, Jim then lay on top of the bed beside me and in seconds he went off to sleep; it must have been the overnight travelling that had made him so tired. Then Mum, seeing Jim asleep, crept in and took the tray away, so there was nothing I could do but doze over myself. So the three of us were all together, and in a contented sleep. Later, I myself awakened to hear laughter coming up from the front door. I recognised Dad's voice, but who was the female I could hear?

Then came knocking on the bedroom door, which startled Jim out of his sleep. The door opened: it was Dad, and beside him stood a young midwife. 'Mrs McCann? I'm the relief nurse, here on behalf of Nurse Thomas.'

I smiled, saying, 'How do you do?' Then I introduced Jim to her. In seconds Dad and Jim had disappeared.

The young nurse was very pleasant, and most efficient, attending to the needs of both baby and I, and when finished she closed her little black bag, saying, 'Most probably be seeing you again, Mrs McCann.' I thanked her kindly, and she then left the room, so both baby and I felt and looked like two new pins.

Jim appeared next, carrying a vase of freshly cut flowers from the garden. Their aromatic scent, mingled with Dettol and baby powder, made the bedroom an absolute refresher of cleanliness.

'I've just been talking to Bob,' said Jim. 'He tells me he goes for his medical today.'

'Yes I know,' I answered. 'I say, Jim, why not take a trip to town with him? I know he'll appreciate your company very much.'

'But pet,' said Jim, 'I don't want to be leaving you. For our time together is short enough.'

'I don't mind really, darling,' I said. 'You go with our Rob, maybe have a drink in town.'

'But what if Bob wants to go on his own?'

'In that case, my darling, you can stay with me.'

But, as I expected, Rob was delighted at the idea of company, so they arranged to catch the Lansdown bus into town together. Meanwhile, Mum was preparing to go to town also, so off they all went, leaving Dad to hold the fort. He kept himself busy preparing lunch, and running up and down the stairs to me, giving me his whole-hearted attention.

Mum was the first to return, saying that she had registered baby, and had got all she wanted in the way of shopping. She showed me hanks of blue and white wool. 'Thought I'd send this wool off to your Auntie Jo in Oxford. She said she would knit some things for baby.' Now Mum was carefully wrapping up the wool again, and remarking, 'I'm sure the young lady that served me didn't take sufficent coupons from me.'

I now could smell the aroma of Dad's cooking: best fried onions without a doubt. Then, at almost 1 o'clock, Jim and Rob returned home. Both appeared happy when they saw me. I didn't ask, only guessed that they had called in somewhere for a pint; after all they were entitled to an appetiser before dinner.

I looked at Rob and said, 'How did the medical come off?'

'They passed me "A1",' was Rob's answer. 'And I've to report at Swindon REME base.'

I then asked the dreaded question: 'When will you be going then?'

'This coming Monday,' replied Rob.

'Doesn't give anyone much time to sort things out, does it?' said Jim. 'Still, you'll be going into a good regiment.'

So Dad was right after all, about Rob going into the REME. It meant a grand opportunity for him to finish off his apprenticeship as a motor fitter. Another thing — Swindon was not so far away, and if Rob was there any length of time I dare say he could always pop home occasionally. I was convinced that the news about Rob had pleased me, and I sincerely hoped Mum and Dad would feel the same way.

When Rob left the room, I was alone with Jim, apart from baby, who was still fast asleep.

'And how's my best girl?' said Jim, who was now sitting on the edge of the bed. And from behind his back he placed before me a small jewel-box. 'A little present for you, pet.'

'For me?'

'Yes, for you, my darling, and with all my love.'

I lifted the lid off carefully, and to my surprise and delight I gazed upon a heart-shaped locket, attached to a fine gold chain. Lifting it out, it gleamed in the sunlight that was streaming into the bedroom. 'Oh Jim, it's beautiful!'

'Thought you'd like it,' said Jim. 'Here, let me put it around your neck.'

Placing the locket around my neck, he fastened it and then chuckled, saying, 'Hope you don't expect a new locket every time our children come along.'

I joined in on his laughter, flinging my arms around him.

Soon afterwards Mum came in with my lunch on a tray. 'You'll be hungry too, Jim,' she said.

'Ah yes, I could eat something now. Oh — by the way, I've something for you, Mam.' Jim produced yet another little box from his pocket, and I'm sure Mum was taken unawares at such an unexpected gift.

'Oh Jim, really.' A surprised look was on her face as she opened the little box and exclaimed, 'Why how lovely!' Then she held up in her hand a most exquisite brooch.

I could see Mum was delighted. She gave Jim a kiss and thanked him, with myself thinking how jolly decent it was of Jim to think of Mum in such a way. And so he followed her downstairs for lunch.

I myself was feeling content and happy. I had only one desire now: that the end of the war would come soon.

Long before baby was born, Jim and I had decided that if we should have a baby boy, his name would be James Paul.

Jim's short leave went over only too quickly, and soon it was time for him to leave. Hugging me so closely he whispered, 'Look after yourself, Paul, and young Jimmy there.' We kissed, and then Jim hurried out of the bedroom, feeling I'm sure full of emotion, as I was.

The following Monday morning it was Rob's turn to leave home. With his case packed he came into the bedroom to say goodbye. I couldn't hold back the tears as he kissed me, although of course the love I felt for him was different from that I felt for Jim: it was a sisterly love of deep affection.

'Hey, Quinner, cheer up! Wouldn't we just be letting our Mum down now? You know her saying, "Never let it be said your mother bred a jibber." We're still at war, Paul. Must go and do my bit.'

'Of course,' I answered, trying hard to smile.

So kissing me again, he said, 'So long, Paul.'

These partings — how I had come to hate them. However, the following day we had a surprise visit from my brother Pat, who was so full of charm as he came into the bedroom to see me.

'Our Paul!' he said, as he came across and hugged me as he always did. He then looked down upon little Jimmy. 'Big babby, Paul. What you gonna call the little fellow?'

'It's James Paul McCann.'

'Real Irish,' said Pat. 'Good Irish name, that. He should go far with a name like that. Mum was telling me he was born with a caul over his face, like when I was born.' He then looked at little Jimmy and said, 'James lad, we both bain't never gonna drown.' Dear brother Pat; now he was leaning on the bedpost. 'When be you getting up then?'

'A week tomorrow will be my fourteenth day.'

'Blimey, thee look in the pink now!'

'Given the chance, Pat, I'd be up this very minute.'

'Never mind, old gal, you've to do as you're told, I suppose. Anyway I'll be coming up tomorrow, most probably with Vi.' Then, kissing me, he said cheerio, leaving me to ponder over many thoughts.

I gazed down on little Jimmy. Already there was a considerable change in his growth, and he was I might add, a most contented baby, for awake in his cradle he would just lie in complacency. I myself was feeling on tops, and longing to jump out of bed. And nearly did that very night, for what did happen certainly put us all on our toes.

At this particular time was were experiencing a lull in hostilities. We were free from air raids, and let's say it made us all lackadaisical in a way. But this particular night the warning siren went at exactly 11 p.m., and with it being such a humid kind of a night, the siren sounded much louder than usual. In less than a minute Mum and Dad were beside me.

'What are we going to do, Pat?' said Mum.

'You take baby, Nell, while I carry our Paul down to the shelter.'

'Oh Dad, I'm much to heavy to carry! And I could easily get out of bed and walk down.'

'You can't, duck,' said Mum. 'Nurse Thomas said you hadn't to be on your feet for fourteen days.'

'Oh Mum, I know I'll be all right.'

But it was no use. So, like a child, I had to be carried to safety. While Mum took little Jimmy, Dad picked me up in his arms, saying, 'Put your arms around my neck, and hang on.'

I knew it was an ordeal for Dad, and it was certainly a struggle, especially around the bend of the stairs. However, we finally reached the shelter in the sitting-room, and what a relief it must have been for Dad, for I was not a lightweight.

I myself appreciated the change of scene, for already I ached with lying in bed too long. So here I was sitting on the mattress with little Jimmy now in my arms. Somehow I couldn't help but think of our Rob; I suppose it was at times like this that we missed him most. Dear Rob, now away in the Army, but settling down please God.

We heard the roar of many planes approaching. It was a job to distinguish if they were ours or not. Then there were thuds, so we came to the conclusion that it was enemy aircraft.

'I'm going in the garden,' said Dad. 'Take a quick look at what is happening.' He went, and returned immediately. 'It's Bristol!' he gasped. 'The whole skyline is lit up.'

I cast my mind back to the time I was with Mr Penny, down on Avonmouth docks, and visualised what must be going on right now, the enemy wreaking their destruction as they did before.

More planes went over, and then we heard the echo of more bombs being dropped. Now I was holding baby that much closer to me.

At long last the air activity quietened down, and the 'all clear' went around 1 a.m.

274

'Thank God for that,' said Mum, who was crawling out of the shelter.

'We could do with a nice cup of tea now,' said Dad, and to his surprise I gave him little Jimmy to hold.

'I'm going to make my own way upstairs, Dad. Under my own steam.'

'But Paul, you cannot walk upstairs.'

This I knew was only too true. Dad was absolutely right — I just couldn't walk, and I dare say even to stand up would have been impossible, for already I had spent many days confined in bed. However, determined I was of making my own way upstairs.

'Don't laugh, Dad, but I'm going to crawl on my bottom.'

'Well I be blowed,' said Dad, and he was amazed at the speed I was going along the passageway.

Before ascending the stairs however, I burst out laughing, amused at the sense of fun it was giving me.

'Did you ever?' exclaimed Mum. And so I proceeded on up the stairs, and on each stair my bottom was going up and down, taking individual bumps.

Now I was beside the bed, and I tried standing on my feet. But alas, my legs were too shaky, so I just fell over into the bed. Still laughing, I buried my head in the bedclothes. Secretly, I had enjoyed every minute of it; it was a challenge, of course, but I was thoroughly proud of myself that I had made it.

The days that followed were more or less routine. Daily visits from Nurse Thomas and other midwives gave me the added satisfaction of knowing that baby and I were both doing well. One morning, I recall, one of the midwives who called lost the heel of her shoe; however, it was found in the lane, and Dad got the last out and nailed the heel back on again.

Then the day I was looking forward to arrived. It was my day for getting up. This was my moment; so sliding off the bed I hung on tightly to the bedpost, my legs wobbling like jelly. I persevered in making small steps, and then found I could walk the width of the bed, but needless to say I was still hanging on to the bed-post with one hand. Then, without any aid, I actually walked a pentameter.

'Bravo!' said Dad, who now had just popped his head in the doorway. 'Can you make it down for breakfast, Paul?'

'You bet,' I replied.

The effort of walking downstairs made me feel amazingly good, and I felt the strength coming back into my legs with each step I took. Feeling as high as a kite, I was never happier. How good it felt to be on my legs again. I wanted to do so much, but Mum's advice was to take things easy.

Just before midday, Pat came up home. I expected to see Vi with him, but Pat said she would be up the following day. Then Pat produced two white silk sashes; each of them was a large silk square which normally hung around a sailor's neck, giving an added array for show to the British Navy uniform.

'Here, Paul,' he said. 'These'll make two lovely covers for the baby's pillow.' The very thought of my baby's head lying on white silk was very appealing; it was what a Royal head would lie on.

'Oh Pat, thank you.'

'Well, old girl, how about a sprint across the fields?'

'Wouldn't I just love that?' I chuckled. 'But I cannot.'

'Never let it be said, our Paul.'

Pat was on his last day's leave, and would be rejoining his ship the next day. 'I'll tell you what,' I exclaimed, bearing that in mind, 'I'll race you into The Retreat.'

'Ah now, I'll take you up on it, our Paul. Hey Mum, can you spare our Paul for ten minutes?'

'Why of course,' said Mum. 'It will do her good to have a walk as far as Sam's.' Mum, now smiling, said, 'I overheard your conversation.'

'You know, Mum, our Paul's going to buy me a pint.'

I was thrilled to link Pat's arm, and so the pair of us toddled into The Retreat. We found Sam, as we expected, polishing the drinking glasses, and when he heard us come in he looked up to greet us.

'Well, it be our Pat! Nice to see you.' Then, looking at me, he said, 'How be you, gal?'

'I'm just fine, thank you.'

'And the babby?'

'Just lovely,' I replied.

'What will 'ee have then, Pat?'

'Usual pint, Sam,' was Pat's reply.

'And you, gal, what do you fancy?'

'Oh, um, a nice long cool glass of orange, please Sam.'

Our drinks were placed on the counter, and while Pat was retrieving money from his pocket he said, 'How much is that, Sam?'

'It be all right,' said Sam. 'The drinks be on me.' So, still standing at the counter, we toasted Sam's health.

We continued chatting a while. Meanwhile other customers were coming in, one of whom I was so pleased to see. It was Horace, Rob's pal.

'Why, it be Pauline,' he said, grasping my hand to shake it. 'Congratulations! It be a little boy then.' And Horace immediately asked what I would like to drink.

'Horace, thank you, but I best be getting back in home. Maybe another time perhaps.'

'OK,' said Horace cheerfully. 'You go in home, and look after your baby.'

I looked around for Pat, and found he had got himself seated at the cribbage table, ready for a game with the locals. My conversation with Horace made me think he was missing our Rob very much, for had he not said, 'You know, Pauline, I would be off into the services like a shot, if it wasn't for my eyes.' This I knew; he had to wear thick pebble lenses in his glasses.

I could only try to cheer Horace up by saying, 'We need good men at home as well, you know. Anyway, our Rob will be coming home shortly.'

'Ah, I suppose it's something to look forward to,' he said.

'Anyway, Horace, must fly.' I then touched our Pat on the shoulder; by now he was engrossed in his card playing. 'I'm going in home now,' I whispered.

'Ah, righto. See you later.'

While I walked up the lane, my thoughts dwelled on Horace. I really felt sorry for him, for he must have felt right out of everything, and it was such a pity he was afflicted by his poor sight; this of course was sufficient to make him unfit for active service, for without his glasses he could see very little.

However, my thoughts were diverted into joy, for there was a letter from Jim awaiting me when I got in home. Jim started off his letter by saying, 'Guess you'll be enjoying your first day out of bed?' How true, thought I, for the freedom of just being able to walk about was more enjoyable than I could have anticipated

The war — what was happening about this time? Well, an allied victory now seemed nearer. General Montgomery and the American General Eisenhower completed the conquest of North Africa, and Mussolini's capitulation was greeted with jubilation.

American help, of course, brought success in the Atlantic, as well as in North Africa and Italy, for United States destroyers helped to end the U-boat menace; 37 U-boats were sunk in July 1943, and consequently less shipping was lost, and imports began to rise once more. The Russians too were sweeping the Germans to their borders.

The sporadic air raids had become almost bearable by now, and when a warning siren was heard many people paid not the slightest attention. Observed by many, it was a strange psychological fact that the sound of the siren gave one almost the sense of pleasure rather than that of fear. Could it be that we thought serious raids unlikely, and so appreciated the tranquillity that somehow surrounded us when the siren went?

It was reported by Mass-Observation, and confirmed by our own limited experience, that many factory workers were actually afraid of the war ending. Could they perhaps forsee a prompt return to the old conditions with millions unemployed? I dare say that, for people much older than myself, memories of the great depression of the 1930s lay at the back of everyone's mind. It was logical: wars created work, and work paid off in wage packets.

We must remind ourselves what happened after the 1914-1918 war: unemployment, poverty, and often hardship. J. B. Priestley summed it up admirably by asking, What did we do for the young men and their wives, at the end of the last war? 'We did nothing. . . . After the cheering and the flag-waving were over, and all the medals were given out, somehow the young heroes disappeared, but after a year or two there were a lot of shabby, young-oldish men about who didn't seem to have been lucky in the scramble for easy jobs and quick profits, and so tried to sell us second-hand cars, or office supplies we didn't want.'

What a sad state of affairs. Would there, could there be, yet another repetition after this war? We could only wait and see.

And so the weeks to follow kept me occupied with little Jimmy, and helping Mum. Occasionally I would help Dad in the garden, and one great advantage was that we were still enjoying the beautiful weather of summer.

Having no pram as yet, I was obliged to bring the cradle into the garden, and in it baby would lie for hours. He had in fact a special place, under the archway of white rambling roses; these lovely little roses protected him from the strong sunlight, and often enough I would watch the little fellow, lying on his back in sheer contentment, gazing up into the masses of small white flowers.

I was now looking forward to Jim's next leave, for there was going to be one great occasion: our baby would be christened.

One Monday morning I received a letter from Jim, saying that he would be home the following Friday. This meant I could go ahead with the christening arrangements on the following Sunday. Overwhelmed with joy, I started making plans. Then suddenly it dawned on me — I must find a Catholic godparent. But who? I had no Catholic friends, and could think of no one. I talked things over with Mum, who suddenly exclaimed, 'I know! Mrs Smith, who lives down in the bungalow beside the farm.'

'You mean the Polish lady?' I said.

'I only know,' said Mum, 'that she is a Catholic, and goes to St Mary's along Julian Road. Pop down and see her, duck. I'm sure she will help.'

So off I went, almost running down the slipway. I did know that Mrs Smith's husband was away in the Army, and that they had a small boy.

Outside the bungalow now, I knocked on the door, and it was opened by the lady herself. Her pleasant smile put me to ease at once, and before I had time to explain my errand, I was invited in.

Having no personal knowledge of the lady herself, I found I was pleased to make her acquaintance. With a quick glance around me, I noticed that her little home was incredibly clean, and it immediately gave me the feeling of warmth and friendliness. At once she offered me a cup of tea, and so in between sips I explained why I had called upon her.

It was in broken English that she spoke. 'Why, that will be lovely. I will be so proud to be a godparent to your little son.'

So happy at what she said, I felt like jumping up and kissing her. For no finer lady in my eyes could be better as a godparent for little Jimmy.

I then explained to Mrs Smith that I would have to make arrangements with the Catholic Priest at St Mary's, a small church which stood off the roadway and was situated almost half-way to town.

I was thankful for Mrs Smith's assurance, for she said, 'Any time you want me, I will be ready.'

I shook hands with her, thanked her for her kindness, and left her standing at her front door. I then hurried back up the slipway. I turned around to wave to her, and she waved back at me. Turning the corner into the lane, I was happy with the thought that I had certainly made a new friend.

Arriving home, I eagerly told Mum all about Mrs Smith, and her readiness in coming forward to be a godparent. Mum on the other hand remained calm; she was interested, of course, in what I had to say, but I'm not mistaken when I say that Mum in her heart was not happy with the idea that little Jimmy would be christened a Catholic. I knew Mum showed no animosity towards Catholicism — in fact, I knew that she respected and honoured all religions — but somehow, for her own reasons maybe, she would have preferred that her grandson be christened in the Church of England. I wondered if it had anything to do with Dad, for he was brought up in the Catholic faith until he married Mum. But, having been married in a Catholic church to Jim, I intended to keep my promise that all our children would become Catholics.

So it was that very afternoon that I made a visit to the presbytery of St Mary's. Arriving at the entrance, I pulled the bell gently, whereupon the door was opened by a pleasant-looking lady who I could only imagine was the housekeeper.

'Good afternoon,' I said. 'Will it be convenient to see the Priest?'

'Please come in,' replied the lady, who then ushered me into a room which looked like a study. 'Please take a seat,' she said. 'I will ask the Father to see you. It's Mrs . . .?

'Mrs McCann,' I answered. The lady then disappeared.

Sitting, I glanced around the room. Simplified as it was, it contained an air of grace, of ecclesiastical living.

I stood up as a young Priest entered the doorway. He smiled, saying, 'Please be seated.' Announcing himself as Curate of St Mary's, he held his hand out for a handshake, and at the same time I introduced myself.

'I'm Mrs McCann,' I said. 'I've called to see you about baptismal arrangements. I would like my son to be baptised this Sunday if possible.' I explained to the Curate that my husband would be coming home on leave this weekend.

'Usually,' said the Curate, 'we like a little longer notice. However, under the circumstances, I think we can arrange for your baby's baptism on Sunday.'

'Thank you,' I said.

'How about godparents, Mrs McCann?'

'Oh yes,' I exclaimed. 'I have already one godparent. A Mrs Smith, that lives on Primrose Hill.'

'Ah, I know the lady. She's Polish.'

'Yes,' I replied. 'And I must tell you, Father, I'm not a Catholic.' I could see I had suddenly filled the young Curate with perplexity. Nevertheless, I continued on talking. 'You see, Father, I was brought up in the Church of England. But it's my belief that all denominations are equal, all believing in the one God. Like a tree divided into branches of different religions, we must all depend on the trunk and the foundation to feed us all with the strength of faith, which is in all of us.'

I felt my cheeks go hot. Had I said too much? Really I had no intention of delivering a sermon, especially to a young Curate of all people. Yet he looked at me in a most understanding way, and then calmly spoke. 'There is no doubt, Mrs McCann, that your faith points in the right direction.'

I suddenly felt relieved inside, more so when the necessary forms were placed before me to sign. So, after that, all that remained was for me to depart. I kindly thanked the young Priest, and we shook hands. 'We shall see you on Sunday then, at 2.30 p.m.' Again I thanked him, and his final words were, 'God bless you.'

I walked across the common towards home, that late afternoon being exceedingly warm. The field on my left, where cattle usually grazed, was adorned with a blanket of yellow buttercups, shining out amongst the long blades of grass. Now I was feeling content and happy, knowing that I had made all the important arrangements for Sunday.

First I wrote to Jim when I got home, and after writing and posting Jim's letter I made yet another visit down to the bungalow to see Mrs Smith. She made me more than welcome, and we talked about the christening over a cup of tea.

'Shall we walk down to church on Sunday?' I said.

'Yes,' replied Mrs Smith. 'A nice stroll across the common we'll all enjoy, providing of course it's not raining. But I'm sure it'll be fine for wee Jimmy's christening.' So final arrangements were made that we would all meet outside the The Retreat at 2 p.m. 'I'm going to look forward to Sunday,' said Mrs Smith. So, saying cheerio to her and her little boy, I made my way up home.

At this particular moment, I was possessed with so much happiness of my own, what with Jim coming home, and the christening of our little son on Sunday, that it all made me forget entirely that there was still a war on.

When I arrived home, Mum was busy gathering up the ingredients to make a christening cake. I knew, somehow, that the excitement would catch up with Mum eventually.

And so Friday arrived, and I was able to meet Jim at the station. I got my eye on him coming through the ticket barrier, with crowds of people who had just got off the train. He was carrying his valise, plus his respirator etc. Now showing his pass to the ticket-collector, he came through the barrier, dropped his bag and kit, and in front of everyone embraced me with a long lingering kiss. 'Hello, pet,' he said.

I could see his face was well tanned with the sun. 'You look well, darling,' I said. Then someone accidentally pushed us closer together, and it was then I noticed Jim flinch. 'Anything wrong?' I exclaimed.

Jim, half smiling at me, said, 'Believe it or not, Paul, but my whole chest is just one mass of watery blisters.'

'Oh no! But how come?'

'My own fault, of course. I would lie on my back in the sun, and falling asleep, my front was exposed to the sun's rays.'

I couldn't help it, but burst out laughing. It was only natural that I saw the funny side of it, and visualised Jim just lying there, not knowing he was being cooked.

Jim was now chuckling to himself, and remarked, 'I'll not do that again.'

Coming out of the station, we decided to catch a Lansdown bus home, and in the bus I talked incessantly of the christening and the local happenings around. In turn, Jim mentioned in his conversation that he was being transferred to Southampton. Suddenly I was confronted with only one thing in mind — embarkation. The perturbing thought of Jim going overseas made me glance impetuously towards him.

'Oh Jim, they are not sending you abroad, are they?'

'Not likely, pet,' replied Jim. 'I'm more value to them here, just driving a few locomotives on the docks.'

I sighed with relief.

'Must be something to do with this invasion everybody is talking about.'

'Are we ready for such an attack?' I asked, but Jim didn't answer and I immediately realised that my conversation had become inadvertent. I remembered the slogan: 'Careless talk cost lives.'

Arriving home, Jim immediately wanted to pick little Jimmy up. 'My,' he said, 'he's getting a fine bairn.'

Sitting down to supper, our conversations were rather mixed, with Dad and Jim being deeply interested in past events and developments of the war.

'Once we get a foothold in Europe, we stand a chance to push an invasion force into action.' These words were spoken by Dad.

The following day I went into town with Jim, with the intention of buying a pram. Articles such as new prams were very hard to come by, and the idea of having to wait for goodness knows how long kind of put me off from buying a new pram. So after looking around I made up my mind I would buy a second-hand one; there were always plenty for sale in the local newspaper.

After doing our shopping, Jim and I went for a drink in a little pub that stood beneath a very old plane tree, in the middle of town. The pub was called the Crystal Palace, and it stood in a square, surrounded by historical houses; the houses were so quaint, so interestingly old-fashioned, that one could easily imagine the scenery that existed a century or two previous. It would just have to be carriages and pairs, waiting for beautiful ladies in their fine bustles and big hats, probably adorned with fine ostrich feathers. And strange as it may seem, I always felt this special kind of elegance in the surroundings; it was a place which Beau Nash must have often frequented.

Sunday morning was here, bringing with it yet another glorious day. Lunch was early, giving us all plenty of time to get ready. Baby was ready first, and I must say he looked a little picture in his long white gown, with a matching bonnet tied with blue ribbon. Mum and Dad were also ready. Jim was still obliged to wear his uniform, but he had cap badges and buttons shining.

Bunched together, we left home, strolling down the lane, and we were just about to pass The Retreat gate, when who should appear but Old Sam, wearing his straw hat.

'You be all looking nice,' he said. 'I'll be keeping bar open until 'ee all come back.'

'OK, Sam,' answered Dad.

A few more steps and we had reached the corner, where Mrs Smith was waiting. And who were the others? Why, it was Mr and Mrs Harding, and a couple of the Billett girls. A few strange faces amongst the locals, who had popped out of The Retreat, and Horace, bless him. He appeared shy, but nevertheless came over to have a peep at the baby. Then, putting his hand in his pocket, he produced a half-crown (two shillings and sixpence), which he gently placed in little Jimmy's tiny hand. But baby's hand was too small to hang on to it, so it slid on to the shawl, whereupon I retrieved it and placed it into the pocket of my dress.

'Thank you, Horace, you are most kind.'

'Don't mention it, Pauline.'

The next thing, Dad was telling us all to get a move on, so our small congregation started walking slowly along the top road. It was obvious to anyone that we were on our way to a christening, all wearing I'm sure our very best attire. Going across the common, much laughter and chatter was going on, and for a wartime christening it was certainly a most joyous occasion.

Arriving at St Mary's, the young Priest was there to await us, and if I was not mistaken he was surprised to see so many of us for the christening. I first introduced Jim to the Curate, and then one by one we gathered around the font, at the back of the church.

When all was quiet, the young Priest started the ceremony in Latin. The Latin most of us could not understand, yet the very reverence in which it was said, I could see, was pleasing to all.

When the final phrase of the service was said, however, the young Curate spoke in English, and while making the sign of the cross with holy water on baby's forehead, he said, 'I baptise thee, James Paul, in the name of the Father, the Son, and Holy Ghost.'

A slight whimper came from little Jimmy. I then looked at Jim, who in turn was now smiling at me. I guess we must have both felt satisfied and happy; all had gone well.

Then, without any hesitation, the Priest gently placed little Jimmy in the arms of his godmother, who, with a contented smiling face, gazed proudly down upon her little godson.

So with the ceremony now all over, it only remained for Jim and I to thank the Priest, whereupon he shook our hands, blessing us as he did so.

It was mid-afternoon when we all started to make our way home, with everyone commenting what a lovely service it was, and Mrs Smith carrying baby with a displaying pride and joy.

I then offered to carry baby, but Jim beat me to it. 'Shall I have the little fellow?' he said. 'Guess your arms will be aching.' Smiling, Mrs Smith handed over baby to Jim.

With much laughter and conversation, we soon reached the outer gate of The Retreat, whereupon I expected saying cheerio to many, but to my surprise Sam came to the gate. He was smiling, and looked upon all with such esteem and pleasure. I couldn't believe my ears when he said, 'Come along inside. There be something laid on for 'ee all. Thee men will be ready for a pint.'

Then, one by one we followed Old Sam along the cobbled pathway that led to the pub itself. And behold — I gasped, and was absolutely amazed at what I saw, for the long wooden tables that stood underneath the veranda were all neatly set out with refreshments. There was beer for the men, and lemonade with ice for the ladies, with plates of sandwiches, home-made cakes and scones, and all covered with fine muslin; there was even a flower-bowl centred in the middle, consisting of scented stock and blue cornflowers.

'Oh, how lovely!' I remarked. I then got my eye on Mrs Harding, now wearing a pinny. I called out to her. 'Mrs Harding, now who could be responsible for all this lovely spread?'

'Well now,' replied Mrs Harding, 'it's like this, Paul, we all chipped in a little bit. A kindly gesture, you might say, from all your old neighbours.'

Suddenly I was emotionally overjoyed with such kindness. How does one feel, when emotion is roused by being taken unawares? I realised the goodwill and kindness that still existed in people, in spite of all the hardship and frustration of war. For I had a fear that the war was responsible for people becoming irresponsible and maybe selfish. But I was wrong to think as such, for the very folk that lived around me had endeavoured only to show their true colours of warmth and friendliness, which forever remained in my heart, and for which always I would be indebted with gratitude.

We all enjoyed ourselves that late Sunday afternoon, in dear Old Sam's garden, amidst the beauty of the flowers. Happiness had certainly possessed us all, making all worthwhile. Baby was content just to be nursed on my knee, and I thought how wonderful it all was, brought about by a little child being christened.

Then someone started to play a piano-accordion, so naturally we all wanted to dance. Giving baby to his Dad, I joined in the fun. We danced up and down on the pathway, while many of us finally finished up dancing on the wooden floor of the skittle alley. What joviality; everybody was happy, that was for sure.

I went back and joined Jim, who said, 'I say old girl, any chance of me having a puff of the pipe?'

I took little Jimmy into my arms while Jim lit his pipe, and the aroma from the old war-horse tobacco made it appeasable.

Mrs Smith then came across to us. 'I must go now,' she said, 'for I've left my little Timothy with Mrs Chubb.'

With my right hand free of baby, I stretched it out to shake hands. 'Mrs Smith, I'm so grateful to you.'

Mrs Smith then clasped my hand in both of hers. 'I'm so happy for you both,' she said, 'and little Jimmy.' Tears suddenly filled her eyes, which simultaneously acted upon me, for I too was emotionally happy, and could not prevent the tear-drops which escaped my eyes, and which fell on baby's white shawl. I guess it was a woman's prerogative to be sentimental, especially on this very special occasion.

Mrs Smith left us, with Jim remarking that little Jimmy had a fine godmother; and never did Jim speak truer words, for indeed she was a fine person, who later I discovered had suffered much in the past. She was in fact in Poland when the Germans invaded in 1939; she herself had a miraculous escape, managing to travel by boat to England. But the saddest part for her was that she had to leave all her family behind and many had been put into concentration camps. From there very few Poles came out alive; thousands upon thousands were gassed, and died.

Our treat in Sam's garden was drawing to a close. Many started to make their way home, and this gave me the opportunity of helping Mrs Harding to clear the tables, while two kind ladies offered to do the washing-up.

So, after thanking Sam and his good lady for their splendid hospitality, we made our way in home, only to find yet another little reception awaiting us. Mum had set a most beautiful table of flowers, with christening cake, plus the wines and drinks to go along with it. Those that couldn't make it to Sam's were more than welcomed in our little cottage, and I was surprised who did turn up. So the forthcoming conclusion was, we just had to have a party; and what made it all so wonderful was the fact that Rob had managed to come home for a few hours from Swindon.

The days that followed Jim and I spent happily together, going for walks, and spending hours in the garden. We experienced no raids, and it was almost like living in peacetime, so our only reminders of war came from listening to the news on the radio, or from reading a newspaper.

Inevitably Jim's leave came to an end, and he had to return to the Army. So, yet another parting; but the realistic must take over. This time it was different for Jim, for he was going to join his new outfit in Southampton. I knew Jim was not going to relish the change. After all, he was very settled at Wem, amongst lads he thought highly of; he was always remarking what a fine bunch they were. As usual, I went down to the GWR station to see him off.

There was a lump in my throat all right, but I knew I could keep back the tears. Jim would be feeling just the same, but we both knew that duty was prevailing, and that we were still at war. We kissed and waved goodbye — and one minute he was with me, the next he had gone.

Now alone on the station, I felt utterly miserable. While descending the wooden stairs in the station, I could have easily have cried, but I remembered the people around me. Then, all of a sudden, I was jolted by my very own thoughts. For I too had a duty to carry out. I now had a son to care for, and parents come to that. So shame on me for wanting to gratify my own self-pity.

I started walking quickly up the Lansdown Road, and I was beginning to feel better, for I had stopped feeling sorry for myself. I was now thinking of little Jimmy. Must hurry, for it was well past his feeding time.

True enough, when I arrived home it was taking all of Mum's time to pacify him. However, strange as it may seem, when Mum spoke to baby by saying, 'Ah, here's your old pot and pan,' he actually stopped crying.

'Jim go off all right then?' said Mum.

I could only nod my head.

'Never mind, duck. Look forward to your next meeting.' That indeed was a nice comforting thought.

While I was feeding baby, Mum produced a letter. 'It's from Matron,' she said, 'She would like me to return to work at the hospital. Getting a bit short-handed they are.'

'Why Mum, you can manage it, can't you?'

'I dunno, duck. Depends on what your Dad has to say.'

'You know Mum, I could do most things at home now.' I was encouraging her because I realised that I was actually responsible for Mum giving up her job in the first place; for had it not been for me, and my confinement, Mum would still have remained at her post as personal domestic help to Matron.

I noticed Mum again glancing at the letter, and felt sure of her interest in it. 'I'll talk it over with your Dad,' she said.

'Do that Mum, for I'm sure I can cope all right at home.' Adding: 'Not as good as you, Mum, but willing to try.'

286

'I know, duck, I know.'

I was aware also, that the earnings Mum would make would certainly come in handy, for although wages had increased considerably, Dad had none to spare; of course he would always share what little he had, for Dad was all too kind, but the extra would be useful.

Dad was due home at 11.30 p.m., so at 11.15 Mum set off to meet him, this of course being her settled tendency of practice, now that Dad kept his bus overnight in the depot, together with all the others. Myself, I settled down to reading the adverts in the evening paper, with the hopeful expectation of seeing a good second-hand pram for sale.

My eye soon caught an advert, appropriate to what I was looking for. A pram for sale; it was, however, at Batheaston, quite a distance away. Still, it was worthwhile going after, for its price was quoted as 2 pounds and 10 shillings.

Mum and Dad arrived home exactly at 11.30, and it was through a light supper that Mum mentioned her letter from Matron. 'What do you think I should do, Pat?'

'It's entirely up to you, Nell.'

Immediately I noticed Mum smiling, and at once I knew she would be returning to the hospital, for now she looked quite satsified.

I then spoke of my findings in the paper.

'Why don't you go after it in the morning?' said Dad. 'I don't start work until midday, and so I can look after little Jim.'

'You don't mind, Dad?'

'Not at all, and you do need a pram badly. For little Jimmy's getting far too heavy to carry.'

So, the very next morning, after attending to baby, I set off for Batheaston, with my purse containing 2 pounds and 10 shillings, plus 6 pence for bus fares. Of these pennies 5 were taken up just reaching there; however, I found the house without any bother.

I knocked on the front door, which was opened by a young lady not much older than myself. 'Good morning,' I said. 'I've come about the pram you have for sale.'

She smiled, and said, 'Do please come in.'

I followed her down a long passage, and then into a kitchen. There, playing with wooden bricks on a mat, was a lovely little boy, who I would say was about 15 months old. Then the young lady pulled back a curtain revealing a very large black pram, with four big wheels, and shining like silver were the chrome fittings.

I was really surprised at seeing a pram so big, yet looking closer at it, I could see it was in perfect condition. The very thought of pushing such a big pram, especially up our steep hills, gave me much to ponder over. I was trying to meditate, and make up my mind, when the young woman must have come to some sort of a decision herself, after realising I was undecided, for she said, 'I really expected getting the two pounds ten shillings for it — but I'm prepared to let it go for two pounds five shillings.'

I accepted, and the deal was closed, knowing that, without any effort on my part, I had made a bargain. I settled up with the young lady, patted the little boy on top of the head, and then proceeded to push the pram back along the passageway and out on to the road. Thanking the young woman, I was soon homeward bound, at last pushing my new means of transport.

I walked briskly with it to town, passing Dad's bus depot at Kensington, and at the end of the Paragon I joined on to the Lansdown Road, now attempting the first hill. It was just a matter of trying out my own strength, I suppose, but alas, up the steeper part I slowed down considerably. However, I was still moving, and I must have made home in record time. Proudly standing the pram outside the front door, I went down the garden in search of Dad and little Jimmy. I discovered that Jimmy was still asleep, while Dad was busy hoeing his late potatoes.

With such ardent eagerness, I almost dragged Dad away from his job, exclaiming, 'I've got it, I've got the pram! Come quickly, and see what you think about it.'

I stood beside Dad as he carefully examined it, hoping that in his opinion I had made a good buy.

Lifting his cap off, he started scratching his head, and then remarked, 'It's a nice pram. Not too big for you, is it? Yes, Paul, I reckon you'll manage it all right.'

So Dad's approval was given, which pleased me. Then, quite excitedly, I told Dad what I actually paid for it, being 5 shillings better off than I expected.

'Good for you,' said Dad. 'You got yourself a bargain. And now you've got me up this far, young lady, how about making your old Dad a cup of tea?'

'Of course,' I answered.

It was while we sipped our tea that we spoke of Mum, wondering how she was getting on down at the hospital. 'Knowing Mum,' I said, 'I think she will enjoy being back amongst so many.' And though Dad and I would not admit it we were both missing her already.

The talk with Dad reminded me that I had to prepare a lunch for us, so without hesitation I set to. But in the midst of it all I was interrupted by loud cries from little Jimmy. I hurried down the garden, only to find that the clothes-line had snapped, and the string of nappies was strewed across the cradle, with one nappy dangling into baby's face.

'What's up?' shouts Dad.

'It's the clothes-line, it's snapped!'

'Coming up,' called out Dad.

So by the time I had retrieved the nappies from the fallen line, Dad had little Jimmy in his arms. It appeared that it was the end of gardening time for Dad, for he nursed baby while I finished off making the lunch.

I had promised Mum that I would cope with everything, but as yet I'm afraid I wasn't off to a fine start. However, we finally got our lunch, and then Dad went off to work.

Then, with baby settled, I decided to clean the pram, using the Dettol lavishly; and when I had put the final touches to it, I stood back and admired its high polish, for it looked almost new.

I then proceeded on with other jobs around the home, and almost forgot to feed the chickens, had it not been for the hens strutting and scratching around the pen.

And so the afternoon passed over very quickly, and knowing Mum would be finished at 5 p.m. I decided I would meet her. With little Jimmy in his own pram, I was like a proud peacock, pushing it down the hill, down the dip, and then along Combe Park, towards the Royal United Hospital. I then continued up the hospital drive, and was almost at the entrance when Mum appeared from the door, with several other women.

Mum looked flabbergasted. 'Why duck, never expected seeing you!' Her first reaction was to look inside the pram. 'The little love is sleeping,' she said.

It was only natural, everybody wanted a peep, and sayings like, 'Bain't he a lovely babby!' echoed in my ears.

'You should see him in his bath,' said Mum. Then Mum, without any hesitation, proudly pushed her little grandson back along the driveway towards the big gates, where we all separated, each Mrs Mop going in different ways, each saying cheerio to the others.

'Well, Mum, how did it go?'

'Splendid!' replied Mum. 'And I'm pleased to see you've got yourself a pram. And you, duck? You've managed all right at home?'

Well, I had to be honest, and replied, 'Only just, Mum.' I wanted to change the last subject quickly. 'Do you like the pram?'

'It's a bit big, but nice,' answered Mum.

'And what do you think, I got it for five shillings less!'

'There!' said Mum. 'You had a long walk back home with it, a good five mile, I'll be bound. But I dare say it's been worth it, and I can see you are happy with it.'

I took over from Mum while pushing the pram up Weston hill, and coming up the slipway we both had to push.

During tea, Mum suggested we pop up to St Martin's to see Gran. I was delighted, for as yet Gran hadn't seen little Jimmy, so that evening we took the bus to town, finally taking another bus up to Combe Down. I carried baby, while Mum carried her basket of fresh eggs, plus Gran's miniature of whisky.

It was very quiet when we arrived on the ward, and in fact Gran herself was sleeping. We tiptoed beside the bed, but Gran must have sensed our presence, for directly her eyes opened, and then her face beamed into a smile at seeing us.

'Hello gal,' were her words to Mum.

'Hello Gran,' I then said.

Mum helped her to sit up in bed, and almost at once I placed baby into her arms.

'God love him!' said Gran, as she caressed him closer to her. So with great admiration, I now looked upon four generations. 'What's his name?'

'It's James Paul, Gran.'

'Another James then,' said Gran. My paternal Grandfather's name was James and there was also my Uncle James, Gran's only son, who had died of quinsy when just a boy. So the name of James goes back to both sides of the family; that may be a coincidence, but is accurately true.

I then produced from my bag a little white box. 'Christening cake for you, Gran,' I said, and handed it over. I then told her all about the christening, and how well everything went off.

Gran was listening attentively, and then spoke. 'You know, Pauline, all my children were christened in the same gown, at the same church in White Whaltham.'

'Oh Gran, how wonderful!' I said, thinking to myself how easy it must be for Gran to reminisce into the past. I then asked Gran if she was ready for her little drop of medicine. I at once saw the sparkle in her eyes, so giving baby to Mum, I placed my handkerchief around the little bottle of whisky. 'Take it in sips!' I whispered, and bless her she did, but just the same it brought the red roses into her cheeks.

It was a lovely hour we spent with Gran, and we wished we could have stopped longer, but it was getting late for baby, so we decided to go. Dear Gran, she almost smothered little Jimmy with her kisses, and I felt in my heart that seeing her great-grandson had made her very happy. 'Take good care of the little fellow,' she said, 'so one day he will take care of you. For he's just a little bundle of treasure.'

I too gave Gran many kisses, meanwhile admiring her countenance, the beautiful snow-white hair and milky skin, not forgetting the temporary rosy cheeks. Dear Gran — I loved her so much, and as we made our way through the exit doors of the ward, we turned around and waved. Gran saw us, and waved back.

Then, outside the hospital, we caught a bus straightaway which took us to town, whereupon a Lansdown bus was waiting, so we arrived home quicker then we thought. In no time at all, I had baby settled for the night.

Autumn of 1943 was upon us only too quickly, and it was, of course, a time when all the fruit had to be picked in. What would we do now, without Rob's help? Previously I had always helped Rob. I liked nothing better than to put on a pair of Rob's short khaki pants, and climb up Dad's apple trees with a canvas bag tied around my neck. It was always such fun and I thoroughly enjoyed doing it.

Dad and I decided to proceed much as usual; and so on this particular day, Dad's day off, I dressed up for the occasion after settling little Jimmy in his pram.

We decided to start with Dad's largest apple tree. So there we were, standing right beneath it and looking up. It was exquisite just to gaze upon the beautiful colouring of the leaves; and dotted amidst the leaves were those delicious-to-eat Blenheim apples. They were, of course, similar to the Cox's orange pippins, but much larger, and so this beautiful fruit had to be picked in most carefully. This is where I came in, and I was ready to climb up the tree.

'I dunno,' said Dad doubtfully. 'Somehow I don't think you should be climbing up trees now.'

I smiled at Dad, assuring him that I would be quite all right. I knew he would have preferred going up the tree himself, but we both realised that he was not so agile as he used to be, for he was now approaching retirement.

Once all was ready, I started to make the climb. Inwardly, I must confess, I was feeling a bit shaky and awkward. Nevertheless, I made a steady progress at climbing, determined perhaps to convince Dad that I was still capable. I was up now on the top branch, where as a child I would sit without a care in the world, eating bread and jam.

Dad called up. 'You all right, Paul?'

'I'm OK,' I shouted back.

Carefully I picked away, placing each apple gently into the canvas bag, giving it an occasional little swing around my neck. And so, with each bag almost full, I would make a partial descent towards the ground, where Dad would reach out with his walking-stick and hook the canvas bag to safety. On one descent Dad remarked, 'Bravo, Paul!'

I could see Dad was pleased with the good crop which the old tree had yielded, for he immediately wrapped the precious fruit in individual pieces of newspaper. This was to prevent a bad apple contaminating the others, but that was not what I thought as a child — I used to think the apples were wrapped in newspaper to keep them warm.

It was about mid-morning when Dad and I decided to have a break, so out came the bread and Gorgonzola cheese. Maybe it was my fancy, but it always seemed to taste that much better, eating in the garden. As we munched away at our snack, we talked of the amount of apples already picked: 6 orange boxes in all.

The break enabled me to feed baby and settle him down again, so once more I was ready to continue.

'Sure it's not too much for you, Paul? Just say so, and we'll pack it in, you know.'

'We'll soldier on,' I replied. 'Providing little Jimmy lets us.'

'Good,' said Dad. 'Maybe, with a bit of luck, we could almost strip the tree. Then, who knows, might even get started with the russets.' These, of course, were little trees and the top branches were easily reached by means of a small ladder.

And so the afternoon, like the morning, went over quickly, and when Mum came home we were still at it.

'I reckon the pair of you have had a good day,' said Mum. And how true were Mum's words, for it was days like these that were my happiest, next to having Jim at home, of course. 'I'll go up and prepare some food for you both,' she added. You must be hungry.' Dear Mum, willing to start again, after a day's work at the hospital. She took a peep at the baby as she went up the garden path, remarking, 'The little darling.'

About a half-hour had passed when Mum called us up from the garden. 'Come on, Paul,' said Dad. 'Let's call it a day.' With which he picked little Jimmy up in his arms saying, 'Come on, my lad.'

I had to smile, for Jimmy's bonnet was on the side of his head, and remained so even when Dad placed him between cushions on the sofa.

Mum had surprised us with a quickly prepared meal, and I must say all our plates were soon empty.

'Very nice, Nell. It'll give me strength to carry up those orange boxes from the garden.'

'I'll help you, Dad.'

'I can manage, Paul.'

'We'll carry 'em up between us,' I said firmly, determined to have my own way.

It was after we had placed the last box in the outhouse that Dad remarked, 'We've done well, Paul.' And I could tell he was pleased.

We then listened to the 6 o'clock news, after which we could all sit back and relax. With one exception — I must write to Jim.

Finishing off my letter, I sat back. But I did feel the absence of our Rob. It was always in the evening that I missed him more. I suppose it was understandable, as Rob and I were brought up together and we shared many of the same interests. But I knew Rob would do well in the Army, continuing his training to be a mechanic.

I had just got up from the table when I heard the front door open, and a voice call out, 'Be thee there, Polly?' I recognised that it was one of the locals who frequented The Retreat. 'It's Jim, he be on the phone.'

I dashed into The Retreat, forgetting that I still had Rob's short khaki pants on, and was only reminded of them by the sudden glances I received from folk who were sitting outside underneath the veranda. In those days women did not wear shorts in public, and I must have astounded them, showing my bare legs as I did. Still, I was so excited with the idea that I was going to talk to Jim that my attire was of no consequence at that moment.

Our conversation on the phone was precious indeed, and we exchanged all news. Jim actually laughed when I told him I'd been climbing trees. We could have gone on talking, but I knew it was costing Jim 2 pennies for every 3 minutes. So, after saying our farewells, I replaced the receiver, and then walked quietly through the flagstoned passageway, hoping I would not meet anybody. I was now conscious of my exposed legs, and wanted to get in home as quick as possible, but sure enough I bumped into Horace in the doorway, for he had just arrived.

'Why, hello Pauline — just in time to have a little drink with me.'

'Not now, thank you, Horace.'

'You told me that the last time, remember?'

I did remember, and felt myself blushing. 'I'm sorry, Horace, but perhaps I really will *next* time — OK?' I felt my cheeks getting hotter, for I realised the embarrassment of my situation: I was not quite rightly dressed, even to be in our little local pub. 'Will you excuse me Horace? Must dash.'

I was still feeling hot with embarrassment, yet inside I was feeling very happy, for I had just spoken to Jim.

It was late autumn, the leaves were falling fast off the trees, and the pattern of my life did not change. I lived somewhat in a routine, caring for baby and watching him grow fast. Time, it just raced along, so much so, that before we knew where we were the

Christmas of 1943 was approaching. When it arrived, we were without Jim and Rob, neither of whom could be at home to enjoy the festive season. However, I was happy to know that Jim would be home in the January of 1944, so it wouldn't be very long.

We spent Christmas at Primrose Hill very quietly, and talked of previous Christmases when we had all been at home together; but, having to accept the reality, we made the most of it. There was one thing: baby was an added joy to Mum and Dad. They were as always devoted grandparents, and I would not be wrong in saying that they just idolised little Jimmy, especially Dad.

I push on now to the spring of 1944. In the spring everything comes alive after the long winter, and even the light showers of snow were melting with the early sunshine.

Dad's retirement was due, and with 38 years' service (interrupted by his time in the Army in the Great War) it was no wonder the Bath Tramways Company had offered him a part-time job in the office. But, knowing Dad, I was not surprised when he turned it down. I knew his heart was at home, where there was always so much to do, especially in the garden. Mum, on the other hand, was a little younger than Dad, and being still capable of a good day's work she could continue on at the hospital. Her work, of course, appertained to the war effort.

The late spring brought us a visit from a lady, a Spanish lady called Mrs La Touche. Mum in the past had done cleaning work for her, and in fact the very idea of her visit was in hopes that Mum would return to her. A couple of mornings a week was all that she asked, but this was out of the question, for Mum was fully occupied at the hospital.

Well, the dear lady was so desperate for help that she even tried to persuade me to go to her. I appeared hesitant, and would have remained so, only Dad intervened, saying, 'I can always look after little Jimmy, you know. And it's only for two mornings a week.'

I felt Mrs La Touche's eyes upon me, her gaze, without doubt, full of hopeful expectations. Of course I was aware of the financial help it had to offer; it would mean little extras for Jimmy. So, smiling at Mrs La Touche, I accepted the post for two mornings weekly. I was to work on Mondays and Thursdays, at the big house on Sion Road. And it was there that I met Mr La Touche, who called himself Alfonso. He was a kindly man, with a typical Spanish accent; his face was deeply tanned, and adorned with a huge black moustache.

The work entailed much of an assortment, from cleaning silver to scrubbing floors. All this I happily did, and the La Touches were very kind to me; they treated me well, and often gave me little titbits to take home. On the dot of 10 a.m. I would make my way to the kitchens, where Cook always had my cocoa and biscuits ready; or, if Cook had just brought some scones out of the oven, I would have a hot buttered one.

Dad, now retired, coped marvellously with little Jimmy, giving always of his best attention, and I knew my son could be in no better hands than Dad's. The few shillings I earned, I saved, and so, when I had a few pounds saved up, off I would go to town to buy little Jimmy new clothes.

About this time, activities on the Home Front were beginning to stir. One night, after the 9 o'clock news on the radio, Mum and I listened to extracts from a speech made recently by Winston Churchill. 'The hour of our greatest effort and action is approaching.... The flashing eyes of all our soldiers, sailors, and airmen, must be fixed upon the enemy on their front. The only homeward road for all of us lies through the arch of victory.'

What did it all mean? What was Winston Churchill trying to get through to us? Invasion of Europe could only be the answer. Certainly it was no secret that convoys were carrying soldiers from their scattered camps to the south coast. Vera Brittain wrote that, 'Our nights echoed to the ceaseless clatter of heavy tanks lumbering down the Bournemouth-Southampton road.' Thousands of skilled men were drafted to small southern ports to make and assemble floating harbours, and, in spite of the number of people involved, the secret was well kept. For the benefit of the enemy, mock landing-craft were assembled on the east coast, in Kent and Essex. I think every man, woman and child was aware of what was going to happen. 'Every time we turn on the radio,' wrote J. L. Hodson in his diary, 'we expect to hear that the great invasion of Europe has begun.'

I suppose one could say that it was the start of the last stage of the war.

All military leave was cancelled, but there was one exception: servicemen could travel within a 20-mile radius from their base. For Jim it meant he could come up from Southampton as far as Salisbury, and so this was to be our meeting-place for many months to follow. I took the bus many times to Salisbury, meeting Jim at a certain place at a certain time, and always I had little Jimmy with me. The few hours we had together were very precious. Nearly always we strolled in the grounds of the Cathedral, and then sat ourselves down along the river bank, where we would enjoy sandwiches and take sips out of lemonade bottles. It appeared that the weather was always kind to us, and Jim and I would watch little Jimmy trying to make his first uncertain steps.

Jim would never speak of what he was doing on the Southampton docks. He had a reason for not doing so: it was for fear I would worry about him, for later I found out that he was actually shunting ammunition trains, filled with firearms, shells, and explosives.

Now we were in the month of June, when all the leaves on the trees came bursting out, and one could feel a new vitality. I was still with the La Touches, and this certain morning, after I had finished work, I made up my mind to ween little Jimmy.

I remember vividly that very evening, for on the 6 o'clock news it was announced that our expeditionary forces had landed in France, and with the help of the Navy and the Air Force our attack had begun. D-day had come at last, on the 6th of June 1944. A BBC news reader announced the successful landings.

Later, Mum took little Jimmy up to bed with her, and the surplus of milk I had gave rise to pain and discomfort. Knowing that it was impossible for me to go to bed and sleep, I contented myself to sit in the kitchen with the radio on so low that it was almost a whisper. Constantly news came through, and I was not even aware of my own little discomfort, for wasn't it just so very insignificant in comparison with the present onslaught that we were now inflicting upon the enemy? I knew only too well that many lives would be lost on both sides, and through the long night I had time to pray.

The 8 a.m. news announced the liberation of Paris. Our advance units were penetrating further, and our prospect of an early victory was at last in sight.

Of course, nothing much changed in England at first, and there were still hopelessly long queues in shops and for buses. And talking about queues, always someone would try the old trick. For instance — and this was especially popular for getting on to buses — one would observe a person walking slowly down the queue, and then looking speculatively along its length. Then the offender would spot a familiar face, and the chatting started, so that when the queue moved up, so would the person in question. This definitely was queue-jumping.

I'm afraid I could not be so cheeky. Maybe I couldn't stand the embarrassment of being caught. Then again, perhaps people had reasons for doing this sort of thing, for let's face it, the women had a lot to put up with, with their menfolk away. They themselves were probably working long hours in factories, having to wear turbans, painting their legs tan with a pencil mark down the back for imitation stocking seams; it was very unfeminine, but that was the dreariness of war.

But now things were changing for the better, for already we had a good foothold in Europe, and our armies were setting people free. For the folk living near the south coast there was much activity to be seen and heard. The flow of soldiers and equipment across the Channel continued, and the sky was dominated by aeroplanes, with bombers and fighters in low formation swishing along at enormous speeds.

I suppose in a way we were relieved that it had all begun, and on the whole people remained amazingly calm. Life began to be a lot easier, for the ships were coming in with more food. Some restrictions were abolished: for instance, the black-out was replaced by a 'dim-out', and gas-mask practice was abolished.

And the enemy, what were they up to? They tried hard, in fact they were desperate to hit back at us, by dropping their first flying bomb on London. It was the V1, and unfortunately it killed many. The V1 was later succeeded by the V2, and Jim spoke of the effect of these at Southampton. 'Never heard them coming, they gave no damn warning, they just exploded.' I wondered myself what effect on morale these nasty flying bombs and rockets would have. However, thank God, the menace of the V1 was largely defeated by the capture of their launching pads in northern France. And, by August 1944, the Allies had landed in southern France.

In December, a German offensive was started in the Ardennes, giving rise to more casualties. Maybe the Ardennes campaign was Hitler's last throw, but by diverting his troops from the East he may have given the Russians their opportunity to advance towards Berlin.

In September 1944, the Civil Defence forces where dispersed, and at the beginning of December Dad came home with the news that the Home Guard was going to be disbanded. This, of course, was good news, but to Dad it meant something entirely different. There would be no more manoeuvres, and no more get-togethers with his old pals. Comradeship had closely united them, developing strong ties among a generation of men with long experience. So I knew that the dissolving of the Home Guard was a shattering blow to Dad. He would miss the company of his pals, and his only other friends were the few locals that frequented The Retreat.

A week before Christmas we had a surprise visit from Uncle Edwin. The dear man was well, but still suffered from the loss of his son, Cecil. At work he was still in charge of the Bath GPO sorting-office, but he was having difficulty in finding staff to cope with the mail. So, with Mum and Dad's approval, I offered my services to the postal department of the GPO. Of course, the very thought of having to leave the La Touches disturbed me, for I had been so very happy with them. They had been kindness itself, I enjoyed working for them, and my little wage had come in handy. However, one had to enhance one's status if it was possible, so a postwoman I became. Mind you, I was solely dependent on Dad to look after little Jimmy, who by now was toddling everywhere; but I had the deep satisfaction of knowing that Jimmy was cared for and loved by Dad, who constantly guided and protected him. This gave me reassurance; he could not have been in better hands.

How well I remember getting up at 3.30 a.m. to start my new job. It was another challenge in my life, and one which I was eager to attempt. I remember the morning perfectly: it was dark and cold as I made my way to town, but walking briskly I arrived prompt at 4.15 a.m. at the sorting-office, which incidentally was situated opposite the Pierrepont Garage. As I glanced over towards the garage, a flood of memories passed through my mind. But I realised that I was now on the verge of something new, so I opened the big entrance door of the sorting-office. There I was confronted by two heavy black curtains, which I drew back, letting myself in, and at one glance I could see folk were busy sorting out the mail and placing all correspondence into different racks, or pigeon-holes. I observed a place unattended, and wondered if that space was for me.

Then I heard my Uncle's voice call out, 'Pauline!' He beckoned me over to his office, and it was in his office that he gave me a tunic and cap to try on. Well, they were much too large for me. Fortunately, Uncle Edwin remarked, 'It's the only one I have, so maybe you might just settle for an armband.' I couldn't agree more. 'Come,' said Uncle. 'I'll show you how to go on at the sorting of mail.'

Soon the mail was sorted out between us, and its destination was Newbridge Road. 'Thought I'd give you something handy to home,' said Uncle Edwin. He was in fact being very considerate, for after finishing my round I would be a mere fifteen minutes' walk from home; this of course would suit me admirably.

Already postmen and postwomen were leaving the building, and it was amazing the amount of mail they carried. Soon it was my turn to leave; my mail-bag was full, in fact it was bulging over the top, and there were also the registered letters which I carried for safety in my hand, not forgetting my indelible pencil which I placed behind my ear. The canvas bag was heavy, but I managed to sling it over my right shoulder, fully aware that it contained some weighty bundles.

My round started a distance of two and half miles away, so I had to take the first bus available. Being a postal worker, I could travel free, and rested my load on the long seat of the bus. The conductor, who by now was eyeing me up and down, said, 'Where do you want to be off, Miss?'

'Oh,' I said. 'Start of Newbridge Road, please.'

The bus stopped for me to get off, and when I did, I swung my bag much too hard over my shoulder, which nearly unbalanced me. I looked up at the conductor, and saw that he was now smiling at me. So, with the first bundle of letters in my hand, I started delivering.

At No. 3 Newbridge Road, I walked up the pathway. There were two letters for this house; the letter-box, however, was situated right at the bottom of the door, and when I stooped my bag almost slid off my shoulder. There must be a knack, I thought, to prevent the bag from slipping. And of course I realised later that, when wearing uniform, the buttoned epaulettes would hold the bag in position. I was learning as I delivered, and I was thankful that my load was getting lighter.

As the days went by, I got better and quicker, and I started to notice the people I was delivering for. One of the buildings in Newbridge Road was a house called Fairfield, a building of distinguished character, somewhat larger than the others. It was owned by a very famous figure indeed, for he was Haile Selassie, the Emperor of Ethiopia. From 1936 to 1940 Haile Selassie lived in this house, together with his family and followers, who had all taken refuge in this country. At the time when I was delivering the letters, there were still a number of Ethiopians in residence. It made me feel privileged and honoured to be delivering mail to such refined people; and to me refined is what they were, for I was always received with politeness, so they were worthy of all the respect I had for them. Maybe it was the salaam that fascinated me; or was it the ladies' sarongs or saris which hung gracefully to their heels; or was it their beautiful dark skins, which blended in with the beauty of their attire? Whatever it was, I was most impressed, for I had known no other people like them before.

Only twice did I have the pleasure of meeting a man whom I believed to be Haile Selassie, and this might not have occurred had it not been for him strolling in the garden as I happened to be walking up the pathway. A small figure of a man he was, dressed in a long robe, and I knew that the very smile he gave me was genuine; on one certain occasion, he thanked me when I handed the mail to him.

During my role as a postwoman, I met all kinds of people, some happy, some sad; I also met a lot of little dogs who constantly yelped at my feet. Or course, being on a job like this, one had to be exceptionally fit, as it naturally entailed a lot of walking. Having reached the age of twenty-three, I thought myself very eligible — that is, until something happened which very abruptly ended my job as a postwoman.

It was the beginning of February in 1945. It was a cold morning, and a thin layer of snow had covered everywhere. However, walking to town that morning was most invigorating, and so I arrived at the sorting-office in good time. The volume of mail was not quite so heavy that morning, so I was quick in sorting it out, and was almost first to leave the building. I was off to a fine start, taking the bus as usual to Newbridge Road, whereupon I was ready to deliver the mail. Happily I went about my work, offering 'Good mornings' to early risers.

I had practically finished my round when I jumped over a wall to get to the next house, and indeed it was a mistake on my part, for as I landed on the thin cushion of snow, I slid forward, twisting my right leg. I finally landed on my backside, with the remaining letters all strewn around me.

I could only blame myself for this mishap, knowing it would never have happened if I had walked the pathways in a proper manner. I tried desperately to get up, but found I couldn't stand on my right leg. I imagined it to be broken, and I felt myself shaking, but I managed to support myself by a stone wall. So there I was, standing on one leg.

Immediately the front door of the house opened, and a man's voice shouted out, 'You all right, Miss?' I was now almost in tears with pain, and must have looked quite pathetic just leaning against the wall. I think the man recognised the predicament I was in, for he came racing across to me. 'Good Lord, Miss, what's happened?'

I now felt myself trembling, when I said, 'I've hurt my leg, and cannot stand on it.' Again I tried putting my foot to the ground, but the pressure on my leg was too much, and it just hurt so. Without any hesitation, the man started to pick up the remaining mail, wiping off the fine snow with his handkerchief before placing it all in the mail-bag. Meekly I thanked him, for he had come to my rescue.

'I best get you to hospital, young lady,' he said.

This was the only solution. I needed medical help, so in a matter of seconds the man had driven his car out of the garage, and soon we were on our way along Combe Park towards the Royal United Hospital.

'I'm sorry to be such a nuisance,' I exclaimed.

'Oh, that's all right, Miss. Anyway, you need medical attention.' And when he left me in Casualty, I thanked him once again.

The next thing I knew, I was sitting in a wheelchair, almost feeling sorry for myself, when a Nurse wheeled me into a consulting room. Strange, but while waiting, I remembered the young German airman. However, my thoughts were interrupted by yet another

300

Nurse, saying, 'Hello, what have you been up to then?' Smiling back at her, I could only tell her that I had had a slight accident with my leg.

After that I was wheeled into another room, where a Doctor and two Nurses were in attendance. One Nurse took my shoe and stocking off, and now the Doctor was examining my leg. 'Tibia and fibula all right,' he muttered. He then carefully examined my knee. 'Ah,' he said. 'I've found the trouble. Possibility of torn ligaments.' He then looked at me. 'You need to rest it for at least six weeks.' The Doctor gave instructions that my whole leg be put into plaster of Paris. He then left the room, and so did the Nurses.

I was still sitting on the examination bed, regretting that I had been so careless, and knowing that all this could have been avoided if only I had walked up the paths properly. Then the door opened, and one of the ward maids had popped her head in the doorway. 'I say,' she said, 'bain't you Mrs Quintin's daughter?'

'Yes,' I answered.

'Thought so,' she replied, and off she went. The next thing, to my astonishment, Mum appeared, looking very perturbed.

'Gawd, duck, what's happened?'

I explained to Mum what I'd done. 'Anyway Mum, it's just my knee. And it was my own fault.'

'Dearie me,' said Mum. 'What about the rest of the mail? I'd better ring up your Uncle Edwin, and tell him what's happened. Then there's getting home. Will you be all right?'

'Sure,' I replied. 'I'll hop if I have to.' Now I was treating my misfortune lightly; anyway, I didn't want Mum to worry over me.

'I'd better go now, duck. And sure you'll be all right now?'

'Of course, Mum. See you later.' She then kissed me, and was off.

Two Nurses then came on the scene, pushing a trolley equipped with the necessary to put my leg into plaster. Finally a Sister appeared, rolled up her sleeves, and got to work on me straightaway. First she moulded the white clay around my ankle, and then she manipulated it with such skill that my whole leg was soon covered. It quickly set, enabling me to stand, and with the aid of a walking-stick I then walked slowly out of the room. Eventually I toddled out of the hospital, looking like a typical wounded soldier, but this time it was a wounded postwoman.

While walking up the driveway, I noticed a GPO mail van coming towards me. It stopped alongside me, and then a head poked out of the side window. 'Hello. It's Mrs McCann, isn't it? I've come to collect the rest of the mail.'

I handed over the mail-bag containing the few letters I had failed to deliver.

'I say, is your leg very bad?' said the postman.

'It's just my knee. Torn ligaments.'

'Blimey! Did they have to put your whole leg in plaster?'

'Appears so,' I replied.

'Got far to go?'

'Primrose Hill.'

'Well, you'll not be able to get in the front seat, but if you can manage to get yourself into the back of the van, I can give you a lift home.'

What luck, I thought, as I slid my bottom along the floor of the van. The van then turned, and headed for home. I must say I appreciated the lift very much, and thanked the postman for his kindness.

I hobbled along the top road into the lane, and as I opened the front door I shouted out, 'Cooee!' There was no answer, so my guess was that Dad and little Jimmy were down the garden. I was right. They were both well wrapped up, and enjoying the crisp fresh air.

I think I startled Dad when he saw me. 'What on earth has happened to you, Paul?' he said, but before I could explain, little Jimmy, excited to see me, came running towards me. I picked him up in my arms, letting my stick fall to the ground, and at the same time I gave a quick account of events to Dad. I explained that it was only an injury sustained to my knee.

'You know, Paul, for the minute, I thought you had broken your leg.'

'Sorry, Dad. It must have given you a shock. I thought it a bit ridiculous putting all this plaster on my leg though.'

'Still, they'll know best,' said Dad, with which he placed his arm around my shoulder. 'Never mind, old girl, let's go up for some hot cocoa.'

Little Jimmy was making his way along the pathway, with Dad behind him, tapping him on the bottom. Shrieks of laughter came from little Jimmy, and how Dad loved playing with him.

So, on the sofa I anchored, beside a fire that shone brightly, which meant a frost was still about. In between sips of cocoa, I told Dad all.

Well, as incapacitated as I was, I remained cheerful. The following morning brought a heavy fall of snow, and Dad remarked that I was lucky I hadn't to plod around in it, for already there was much drifting. Fortunately for Mum, it was her day off, so it remained only to stay indoors and keep warm.

I wrote to Jim, and I dare say when he received my letter he was concerned over my injury, for when I got his return letter he said that there might be a possibility of him coming to see me. Apparently the ban on leave had now been lifted, so it was no surprise when Jim landed home the following Saturday morning. The short and unexpected leave that Jim had managed to get made a very happy weekend indeed, and with the help of the walking-stick I managed to hop around, even to go into The Retreat with him.

We talked of the future, and longed for the end of the war, so that we could settle down in the north-east of England. Jim expected to have his original job to go back to, driving steam-rollers for the Gateshead Council; that had been the work he had done before becoming a train-driver.

All too soon, Jim's short leave was over, and he had to make his way back to Southampton, with myself regretting that I could not see him off at the station. However, I watched him walk down the lane; he waved, then turned the corner. Meanwhile I just stood, feeling big tears flowing down my cheeks, my emotions being too strong for me. Anyway, it didn't matter. I was alone with my sadness, and maybe after the tears I would feel better.

As the weeks went by, I kept in touch with my brothers through letter-writing. Pat was still on convoys. Tim was still instructing recruits, while Tom was somewhere in Burma. Occasionally we would have visits from my sister-in-law Rene, and the children, Alfie and Iris, who were now growing up very fast.

I recall an incident which happened at home, bringing much grief to the folk that remained on Primrose Hill. It was the sudden tragic death of Mr Chubb, the farmer who lived at the bottom of the hill. Oh yes, I cried when I heard about it, for he was killed by his own tractor which accidentally toppled over on him. He was well respected, for there was no other kinder. In my eyes he was a typical farmer, with cheeks always like red rosy apples, and always smiling he was. I recall when a young girl, and when I used to go wooding, he would let me through the farmyard, saying, 'Take short cut, gal. But for heaven's sake don't thee be letting cows out!' I knew the farm could never be the same without him, for I'm sure he loved his animals as himself.

The early spring sunshine in March 1945 was accompanied by good news of the war: Cologne and Danzig were captured, and without doubt the end was now in sight.

The time came for my plaster to come off, the six weeks being up, so one morning I went off to the Royal United. I was taken in to see a lady Doctor, who carefully started taking off my grimy-looking plaster. When it was almost all off, the lady Doctor looked at my leg with astonishment and then remarked, 'My dear young lady, this plaster should have never been put on your leg. For you have a highly sensitive skin, which naturally rejects plaster, or anything else come to that.'

It was true my leg felt sore, particularly underneath the knee, and with a quick glance I saw that my skin appeared very red and blotchy. This then accounted for the irritation I had felt over the past week especially. Anyway, I was relieved to have the plaster off, and thankful to the Nurse who put a soothing cream on, and a soft crêpe bandage around my knee to give a firm support. I stood down on both feet, feeling no pain whatsoever.

'Keep the bandage on for at least two weeks,' said the lady Doctor. 'By then you should be all right.'

So, in the two weeks that followed, I was able to move around in comfort, catching up with the little jobs that had been neglected.

We were now in the month of April, and it was necessary for me to visit old Doctor Scott-White, who informed me that I was once again pregnant. The news we all accepted gladly, and Jim in his letter announced his delight and joy.

On the BBC news the announcer spoke of the American and British advances in Germany, and told us that Alexander had completed the conquest of Northern Italy. In the space of a few days, sensational events occurred. First we heard that Mussolini had been shot, and then that the Germans in Italy had surrendered, whereupon Hitler and his mistress committed suicide. And in conclusion, on the 7th of May 1945, at Rheims, General Eisenhower accepted the Germans' unconditional surrender.

Following such happenings, Churchill spoke to the people the next day. 'The evil-doers,' he said, 'are now prostrate before us.' His broadcast was relayed over loudspeakers to the crowds in Whitehall. Meanwhile, in our humble kitchen at home, we all experienced a sense of profound relief, for the war was now practically over. I shall always remember Mum's words to Dad: 'Thank God it's over, Pat, and we've all been spared.' Myself I was so happy, I almost cried with joy.

The 8th of May 1945 was VE Day (Victory in Europe). This, of course, was not totally the end, as events surely followed, but for the time being at least we could rejoice.

At home we celebrated quietly, but we were aware of the wild excitements which marked that very special day, such as the singing that came from open windows. In the streets many women wore flags in their hats; some women were even draped in Union Jacks. The following day we read in the newspapers that The Mall, in London, was one solid mass of people linking arms and singing. One journalist described his experience as follows: 'In one crowded crazy day, in one small patch in London, I was passionately kissed by three girls. I sang "Land of hope and glory" until I was hoarse.

I climbed my first and positively my last lamp-post and I nearly persuaded myself, but not quite, that the war was over.'

Myself I was now making preparations for my second baby, who was due in November, so in the weeks to follow my life again was kept in something of a routine. Dad and I were glad of each other's company, for Mum was still working at the hospital. Anyway, Dad and I coped at home, with Dad giving all his loving care to both little Jimmy and I.

Jim was now coming home more often, but I think we could only pretend that we were living in peacetime, for we were still reminded of the horrors of war. In the Far East the fighting continued, and on the 6th of August 1945 the whole world was shocked by the dropping of the atomic bomb on Hiroshima in Japan. Thousands were killed, and thousands more were maimed. Although the Japs were still our enemy, I did feel for those innocent victims who must have suffered terribly through this sudden monster that had dropped upon them. Consequently the Japanese surrendered on August the 14th 1945, only eight days after the atomic bomb had been dropped. Now the war really was over, once and for all, and we could all begin to live normal lives again.

September came, and we had a good harvest of those delectable delicious figs, which Dad sold for threepence each to a large fruiterer in town; they were subsequently sold to customers for sixpence each, so the fruiterer made a good profit in comparison to Dad's yield.

Then again it was time for apple picking. We had no problem this year, because Alfie, now getting a big boy, was able to climb up the trees. Mind you, I still did my share, catching the falling apples that came down. Sometimes Alfie would call out, 'Auntie Paul — catch!' So down would come an apple; but of course I couldn't catch them all, so many I'm afraid got a bash on the ground. Still, they made beautiful apple pies.

With the late September came the early mists, bringing in the crop of mushrooms from the surrounding fields. Actually we lived pretty well, with all the fresh vegetables and fruit.

We had a letter from Rob saying that he had been transferred to Southampton and was now a fully qualified mechanic. Brother Pat was now back in the naval barracks at Devonport, and Tim was at Yeovil, so they were all able to come home often, except of course Tom, who was still out in Burma.

The gradual change-over from war to peace continued. Many people were now returning to their patched-up or temporary homes, and evacuated children were coming back to their families. A steady increase in lighting in public places was appearing, and this in itself gave us all an added sense of security, a feeling that we really were living in a peacetime England.

About this time, however, we were all getting concerned over Gran, for in the past few weeks she been unwell, and sleeping rather more than usual; so Mum and Dad were making frequent visits to the hospital.

Myself I was more or less confined to home, but I would have dearly loved to visit Gran. I recall Mum and Dad returning one day, after seeing her, and I could tell Mum had been crying.

'How is Gran?' I asked.

'Very poorly, duck. I cannot see her pulling through.'

I suddenly felt so sad, for I dearly loved Gran, and knowing that there was nothing we could do made our hearts heavy. It was left now to the Good Lord, and so, in the following week, my Gran entered the gates of Heaven. I knew only that Heaven was a good place, so it just had to be the best place for Gran.

The funeral was very quiet. Well, Gran would have wanted that, and I was glad Jim was home at the time to give me support. After the funeral I did not feel quite so bad, and could think of nothing else but Gran's favourite tune: 'Daisy, Daisy, give me your answer do.' Losing Gran was a big blow to us all, for we all loved her so very much.

Anyway, Jim, bless him, did his best to cheer me up by saying, 'Home for good in six weeks, Paul.'

'Yes,' I answered. 'How wonderful! And Jim, I've just been thinking — you'll be home just in time for our new baby coming.'

And so it was that on the 19th of November 1945, Jim came home in a demob suit. It was grey in colour, with white stripes. It was double-breasted too, with wide lapels. Somehow, to me, it did not do Jim much credit; maybe it was the strangeness of seeing him in civies.

Jim was now laughing. 'Oh, Paul, you should have seen us all getting demobbed. We were all given a large flat box, containing a suit, a shirt, two collars with a stud, two pairs of socks, a pair of shoes, a tie, and a hat, along with a resettlement book. Well, what a carry-on. Men were swopping things with each other. Talk about a free-for-all. I gave up at the finish, and hoped that what I got fitted me.'

I couldn't help but laugh at the way Jim was expressing himself, for I imagined all the chaos which the process of demobilisation would cause; there were 380 of these dispersal centres, all ejecting a flow of men, each man carrying his own personal wearing apparel. In a way it was just another large army of men all dressed the same, but my guess would be that they would all be jolly glad to be wearing civies. For wasn't it a first step towards home? But not all would be glad to return home, I realised, for there could be the added stress of returning as strangers to their wives and families; then again, there was the additional problem of finding work for themselves.

With the excitement of Jim being home, I was forgetting about myself and our new baby that was due any time now. Yet I had everything in readiness, almost exactly as when little Jimmy was about to be born.

On the morning of November the 20th, I awoke with considerable backache, which I had previously not experienced. However, paying no heed to it, I got up as usual, and managed to get around.

The day went over normally, with the added happiness that Jim was home with me. Around 8 p.m. Dad and Jim went into The Retreat for a game of crib, but at 8.30 I began to have more severe pains in the back, so much so that I could not stand up.

Mum decided it was time to fetch Nurse Thomas, so off she went into The Retreat to fetch Jim, who came dashing in, with Mum following. I could see Jim was worrying and he remarked, 'The bairn must be due now.' So, listening carefully to Mum's instructions, he went off in pursuit of Nurse Thomas.

Meanwhile Dad came in. 'Anything I can do, Nell?'

'Yes, Pat,' answered Mum. 'Would you like to put the fire on in the bedroom.'

Mum helped me upstairs, and it was 9.30 when Jim returned. He was puffing and blowing, and I guess he had run up the hills, so in between pants he exclaimed, 'I've seen the midwife. She's on her way.'

Then Dad spoke. 'Come on, Jim, let's go in for another pint. Only be in the way if we stop here. So we'll leave it to the ladies, shall we?'

I could see Jim was a little agitated. He looked at me, saying, 'Will you be all right, pet?'

'I'm in the best of hands, Jim,' I replied. 'So go along with Dad, and finish off your game of crib.'

'I'll have a peep first at little Jim.' He came back, saying that our son was fast asleep, without a care in the world. 'Sure you'll be all right, Paul?'

'Of course,' I answered. 'Anyway, it'll be all over shortly.'

He kissed me, then held my hand tightly. 'If I can do anything, Paul, I'll be around.' Which was a comforting thought.

It was around 10 p.m. when Nurse Thomas arrived. She had been hurrying, for she too was out of breath, and I could tell she wasn't very pleased when she remarked, 'These babies arrive at some of the most awkward times.' Then she smiled, which put me at ease. Next she examined me. 'Baby is ready,' she announced. Then, still looking at me, she said, 'You've had back labour, young lady. And if you had fetched me before now, I could have saved you hours of pain.'

It was then in a feeble voice that I answered her. 'I thought my backache was of no consequence, and I didn't want to bring you out on a false errand.'

Nurse Thomas smiled. 'I wish all my patients were as considerate as you, my dear! Anyway, baby shouldn't be long in coming.'

Nurse Thomas was right, for at exactly 11 p.m. a new baby son was born. The nursing procedure, as before, was done with the highest efficiency and Nurse Thomas soon had my new baby swinging in a net bag.

'Ah,' she exclaimed. 'Exactly nine and half pounds. Not as big as the first maybe, but big enough.' And needing no further medical attention, both baby and I were fine. 'Get a good sleep now,' said Nurse Thomas, as she put on her gabardine coat and navy-blue hat. 'I'll come back in the morning to see you both.'

It appeared she was in a hurry to get home, so Mum didn't delay her by making her tea. 'Thank you for everything, Nurse Thomas,' I said.

'Thank you, my dear, for being a good patient.'

She closed the door quietly behind her. I then heard voices, and knew she would be talking to Jim and Mum and Dad. Then I heard the front door close, and within seconds Jim was in the room beside me.

I looked at him, and saw that big tears were streaming down his face. 'I feel so damn happy,' he said. I knew his affections for me were so deep, and he just placed his arms around me, as if he never wanted to let me go. 'Oh, darling,' he said, 'I feel so proud of you. Now two sons.'

Meanwhile Mum and Dad came into the room to have a look at their new grandson.

'Image of little Jimmy,' said Dad.

I looked at Mum, and she must have guessed my thoughts, for she said, 'How about a nice cup of tea?'

Then Jim said, 'I think I'll take a stroll.'

'But it's so late,' I remarked.

'Just you don't worry now, and settle down for a good sleep.'

Alone with baby I must have dropped off to sleep, until I was woken by the tiny cries of my new baby boy. It was 3 a.m., and time for his feed. I stretched over and lifted him out of the cradle, and his little cries stopped when he settled down to feed. It was then I heard the front door open, which almost startled me, but I knew that the quiet steps coming up the stairs were Jim's.

'Why Jim,' I exclaimed, 'where on earth have you been, dear? It's after three a.m.'

'I knew I wouldn't sleep with all the excitement,' he said, 'so I just had to go for a walk. Well, I walked across the common, and sat on a seat, and enjoyed my pipe. It's a beautiful night. Full moon, too. See how it shines through the window.' I too had noticed the moon shining. 'Well,' said Jim, 'the next thing, I was joined by a bobby, who sat talking with me for ages. For we discussed all manner of things. I suppose he was curious to find me sitting on a bench at that time of the morning, but after he had heard my story, my explanation must have convinced him.'

'Jim,' I said, 'why don't you go downstairs and make yourself a hot drink?'

'A good idea,' replied Jim. 'And what say you to a nice cuppa?'

After settling baby down in his cradle, I felt wide awake, and enjoyed a cup of tea with Jim. We talked in whispers, for fear of awakening Mum and Dad.

We must have chatted on and off for such a long time, for the next thing we heard was a clattering coming up from the farm. Now I was thinking of the farmer's wife, boldly carrying on after her husband's tragic death, and thought it a blessing that she had the help of two land-girls.

Maybe I was too excited about everything to go off to sleep again, but I was pleased Jim did, for when Mum brought up my breakfast he was still in sound sleep. I put my fingers to my lips. Mum smiled and then left the room quietly, but meanwhile I tucked into tasty rashers of bacon and egg.

It must have been the delightful aroma from the bacon that aroused Jim from his sleep, for he stirred, then opened his eyes, and looked surprised at seeing me sitting up in bed, and enjoying my breakfast.

'Hello, darling, had a good sleep?' I said.

'Must have gone off sound. Anyway, no need to ask how the patient is.' With which he kissed me on the cheek. 'Did you sleep, Paul?'

'Kind of dozed,' I replied. 'Guess you'll be ready for some breakfast, Jim.'

'Yep,' said Jim. 'I'm going down to see what Mam is cooking.'

So off he went. Meanwhile I slithered down into the bedclothes, and I soon went off to sleep, with the most happy and contented feeling ever.

I was awakened by baby crying for attention again, but Jim was on the scene. He carefully handed me his young son, saying, 'Come on little fellow.'

After feeding baby, I dozed over again, but then I heard little Jimmy crying downstairs. I imagined he was missing me, so with ·the walking-stick that rested beside my bed I gave three little taps on the floor.

Mum was up immediately. 'You're awake then, duck.'

'Hello Mum. Is little Jimmy all right? I heard him crying.'

'Ah yes, little love was out beside the chicken-run, when he fell. Just grazed his knees a bit.'

'Ask Jim to bring him up, Mum.' When he did come up with his Daddy his little eyes were red, and I detected that he had a bit of a runny nose. Anyway, he was soon into my arms for a cuddle. Then he sat upright and looked around him in a bewildered way. Jim picked him up, saying, 'Let's take a peep at your new brother.'

Little Jimmy stood beside the cradle. He peered through the bars and said, 'He got fingers, he have,' for already he was using the Somerset vocabulary. The next thing, he was in my arms again.

Nurse Thomas was my next visitor. She was puffing a bit, and declared, 'I'm sure those hills are getting steeper.' So off came her hat and coat, and then on with her white starched apron. 'Well,' she said, 'how's mother and baby doing?'

'Just fine, thank you,' I answered.

First she attended to baby, bathing him, then putting on all clean clothes, including a binder which she firmly wrapped around him to support his little back. Then, after Nurse had attended to me, Mum presented herself, carrying tea and biscuits on a tray for our visitor.

'Thank you, Mrs Quintin. And how are you coping? Having a busy time just now, aren't you?'

Mum made no comment, only smiled instead. Dear Mother, I thought, what would I have done without her, for ceaselessly she carried on working around the clock, and it was a blessing indeed that she had acquired two weeks off work. 'Must be at home, when baby arrives.' That's what she would say.

The sweet delicacy of the room was filling my nostrils, and Nurse Thomas was already about to leave.

'Will call tomorrow, about the same time,' she said as she left the room.

I was feeling on top of the world, for everything at that moment was perfectly rosy, for my husband was home with me, and now I had two lovely sons, along with loving parents. What more could I ask for? The war was almost completely over, and it would just be a matter of time before all my brothers would be home for good.

As I was lying there, happy with my thoughts, Jim entered the room, holding an envelope in his hand. 'A letter from my folk in

Gateshead,' he said, as he handed it over for me to read. After reading it, I nodded in approval at its contents. 'Do send off a telegram today, Jim. For they'll all be anxiously awaiting news.'

'A good idea, Paul. I'll enjoy a walk into town. And if there's anything you want, any messages I can do, I can do them when I'm down.' It was an excellent idea, for I needed extras for baby.

The days I was confined to bed went over much quicker than I expected, for already it was my twelfth day, and to our surprise we had a visit from Rob. He came bursting into the bedroom, giving me such a hug, and when he had kissed me, he said, 'Well, how's our Quinner?'

Jim joined us, remarking, 'Doesn't she look well, Bob? Pity we can't take her into The Retreat.'

I was pleased Rob was home for a while, for he was good company for Jim and they always got on well together. So the days that followed were indeed happy times. Rob, who had seen so little of young Jimmy, was captivated with love for his nephew. I could only think of it as a great love that started when Rob had to cycle to town to fetch Nurse Thomas, and then that other dash he made to fetch the Doctor afterwards. Whatever it was, little Jimmy was loved and admired by his Uncle Rob, who played with him for hours on end.

My fourteenth day was up, and I was ready to leap out of bed. I mention leap, but this was entirely out of the question, as my legs felt unsteady as I stepped out of bed. However, hanging on to the bedrail for support I made good progress.

Jim's head appeared above the bedclothes. 'Keep it up, pet,' he said. 'You're doing fine.' However, having said that, he disappeared underneath the bedclothes again. I couldn't blame him, for it was very early in the morning, not even milking time down on the farm, but I was eager to get out of bed. Now I was walking without the aid of the bedrail, and even surprised Mum when she came in with the early morning tea.

'Hello, duck. My, you're up early. Don't overdo it now.' And so it was after breakfast that I first ventured downstairs, with everybody wanting to do so much for me.

This very morning, Jim had received a letter from the Gateshead Council, begging for his return immediately, as there was much work to be done in all areas of Gateshead.

'You must go, Jim,' I said. 'It'll make secure your job. Anyway, she'll be waiting for you, that old steamroller of yours.'

Jim smiled and said, 'I guess so.'

'And besides,' I said. 'It'll give you the opportunity of looking for somewhere for us to live.'

'Yes,' Jim answered. 'I must look for a place for us.'

So it was settled there and then, that Jim would return to the north-east as soon as possible. We both realised that it was so near Christmas too, a time when we should all be together, but circumstances as they were, Jim's job had to take priority; it was our bread and butter.

Very reluctantly Jim made preparations for leaving. However, when I did see him off at the station, we both consoled each other, knowing that the parting would not be for long, and that the next time we met, we would be together for good.

It was understandable that I should miss Jim very much, and so did little Jimmy, for he kept asking for his Daddy. Still, I had my hands full, and I was to make preparations for our new baby's christening. We decided from the beginning to call our baby son Patrick, after my Dad, and brother Pat. There was only one regrettable thing: it meant that Jim would not be at home for the christening. But it was a blessing that we had Rob, and he headed our little procession down to St Mary's Church, one cold snowy afternoon.

I think we had more laughs than enough that afternoon, especially walking across the common, for we were all slipping and sliding, and it amazed me how Rob was so steadfast on his feet. Mind you, I was glad, for he was carrying baby.

Although not as elaborate a christening as little Jimmy's, this one was quite an occasion. Mum made a lovely cake with all the trimmings, and it all went down with a glass of best port wine. That evening, around the piano, we had a singsong, celebrating of course baby Patrick's christening. The nearest Jim was able to get was on the phone. I know how he must have felt, being away at such a time, yet I could tell he was happy to know that everything had gone off all right.

It was on the phone that he spoke of his steamroller. The old lady is playing me up,' he said. 'I think she'll be ready for a new boiler shortly. Meanwhile,' said Jim, I'm searching everywhere for a place, so keep your fingers crossed, darling. I'll have you up with me as soon as I can.'

One week later, a letter came from Jim, saying that he had found a place in a select part of Gateshead, Lowfell to be precise; the accommodation consisted of two large rooms, with the use of the bathroom, and the rent would be 10 shillings weekly. I read on. 'How about coming up for the New Year, Paul?' It all sounded so exiciting.

I told Mum and Dad all the news that Jim had given me in his letter, and I'm sure they were happy for me, yet I somehow detected a melancholy that was within them. And, needless to say, I somehow felt the very same way.

'You'll soon be leaving us, duck.'

'Oh, Mum, I'll be leaving, but not for good. We'll always be coming back to see you.'

Dad remained silent.

It was then Rob's cheerful voice that echoed. 'So, our Paul's going up to Geordie-land then? One thing, we will be able to go up for holidays.'

Dear Rob, how thankful I was to have him around. Although he was not out of the Army yet, his extended leave would carry him right through until mid-January, so it meant that if I left home in the New Year, I would not be leaving Mum and Dad entirely alone.

Leaving home would be a big wrench for me, for I knew no other life than to be at home always, under the loving care of both my parents. But now I was quite prepared to stand on my own two feet, and to care for my two children as my parents had cared for me.

This, I realised, would be the biggest change-over of my life.

In a way it was a blessing that the festive season was almost upon us. We were all so busy with extra baking and preparations that my forthcoming departure on the 1st of January 1946 seemed almost forgotten.

Christmas finally arrived, and with it came a heavy fall of snow, with much drifting over the hills. It was a scene forever to be remembered. It was our first peaceful Christmas in seven years, and a time when the horrors of war were best forgotten. Christmas Day of 1945 was a happy one, and we exchanged presents after our early morning tea. With the decorations up, and holly that hung on the pictures, the festive season had begun.

Jim rang me up early, long before Old Sam had time to open, whereupon we exchanged our love and greetings. Then, while the roast chickens were giving off a lovely smell from the oven, we all celebrated with a glass of sherry.

Dad and Rob went into The Retreat for a half-hour, leaving little Jimmy just content to play with his new toys on the mat, while baby Patrick was as good as gold. I was not used to drink, and the sherry gave me a kind of exhilaration. I even felt like singing, knowing that the world was at peace. During the evening we did indeed gladden our hearts around the piano. The big logs burnt brightly on the large sitting-room fire, and in the grate we were roasting chestnuts. Our lights shone out through unshaded windows; we were happy, each one of us counting our blessings.

With Christmas Day departed, Boxing Day was spent cleaning up, yet we still enjoyed being in the festive mood. And finally, with

313

the holiday season entirely over, it was time for me to prepare for my journey north.

One surprise I did get; Jim sent his youngest brother, Frank, to fetch me up. Being recently demobbed, Frank was free to come down to Bath — in fact he offered to, because he wanted to go back to Frome, some 10 miles from Bath, recalling memories of his first Army base. So all was well; I was going to have an escort to take me and my children to our new home.

When the morning of January the 1st 1946 arrived, snow still lay about, and it remained bitterly cold. Dad insisted that he should travel up as far as Mangotsfield with us, for I had such a lot of luggage, including a heavy wooden play-pen.

The time came to leave home, with Rob hugging me as he never did before. 'Take good care of yourself, Quinner, and that little family of yours.'

Then the moment came to hug and kiss Mum, and oh dear we both cried. The suddenness of the big parting had come.

'God bless you, my darling,' said Mum. And between gulps I managed to say, 'God bless you too, Mum. And thanks for everything.'

Suddenly we had to tug away from each other, and so I started walking down the lane, with baby in my arms, and a big bag swinging on my shoulder, and the tears, they just simply flowed down my hot cheeks.

As I turned the corner of the lane, I waved back, and I could see Rob had his arms around Mum, and I was glad. I waved my last wave, wiped my eyes on baby's shawl, and then hurried to catch up with Dad, Frank and little Jimmy.

We had to walk to town, and it wasn't easy with so much luggage. However, we arrived at the LMS station at Green Park in plenty of time; there the local train would take us up to Mangotsfield.

Almost occupying a whole compartment, we were now in the little local train chugging its way up to Mangotsfield, and I recall being conscious of one thing: I was going to have to face up to yet another parting from my dear Dad, which I knew would be equally felt as when I left Mum and Rob standing at the doorway of our little cottage. I realised that this parting would be heart-breaking for Dad, for I knew full well how he idolised little Jimmy.

The local train stopped at its destination, and we all got out, dumping the luggage in one place. Of course, with it being a somewhat derelict and desolate station, we kept together.

I was feeling sad in my kind of way, and I knew Frank in his kind of way was trying hard to ease the situation, by being as jovial as possible. I looked at Dad. The turned-up collar of his navy-blue overcoat made his face look so pale and drawn. All I wanted to do now was fling my arms around his neck, for the very thought of having to leave him alone on such a station made me so utterly miserable.

We stood and waited for what seemed eternity. Then a green signal flashed up: the north-bound express was coming.

My heart was heavy, and God knows what Dad was feeling like. Then the big steam engine roared into the station, pulling behind it many carriages. It finally stopped, with steam from the engine hissing out everywhere. Then the guard, with his flag in his hand, started shouting, 'All aboard for the north.'

Frank had now disappeared. I guess he was after finding us some seats. I glanced at Dad and could see his eyes were misty, yet he was trying hard not to show his feelings by gathering up the luggage.

Frank appeared, shouting, 'I've found some seats!' Whereupon he put the luggage on the train, with the play-pen going into the guard's van.

Then Dad picked little Jimmy up into his arms, saying, 'Be a good boy for Mummy.'

I was now alone with Dad, except for baby Patrick in my arms. Then Dad, sure he didn't know what to say to me, but his loving arms were around me, and when he kissed me, he whispered, 'We're all going to miss you, Paul.' It would have been so easy just to cry, for my heart was heavy, having to leave my Dad this way. 'Better get on the train, Paul.'

With one last kiss, I got on the train and took up position beside Frank. Then, suddenly, without thinking, I made one impulsive move. I placed baby Patrick in his Uncle Frank's arms, exclaiming, 'Won't be a minute.' I dashed back along the corridor, jumped out on to the platform, and I just flung my arms around Dad's neck. Both our eyes were filled with tears, for our affections were so deep; it was only natural that our emotions were simultaneous.

'Come on now, our Paul. You can do better than that.'

For Dad I managed a brave smile.

Then a porter came along, banging all the doors. 'You on this train, Miss?'

'Oh yes,' I replied.

'Well 'ee best get on. Now!'

I started talking quickly. 'I'll write as soon as I can, Dad.'

'God bless you,' said Dad. 'And a safe journey.'

Momentarily I stood, with a hot face, with tears still streaming down, but I made a tremendous effort to smile.

I got on the train and stood at a window in the corridor. The train started to pull out, and through the smoke from the engine

I watched the figure of Dad get smaller and smaller. I hoped he could still see me waving.

Now, completely on my own two feet, I made my way back to Frank and the children.

I sat down beside Frank, taking baby Patrick into my arms, for he was only six weeks old. Then Frank, placing his hand on my forearm, remarked, 'I know exactly how you must feel.' The next thing, little Jimmy was climbing on to his Uncle Frank's knee.

We were silent for a while, and it was only little Jimmy's childish talk and laughter that brought me back to reality. So now I was speeding north with my little family, to my husband, and our new home, however humble it may be.

And so, as the miles went by, I was beginning to feel better, retentive of the past, but now moving towards a new era, thinking of the prospects of the future.

I have come practically to the end of my story, but I think I should give a summary account of what the end of the war meant:

> President Roosevelt's death.
> The end of American Lend-lease.
> Britain's external debts having increased to some £4,000,000,000.
> We had lost almost a third of our shipping.
> The loss of about 300,000 men in the armed forces, and 60,000 civilians in air raids.
> And with still a shortage of major things, rationing continued, with bread rationing yet to follow.

To conclude, I remember what Churchill said in a speech. After thanking the British people for making possible the victory in the war, he spoke as follows: 'I have laid down the charge which was placed upon me in darker times.... It only remains for me to express to the British people, for whom I have acted in these perilous years, my profound gratitude for the unflinching, unswerving support which they have given me during my task.'

When his Doctor mentioned the people's ingratitude, for failing to re-elect him as Prime Minister, Churchill replied at once, 'Oh no, I wouldn't call it that. They have had a very hard time.'